DIVORCING OEDIPUS

A MODERN DAY GREEK TRAGEDY

M. OPHELIA

m.ophelia@divorcingoedipus.com

Publisher: Franklin Rose Publishing
www.FranklinRose.com

ISBN: 978-1-952146-06-0 (Paperback)
ISBN: 978-1-952146-07-7 (eBook)

Library of Congress Control Number: 2020904019

I dedicate this book to God, to Mothers, and to codependents, addicts and any family unit struggling with mental health issues.

TABLE OF CONTENTS

POOR LITTLE FELLER

CHAPTER 1

It was the summer of 2006. I was waitressing at The Dive and Dine to earn money for the fall semester. It was my junior year at the University of Washington. Late one evening, as I was closing, Trey walked in. He was wearing cologne, a refreshing change from the typical fish-gut aroma. I was intrigued. He was definitely not from Kodiak. Even though he was alluring to all five of my senses, I tried to avoid him. After being hounded all summer by extremely lonely fishermen, I was not in the mood to be friendly. In fact, when I took his order, I did not even look at him. Then he asked if I was going to the prom. I was appalled! I was twenty-two years old and, clearly, too old for a high school prom. I looked into his licorice dark eyes. Time stopped. He took my breath away. I fell into a cosmic trance, a karmic black hole, but at twenty-two, I felt it as love.

We talked for three minutes, tops. Then, we exchanged numbers. At home, I told my mom I had met the man I was going to marry.

Soon after, Trey hired me to work at his parents' boating and yurt outfit, The Salmon Express. Our relationship blossomed. He introduced me to his parents, Simon and Phyllis. Simon was unhappy that Trey had decided to date someone whom he hired. In fact, when I met him, he pulled me aside and said, "Please do not fall in love with Trey. We go to Las Vegas often... if you know what I mean." Simon practically offered to pay me to stop seeing him. I thought he was a strange controlling man, who perhaps used cash to compensate for his small stature and unusually large feet. His mother Phyllis acted oblivious to the matter and was friendly despite all odds. She was charming, and appeared to have a fondness for cosmetic procedures. She was medium height with long blond hair, dark roots and a fragile frame. If only she were taller, I would think she was a living, breathing barbie doll. Her brown eyes reminded me of an eagle, with an air of keen awareness hiding a huntress' glare. Regardless of his parents' approval, Trey and I were in love and nothing was going to stop our blossoming relationship. Two months later, we were engaged and planning our future together.

After the summer ended, we moved into an apartment in downtown Fairbanks. I transferred to Alaska Pacific University to continue my studies. Trey continued to work for his stepdad at Hamilton Enterprises.

One evening, a few months into our cohabitation, Trey did not come home from work. After several hours and numerous unsuccessful attempts to contact him by phone, I began to panic. Eventually, all my calls went to voicemail. I called Phyllis, his mother, to tell her I could not find him. She told me not to worry; he was fine. I found her reaction detached and cold. This behavior was unlike him. I could not accept that he was fine.

I went to the police, and they told me to come back in forty-eight hours. Hours turned into days. Still, there was no sign of Trey. I was in full panic mode, replaying the worst-case scenarios in my mind's eye. I wondered if he had been kidnapped or left for dead on the side of the road. His mother continued to act as if everything was fine. Her cold response confused me. After the allotted time had passed, I filed a missing person report against his mother's wishes.

Later that day, around 3:00 in the afternoon, I received a call from an Alaska State Trooper.

"We found Trey's abandoned jeep wrecked off Chena Loop Road."

The trooper told me not to come.

I went anyway.

Chena Loop was a scenic, windy road outside of Fairbanks, beautifully situated between the natural reserve of Potter Marsh and the Chena River. On the drive down the Chena Loop hill, I saw where Trey's jeep had slammed into a tree, a t-shirt now hanging out of the gas tank. Had someone taken him hostage and were trying to discard the evidence? Then, I noticed lights and sirens at the bottom of the Marsh. The Marsh was a 564-acre wetland just below the hill where Trey's jeep had crashed. It looked as though he wrecked his jeep, walked down the prickly hill and got stuck in the Marsh.

I drove down to the Marsh. A big commotion was afoot. Fire engines, police cars, and the media gathered. I made my way through the emergency response teams and noisy passersby. I felt my heart drop to my stomach. I feared he was dead, and they were retrieving his body.

Finally, I saw Trey. He was stuck in the marsh up to his waist, unable to move, and shivering. It was fall, and the temperature was in the forties. His lips were turning purple.

When he saw me, he began to yell my name while slowly waving his arms. From my gut, I felt a need to comfort him. He was crying for help. For my help.

The coast guard had already launched several boats to rescue him. I watched as men in wetsuits heaved Trey's gigantic, six-foot six-inch body into their little rowboat. His legs dangled over the bow. He was transported by ambulance to a local hospital.

Trey made the nightly news, and bloggers had a field day with his daredevil escapade. No one had any compassion for him; people labeled him as an idiot and laughed it off. I felt defensive and protective of him. At his mother's insistence, his step-sister (a local TV personality) had the media stop playing the footage of Trey being wrestled into the rowboat. She also managed to have his real name removed from all respective stories. The following day, his mother left town with his stepdad. His family acted nonchalant about the entire situation.

I was left alone in Fairbanks, while Trey was placed on a mandated forty-eight-hour psychiatric hold. I had long days and sleepless nights. I was worried for his life. All I could imagine was that he was running from kidnappers or maybe a hungry grizzly bear?

After forty-eight hours had passed, I met Trey's biological dad, Dick, in the hospital lobby. I was pale and thin, with dark circles encasing my eyes. He looked green off the golf course, wearing khakis, a lavender polo, and a dark blue visor nestled in his thick curly blond hair. I pressed him for information about Trey. All he would say was, "Phyllis won't let him hit rock bottom." After one hour had passed, Dick said he had an appointment and left. I waited an hour longer before I was finally allowed to visit. Upon seeing him, I rushed into his embrace. He was wearing green hospital scrubs, his facial hair scratchy to the touch, his lips covered in blisters. His dark eyes now looked lost. I sobbed. Just having him back to hold, I felt so much better. Trey told me he had a cocaine problem, and that he had hallucinated that the FBI was chasing him. At first, he wanted to blow up his truck by sticking his t-shirt in the gas tank and lighting it on fire. He said, he chickened out and decided the only way to safety was through the Marsh to the other side of the road. So, he raced down the Chena hill and halfway through the marsh he got stuck. Someone driving by Chena Loop Road pulled over and called for help. Trey said he sobered up in the cold Marsh, realized what he had done and wanted to kill himself for disappointing me. I can identify this as the moment my co-dependency with Trey began. He gave me a lot of information to digest, but the one thing that stood out in my heart was that he was all alone, and he wanted to die for disappointing me. I didn't want him to die because of me. I could not leave him like this. What kind of person would I be if I did?

I thought he needed love over punishment. I thought he was a lost soul who needed someone to care for him and love him unconditionally. Someone to teach him right from wrong. At twenty-two years of age, with no experience with a substance abuser, I declared myself fit for the job. I told myself I could do it. I could heal all his brokenness. I decided to pour my heart and soul into fixing Trey. God wanted me to save him. Are we not supposed to fix and heal the broken? Is that not my Christian duty? Is that not our highest calling on Earth?

I took him to get Suboxone; I took him to AA and NA meetings. He got a sponsor. He got sober. Somewhere in there, we got married and had two children.

My name is Faith Nathaniel, and when everything came apart, Trey and I had been together for eleven years. We lived in an upper-class neighborhood in one of the most affluent parts of Fairbanks, Alaska. Our children, Maggie and Alex, were seven and four years old. They attended a private Catholic school. Trey had been sober and functioning at a high level for seven years. His family employed him at St. Mary's Alcohol & Drug Rehabilitation Center, which they owned. Once he earned his master's degree, he was in line to take over St. Mary's management, securing the future of our children. We were idolized and in an enviable position. On the outside, things were picture perfect.

On the inside, our relationship was in turmoil. We had battled the depths of addiction together. Our common goal was his sobriety, the children, and building a stable life. But after Trey began working at the Center, love was soon replaced with family business obligations. No one was living out their heart's desire. We were so busy trying to maintain a lifestyle and image that did not suit us, that we lost our connection to each other. In the process, we began to resent and then despise each other. We cast blame in the shadows for what our life had become, a life of fakery, of pretentious projections—a world blended in realities that were not real.

Trey's stepfather, Simon Hamilton, was a successful plastic surgeon and businessman. He worked day and night until his health caught up with him. To the exclusion of Simon's other businesses, Trey's mother took the lead at St. Mary's. Phyllis needed Trey, and she demanded to be the focus of his life. If he did not give her his absolute attention and devotion, she punished him by withholding money and approval. Trey was miserable working for his parents. He walked on eggshells at St. Mary' s around suspicious employees who always questioned his worthiness. He often found comfort and validation in the bosom of his mother.

I was burnt out, too. During the week, I took care of Trey's stepdad, Simon, our children, social obligations, whatever odds and ends Phyllis needed, and Trey's master's degree. A master's degree was required to qualify as an administrator for St. Mary's. Trey and his mother agreed that I would pursue his master's degree through the University of the Arctic, so he could focus on work. The Hamiltons were experts at wielding power through charitable contributions. So, the University was extra supportive of Trey's educational pursuits which allowed me the flexibility to complete his assignments.

On the weekends, Trey was at his mother's house to help Phyllis with Simon. Sometimes he took Maggie with him. This was "Nathaniel normal," and life went on, albeit with an air of tension we were content to live with...or so I thought.

Recently, we had hit a brick wall in our relationship. I tried talking to Trey; he ignored me. I tried taking him to counseling; he refused. I tried being romantic; he wasn't interested. As a last resort, I tried spicing things up by surprising him with an August trip to New Orleans for our eleventh wedding anniversary. When I presented him with the idea, he said, "I guess I can try to go. I'll have to ask my mom."

That was strange, but he was a mama's boy. Still, as the trip drew closer, Trey pulled further away. He began making excuses for why he should not go: his mother needed his help with Simon; he wasn't feeling well; he was too important at St. Mary's to leave. Trey's trepidation dumbfounded me because prior to going on a trip previously, Trey was always ready for a vacay.

In New Orleans, things did not improve. Trey made every effort to remind me that he did not want to be there and, sure as hell, not with me. We did not even make love, not one time during the entire five-day trip. Who goes on an anniversary trip and does not make love? Trey always had low testosterone, but this situation was disappointing even for him.

Our bickering climaxed at Britney Spears' concert. He just left. I was moderately intoxicated and had to find my way back to Trump's hotel in the middle of the night. Back in the room, Trey pretended to sleep as I packed. I was miserable, hurt, and angry. I stomped through the room akin to a herd of elephants, waiting for him to wake up and apologize, to care, to worry about me, in vain. My waiting eventually translated into action and took me to the airport, seven hours early, for a flight home. He did not call to check on me, not even an emoji frowny face or a texted *I hate you* to establish contact. As I sat in the deserted airport in the wee hours of the morning, sobbing tragically, I wondered what had become of our marriage. Why was he so hateful? Why had he given up on us?

Trey showed up well-rested and freshly showered at the airport. He was right on time to catch the same morning flight home. He was cold, unfeeling, and seemed unmoving in his conviction that he just did not give a fuck anymore.

Back in Fairbanks, we had to attend the wedding of Simon's twin brother, Peter. The wedding was held in Peter and Simon's hangar, where he usually parked his private jet, helicopter, and other boating mobiles. On this day, the room was beautifully transformed with black linen round tables, red roses, chandeliers, and a wedding arch. The children and I were in the wedding party. I found myself desperately trying to keep it together. I stuffed my emotions so far down that I felt automated. At the reception, Trey sat at the head table, texting. Intermittently, from a distance, he glared at the children and me. Everyone had been worried that Lonnie, (who was a known party girl) would be the train wreck at the reception, but she was managing fine. She was giggling, tossing her blond hair around, while filling wine glasses for everyone. I was the one lingering on the edge of fragility. My husband did not appear to love me anymore, not only privately, but also publicly.

Lonnie's husband, Jacob, approached me. "I have been watching Trey text on his phone all night. You looked beautiful, and I am so sorry he missed you walking down the aisle. He should have captured that moment." Jacob used a hand gesture to add emphasis on the word "capture," I felt an internal gasp of searing pain, and looked away from his piercing blue eyes.

"I am sure he is busy with the Center," I curtly responded. I felt hurt and paranoid, like he was poking me for an emotional reaction. Why was

I always so protective of Trey? No matter how he behaved, I was loyal to him. For the past six months, I had found myself repeating this over and over. *Trey can't come, he is busy at the Center.* It had become rather contrived.

Jacob felt sorry me. I felt sorry for me, too. People were noticing. All I knew to do was cover it up and pretend, like I had seen them do for years.

"Drinks for everyone!" Lonnie grabbed two wine bottles, one for each hand and began pouring. I decided to help her—it was a welcome distraction to recuse myself from flame- thrower Jacob. It was nice to see Lonnie happy, although I knew she was faking joy to suppress her current battle with her stepmother, Phyllis, relating to her father's annual fishing trip.

Simon, Lonnie's father, hosted an annual all-male fishing trip in King Salmon. Simon's health was in rapid decline, and this year's trip might be his last. About two weeks before, Simon's old, married fishing buddy invited Lonnie to attend. His invitation was seductive. Lonnie was eager to go. She loved fishing and the idea of being the only female in a five-hundred-mile radius. That was until Phyllis found out about the invitation and uninvited her.

Lonnie begged Phyllis to change her mind, to no avail. Phyllis even encouraged Simon to call her up and tell her, "No," just to establish superiority. It made Lonnie fume. She was a rage texter and let loose one evening on Phyllis. She texted her for hours, things like, *You bitch, this is my dad's last fishing trip. I hate you. You bitch.*

The whole family, especially those two, were up in arms continually.

The wedding reception was nearly over by the time the Hamiltons—Simon and Phyllis—arrived. Simon was wearing a black suit and using a walker. His hair was white and untamed. Phyllis was wearing a long brown form-fitting dress that matched her eyes; her long curly freshly dyed reddish hair delicately framed her face. I walked out of the hangar to greet them. I took the kids, Lonnie, and Trey with me to escort a freshly operated on Simon inside the hanger.

"Grandma, Papa!" Maggie and Alex ran to them for hugs.

"What a beautiful girl and handsome young man you are," Grandma Phyllis said and squeezed them tightly.

"Whoa, be careful, Alex," Papa Simon slurred as Alex wrestled his leg from behind the walker.

Lonnie moved Maggie aside from Phyllis, dropped to her knees, and grabbed Phyllis's hands. She kissed them and pleaded, "I am so sorry; please forgive me. I am so sorry." She even squeezed a tear from one eye. It was humiliating.

Phyllis shyly nodded her head. "Okay, okay," while I watched her joyfully declare victory over conquering Lonnie once again.

When we walked back into the wedding, the band was playing Charles Trenet's "Beyond the Sea." I grabbed Alex in his grey tuxedo, and we danced. Afterward, Simon, unsteadily using a cane, gave a toast to the newlyweds. He lifted his glass and said, "My brother marrying Denali is the best decision he has ever made."

As he spoke, I saw Denali anxiously shuffling her hands. She and Uncle Peter had every right to be concerned over a Hamilton shit show taking center stage at their wedding. You never knew what a Hamilton would do or say at any given time. The rules did not apply to them. Phyllis and Simon were the self-declared King and Queen of the Arctic and demanded to be treated as such by the mere commoners that served them. People let them do whatever they wanted because Alaska is an oligarchy, and people feared retribution from the elites. Phyllis fought the change being thrust upon her by Simon's declining health. She had become increasingly aggressive with each passing day. I could not tell which she feared most, losing Simon or losing power. Simon, in his poor health, no longer gave a shit about those pretenses. He just wanted to know he was loved by his family and eat cheeseburgers from Dairy Queen.

Overall, I appreciated the symbolism of the wedding, even though the rift between Trey and me was clearly on display. The love that Uncle Peter and his new bride shared was healing for me, especially after the anniversary trip. I was even inspired to rekindle the connection between Trey and me. When Nat King Cole's song "Unforgettable" came on, I whisked him to the dance floor.

After weeks of alienation, he thrust his hard penis against my leg and, halfway jokingly, said, "I was jealous watching another man walk with you down the aisle. If you ever cheat on me, I'll kill you."

What a nice intro to mending fences. I said, "Things have got to change." But then, as usual, I rationalized his behavior as something beyond his control. My excuse log for Trey contained variations of the following themes: One, his stepfather was ill. Two, his job was difficult. And three, he was having a hard time, the poor little feller, and taking it out on the person closest to him. He did love me. After all, he cared if I cheated on him. I still inspired jealousy, so surely, he must love me, right?

That night, when Trey and I got home, he wanted sex. I felt so lonely. The best I could pull out of him was a death threat over imagined future infidelity. Still, I gave in. I guess any connection was better than no connection.

NO SEX, NO SEX

CHAPTER 2

It was October 19, 2016, 10:01 p.m. in the Nathaniel household. I was exhausted. I had been training all day for the Kairos Retreat—a women's ministry that would travel to the local prisons and minister, once properly trained, to inmates. It was a chance for an objective person to give a prisoner compassion, a voice, and a chance for salvation. The Kairos Retreat resonated with the theme of my life: by helping others, I could help myself; I could heal myself, or so I continued to believe.

That evening during our training, the lead minister said, "The devil doesn't like what we are doing here; if you have never been attacked by the devil, get ready."

She jolted me. I had seen the devil. I had seen the dark struggles of addiction; I knew the devil. Her words had been playing on a loop in my head ever since. Not to mention a foreboding dream I had the night before. Trey, the kids, and I were at a ski resort. Someone came up to me, a stranger, and threw acid in my face. Then, Trey took Maggie to the bottom of the mountain. He left

Alex and me there to deal with the fallout. In the next scene, I was suddenly in the hospital. Trey was crying over me, apologizing. I got up from the hospital bed. I looked in a mirror mounted on the opposite side of the wall, and I heard the words "I am perfect in the eyes of the Lord." Next scene, Trey was with a woman with long brown hair having a romantic encounter. I was in our bedroom, my face scarred from the acid, crying over him. Suddenly, I am in a yoga studio sitting in front of a man, with deep love and acceptance in his eyes for me. He had a name that I was familiar with, a family name. The dream was vivid. It wasn't an ordinary dream, but a dream with a message—a message I wanted to ignore.

That night, I was in a maroon-colored bed, in my white peppermint-scented pajamas, reading "A Course in Miracles." Trey was in the bathroom, taking a shower. He had left his phone on his nightstand—something he never did; it was always attached to his body, like a kangaroo mama's baby pouch. His phone dinged—text message.

A thought pressed into my mind: I am going to catch him. Out of character and without hesitation, I leaped over to his side of the bed. The text was from someone labeled in Trey's phone as *Pichaard.*

Pichaard: *Are you home? Can we talk?*

Trey works with an elderly man named Pichard. He spells his name with one "a"... Why would Pichard be texting my husband this bizarre message at 10 p.m.?

Me: *Where are you?*

Pichaard: *At my mother's house where I should be*

I thought, Pichard is 75 years old; praise God if his mother is still living.

I took the phone, walked downstairs to the laundry room and shut the door. I leaned my body against our brand-new dryer. I dialed the number.

A woman's voice said, "Hey, how's it going?" She sounded jolly and seductive.

I felt breathless, "My name is Faith Nathaniel. How do you know my husband?"

Her tone changed from carefree lover to nasty bitch. "You should talk to your husband about that."

"Please tell me how you know my husband?"

"Talk to your husband about that," she responded with coldness and satisfaction, followed by a smug laugh. She hung up the phone. My eyes bulged, my heart fell to the floor.

Trey came running down the stairs with a towel loosely draped around his waist. He rushed me like a linebacker. We tussled over the phone. His towel fell off, exposing his bare pecker—his weapon of choice. I shrieked and ran into the formal living room to get away from it.

"Give me the fucking phone!"

"No!"

I wanted to break his phone into a thousand pieces, and then take a hammer and break it into a thousand more. He pushed me, knocking over our bookcase—our family photos crashed to the floor. He squeezed my hand so tightly I felt it crack, I relented. After all, he was a foot taller and a hundred pounds heavier than me.

"Who the fuck was that?" I screamed.

"No sex, no sex!"

By this time, Maggie had woken. I looked up and saw her peering over the iron balcony that overlooked our formal living room.

"What are you doing?" she asked rubbing her eyes.

I ran upstairs, high on adrenaline, and ushered her back into her room. "Maggie, no matter what you hear, stay in your room." I tucked her into bed, turned on her tv to "Berenstain Bears" and walked back downstairs. Trey was sitting on the sofa with his arms folded, legs crossed, and the towel securely attached to his waist.

"Who was that?" I asked. "What is her name?"

"Eve."

"Does she work at the St. Mary's?"

"No, and it's none of your business."

I thought, "Motherfucker, it's none of my business who you are sleeping within our marriage? What planet do you live on? I will beat you to death."

I tried to slap him; he ducked, stood up and grabbed my arms from behind. I wiggled loose and punched him multiple times. He grabbed my arms and held them tighter. His towel fell off again from all the commotion, his bare pecker flopping about. This time I tried to punch it.

"Gross! Get off me!" I yelled.

He dropped to grab the towel, letting me go.

I ran up the stairs to our bedroom and started throwing his clothes over the balcony. I aimed them at his head. I wanted him to leave. I wanted him to feel the pain of rejection that I felt at that moment. I wanted to see him hurting any and every way possible. I was in agony. If he had been bleeding out, I would have pushed the knife in harder. "Get out, get out!"

"No. This is my house. I am not leaving." In between the laundry assault, he managed to get dressed.

"I am calling the police," I screamed again. Trey knew from the past that this wasn't an empty threat. I was proud to be a cop caller. As I threw his clothes over the balcony, he gathered them up in garbage bags. On reflection, I can define this moment as our last time working together as a team.

Trey's face looked swollen. He talked out of the side of his mouth like he was stricken with Bell's Palsy. He called for a taxi to take him to his mother's house, but I wasn't going to let him leave so easily. I needed answers. I walked back downstairs.

I confronted him again. "Who is this woman?"

"Eve. We went to school together." Trey stood away from me.

"Give me her phone number? What is her last name?" I approached him.

"I am not telling you. It's none of your business," Trey repeated, protecting this strange nobody over me. Yet I was the person who was working every day to care for him. I cared for our children, his stepfather, earned him his master's degree, maintained our household, cooked his food, did his laundry, showed up as a perfect little wife, stroked his ego....

"Are you stupid? It's none of my business? What does that mean? We are married with children. Who you are fucking is my business!" My mouth gaped open. My hands were raised in the air in disbelief.

"No!" He pushed me.

I stumbled, backward, onto the soft leather sofa. I stood right back up, ready to fight from a different angle. "Well then, I guess all we have to talk about is how we are going to co-parent in the future. Now get the fuck out." Being the lady I am, I opened the front door for him to leave. He walked through with garbage bags full of clothes clutched in his hands. Mid-way, he turned back to me with indignation in his spiteful dark eyes.

"You stupid bitch. You can't survive without me."

"No, motherfucker, you can't survive without me."

I slammed the door in his face and locked it, wishing he would fall off the porch and break his neck. I watched him as he waited outside in the cold for the taxi to take him away. It was surreal. I was completely distraught.

In the meantime, I thought Phyllis should know what was going on, before he made up some wild tale about me. I called Phyllis; she did not answer. I called again.

"Hello, what is going on?" She sounded groggy.

"Phyllis, Trey is having an affair. Some lady called his phone, and I talked to her. I think it's someone from the Center," I said, fishing for clues.

"People are trying to sabotage him; they are so jealous at the Center. It's not true. He's half Greek, we are devoted to family."

"I think it's real, and he is going to your house."

I hung up, bewildered. Trey's reaction to my accusations had been far from normal. Why would Phyllis have me believe that someone from St. Mary's was intentionally trying to sabotage our family because of jealousy? What kind of sadistic prank was that? It seemed like a pretty elaborate scheme. Did this great deceiver also program Pichaard into Trey's phone? What was this? *General Hospital?* Little did I know the events to unfold would rival any sitcom melodrama.

ANOTHER TREY-PISODE

CHAPTER 3

"You two will work it out, don't worry. Trey is too lazy to cheat. Cheating requires a real effort. He is not a cheater."

"Mom, please fly up here."

"Maybe in a week or two. I'll give you time to work it out."

My mother talked to me like she worked at a crisis center. She had witnessed too many of Trey's stunts. Over the years, we had begun to call them, un-affectionately, Trey-pisodes. I didn't blame her for not wanting to get involved. I understood that sympathy ran out for the long-term codependent. That is why I always kept everyone at a healthy distance. "Poor Faith" over time turns into "Stupid, whiney, broken-record, annoying, pathetic Faith." I had cried wolf too often on Trey's account, and because of it, I was alone at the worst time of my life.

The following morning, I walked downstairs and stood in the empty space of the living room—the crime scene—where promises were broken and death threats were made. I felt numb. I adjusted the dark brown bookcase and put the family photos and other items back on the shelves properly. I had to maintain a stable household. My children had a high level of awareness now; this was where real psychological damage could occur. Their welfare overrode any obligation or deep animosity I felt toward Trey.

I checked on Maggie and Alex to make sure they were getting ready for school. In my bathroom mirror, I saw my puffy eyes, the red circles, the peaked face—all signs of the broken spirit of a battered wife. I asked myself, Where did my reflex to protect Trey begin, and where did it end when it came to the children? So, in good faith, I picked up my wedding band off our white quartz counter top and put it on. In our closet, the empty spaces stood out at me like water rings on a fine coffee table. My closet felt so lonely, empty, deserted. I quickly dispersed my clothes evenly across the racks. I loosely placed my shoes, purses, and cosmetic boxes, from the top shelf to the lower shelf. I got dressed quickly, in a pair of leggings and a purple sweatshirt.

The kids were downstairs, watching Dora the Explorer. I made breakfast. I was like a zombie, going through the motions, putting on a happy face, pretending the first rocket of World War Three had not been launched in my house the night before. The kids were not to know how I was tangled inside; I had to keep smiling and being cheerful. I had to keep them feeling safe and steady. I served pancakes and drew smiley faces with whipping cream, something I usually reserved for Saturday mornings.

Alex rushed to sit in the bronze kitchen barstool. "Pancakes, my favorite!"

"Yes, honey, eat up! Try to keep your uniform clean." I patted him gently on the head.

Every interaction seemed more profound than usual. I watched Alex beam with excitement over pancakes and thought, 'that is the joy I must harness inside them, no matter what happens with Trey. Their lives should remain so carefree that the thought of pancakes and whipping cream sends them over the moon and back, on a rainbow.'

"Where is daddy?" Maggie asked with a perplexed look on her face taking a seat next to Alex.

I pushed her brown hair out of her face. I took a sip of coffee and swallowed slowly, to allow myself time to gauge a proper response.

"Daddy will be staying with Grandma and Papa for a while to help take care of Papa Simon; he is sick."

"I hope Papa feels better," Alex said with a mouth fall of food.

"Me too." I hugged them tightly from behind as they scarfed down breakfast.

I congratulated myself on this cover story. Now, daddy had an easy path back to us, and he looked noble. What other option did I have? I could not tell them, "Hey kids, guess what? Your dad's a dick. He left us for some skank, and he is never coming back. *Bon appetit.*"

On the way to school, we recited our morning prayer by Marianne Williamson. I needed it as much as the kids, to stay grounded and rooted in gratitude. After all, we still had clothes, food, a great school, and a warm house.

Dear God,
I give this day to You.
May my mind stay centered on the things of spirit.
May I not be tempted to stray from love.
As I begin this day, I open to receive You.
Please enter where You already abide.
May my mind and heart be pure and true, and may I not deviate from the things of goodness.
May I see the love and innocence in all mankind, behind the masks we all wear and the illusions of this worldly plane.
I surrender to You my doings this day.
I ask only that they serve You and the healing of the world.
May I bring Your love and goodness with me, to give unto others wherever I go.
Make me the person You would have me be.
Direct my footsteps, and show me what You would have me do.
Make the world a safer, more beautiful place.
Bless all Your creatures.
Heal us all, and use me, dear Lord, that I might know the joy of being used by You. Amen.

I asked the kids to name one thing they were grateful for.

"I am grateful for daddy."

"I am grateful for *Skylanders.*"

I dropped the kids off at St. Joseph's. I remembered we had a PTO meeting. I could not bring myself to go. I texted my friend and PTO President, Chelsea.

Me: *Sorry Chelsea, I can't make the PTO meeting this morning.*

Chelsea: *What are we going to do without the VP? Joking. No worries! Ttyl.*

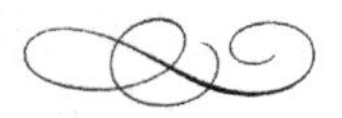

On my drive home, last night's nightmare was ever-present: the words, the looks, the physical encounters, the complete blur of ugliness that had unfolded. It was haunting. I couldn't be with a cheater. Once a man cheats, he never stops. *Once a cheater, always a cheater*, that is what I had heard my whole life. What if he had cheated before and I hadn't known about it? What if he had other girlfriends, and she was the lucky one I just happened to talk to? What if she got pregnant? What if he gave me AIDS? What if the children had AIDS?

My mind wandered from the worst-case scenario to the best-case scenario.

What if it was a one-time thing, and they never had sex—like he said, just an emotional affair? The tone of her voice had suggested otherwise. Obviously, she knew about the kids and me and didn't care or have an ounce of remorse. Why else was she so determined to protect their relationship from me? Then his curt remark, that it was none of my business.

This had to be a serious affair. Trey was protecting her over his own family. Who was this mystery woman? A gold digger? A young hot stripper?

How much could one person take? I had survived Trey's drug addiction, his legal battles, incarcerations, multiple jobs, and moves from state to state. I had thought that we finally had a stable home and a stable family life, that all my hard work, love and devotion had paid off. That Trey had grown up.

My mind wandered, and so did my silver SUV. I realized, once I saw those two ugly orange tiger statues that hugged the driveway, that I had driven right up to Simon's bright yellow house. Phyllis had an obsession with wild cats, particularly tigers.

"Oh, shit!" I said aloud.

I saw Phyllis's gold Mercedes. The car door was open as if she had run inside for a split second and was already on her way back out. I turned around and sped off, this time with a renewed alertness to arrive home in one piece.

My brain had been trained well over the course of several years. After dropping the kids off at school, I would typically go over to the Hamilton's house to help as needed. Recently, I had been going to help Simon get dressed and ready for the day. I would take him to his office, Physical Therapy, or other appointments. Sadly, I had no desire to go over there today. I felt terrible about disappointing Simon, but how could life go on as normal while Trey was boning some bimbo? I needed resolution and recognition that an injustice had been done to me. At the very least, an apology would have been nice.

Once at home, I crawled into bed, sick with unknowingness. I wondered why Trey wasn't calling me? Didn't he care? Was he thinking about the consequences of his actions? Maybe he was reflecting and was going to come forth with an honest, heartfelt confession. I prayed for God's wisdom and strength to hold me up.

My phone dinged around lunchtime.

Trey: *I am listing the house for sale.*

Wow! I was dumbfounded that he wanted to keep fighting. Aren't normal men supposed to take pride in providing for their children, even if they hate their wives?

This was not like him. Before, when I'd caught him red-handed lying, or using drugs, I'd torture him for some amount of time, usually by locking him out of the house or withdrawing communication. Then, he'd beg for forgiveness, make a grand gesture, and all would be well. I suspected he had his mother's full support this time. The Trey I knew was a milksop. I rationalized, Phyllis isn't fully aware of what she is doing. He must have her on a hamster wheel, too.

In the past, Phyllis had allowed Trey to live by a different set of rules. Instead of standing her ground with him, she afforded him the luxury of checking out and behaving like a spoiled, rich teenager whenever he pleased. Money had always bought him a get-out-of-jail-free card. Part of her was anguished when he acted out, while another part of her relished the drama and the battle for control over him. Meanwhile, the rest of us had to toe the line and keep things together for his flawless exit and re-entry into the family.

After the initial hurt of his wanting to go another round with me, I felt justified in my anger. Well, fuck you, I thought, but I knew I could not allow him to see my angry side. He would use it to justify his abusive behavior towards me. He was baiting me, and if I started throwing mud back, I would lose my power. The only power I had was my voice of reason. Any cruel words from me would overshadow his cruel actions. After all, Phyllis and Simon were the power-wielding Hamiltons, who rubbed elbows with Senators and judges alike, and I was a weakling, a nobody. I was not about to lose my victim status by texting profanity, even though it was what I wanted to do. I bit my tongue.

Me: *I am heartbroken. You can't have an affair and then kick us out so you can get a payday.*

Trey: *I am not paying the mortgage for you, Faith. All we have to do is figure out the kids. That is the only thing you have to be proud of; you have done nothing with your life.*

I guess I should have conquered Mount Everest with a baby on my hip and one hand tied behind my back while blindfolded? It sure would have been easier than trying to keep an addict sober. Clearly, being a simple caretaker, devoting one's life to others, was for losers. The Hamiltons only respected people with great financial success. If you could not do them a favor, or plunge the toilet, they had no use for you. I concluded I was no longer someone who could do them a favor, and I sure as hell was not about to plunge their toilet.

Trey's text went on: *I want time with my kids, and you will not allow it.*

Why would he say that I was keeping him from his kids when I had only kicked him out last night?

Was he referring to the hour and a half they had been awake that morning to eat breakfast, bathe, and get dressed before school? At that moment, I realized he was trying to build a custody case against me. The person I was talking to was not my husband; this was a man with a plan, trying to out-smart me. He would not think to say that. He wasn't that clever. This line came directly from his mother. I felt a double betrayal. Luckily for me, I had seen Lonnie unsuccessfully navigate the inner working of Phyllis, so I knew what not to do.

I regained my composure. This wasn't amateur hour. I was the victim of the adulterous affair. This time, I refuse to be bullied and intimidated by them just because Phyllis has a big purse and a loudmouth. Whatever she kept inside of that rattlesnake-skinned purse was not worth bartering the little self-respect I had left.

Me: *My house is built on stone. Your house is built on sand. I have plenty to be proud of; I am blessed. Let's get divorced, so all of your lies will be exposed.*

I waited several minutes but received no response.

The phone rang; it was my mother. "Phyllis emailed me," she said in a low monotone, her emotionless voice full of dread.

"Did she wish you a good day?"

"She said she took you into the confidence of the family, and now you have threatened to expose all of their secrets."

"I'm not sure why she feels the need to interject herself into Trey's life, and now his marriage. Isn't it enough that he moved in with her last night, and they work together every day? Maybe *she's* the other woman!"

"She said she's hiring an attorney."

"For what? Quoting a biblical scripture? I know Trey doesn't believe in God, but this is taking it too far. Can't he fight his own battles, with his own wife, instead of using his seventy-year-old mother as an attack dog?"

My mother sighed. "Well, maybe I do need to fly up there."

That evening I was supposed to go over to Ralph's house for a party. Ralph was family friends with Simon. He and his family lived in a 10,000 square foot high-end Alaskan log-cabin, built for entertaining. He was a sociable fellow who had parties nearly every weekend. His house was right across the river from Trey's parents.

My first instinct was to cancel. I was not up for it. Then, I thought about Phyllis and Trey trying to build a potential child custody case against me. I didn't want Trey, and now Phyllis, to believe they had defeated me into retreat mode. I thought, *I need to keep my life as normal as possible and keep doing things I would normally do with a smile on my face.*

It was best for me to stay present in the community because all I had was my voice. Also, I was counting on Phyllis's fear of "What will the neighbor think?" to keep her reasonable.

I fed the kids dinner: Little Caesar's pizza, always a winner. Afterward, we peered out the window for our favorite nanny's arrival. Bea was a purple-haired fun, artsy high schooler, with an old soul. When she pulled into the driveway in her big, brown, noisy bronco, the kids flung open the front door and rushed to her, arms wide open. Bea was wearing a long black gypsy looking dress. She said she had come from drama club.

"Bea, let's go to the playroom and play dress-up!" Maggie grabbed her hand.

"No, Bea, come watch me play *Skylanders* on my Xbox!" Alex suggested.

"I can do all of that at the same time; I have special powers!" Bea said and wiggled her fingers at us. We laughed.

"I need to talk with Bea alone for a moment, kids."

In our formal living room, Bea and I sat next to each other on the brown leather sofa in front of the bookcase.

"Are you okay?" she asked me. "Have you been crying?"

"Bea, you should know in confidence that Trey and I are going through a difficult time. He isn't living here, and I don't know if he'll ever come back. I am worried about the children. Let me know if they say anything, okay?"

As I told my adorable, innocent seventeen-year-old babysitter the status of my marriage, I broke down once again, the tears flowing freely this time. Thinking it inside of my head was different than saying it aloud in-person to an unrelated third party. Saying it aloud made it real; it shattered the image, and once the image is shattered, there is no going back. Even if it's glued back together, it never quite looks the same.

"I am so sorry. You are going to be okay. This has happened to a lot of my friends' parents. My friends are fine. Very normal, you'll see." Bea stood up to give me a friendly pat on the back, and she looked warmly into my eyes.

Initially, I was confused. Then I realized, she was comforting me! I could not fathom someone comforting me over a Trey-pisode. I was not allowed to let anyone see my vulnerabilities or the realities of my situation, so I rarely received genuine comfort. Bea saw me as a person with feelings, a valid human, not a target to throw darts at, or a sad sap who cries wolf too often.

It was such a simple gesture of love, from an innocent girl with a big beautiful heart, unshaped by the cruelty of this world. Her fresh eyes and words planted a seed of validation in my soul. I did have value, maybe no longer to Trey or Phyllis, but to others. I had a place here. Other people cared about me. I was not defined by what Trey and Phyllis thought or did. Why should I give credence to their accusations against my character, because Phyllis had a big purse? I wouldn't buy into that storyline any longer.

"Thank you, Bea, I can't tell you what your sentiment means to me." I felt renewed and empowered and called the kids into the room. "Group hug!"

On the drive over to Ralph's, I listened to Joel Osteen's CD "Think Better, Live Better." It was about going through the valley of despair and rising up, stronger, wiser, more powerful. Joel declares: "I will have beauty for my ashes. I can give God my anguish, pain, and loss, and he will fully restore me, with more beauty and more blessings." Joel's words helped me to stay strong and positive, to keep the momentum going of a sane, happy person. I parked my car outside Ralph's ocean-front Alaskan lodge.

Inside, I ran into Lonnie. She was wearing a grey form-fitted turtleneck with black jeans. She was always so beautiful. "Where is Trey?" She handed me a glass of wine.

"Taking care of your dad. Phyllis needs extra help." I said to her. She flipped her dark blonde hair. "Hm."

I examined the tone of her voice and her facial expressions to decipher if she knew anything or not. She appeared clueless. Jacob walked up to me, and we hugged. I gently patted him on the back a few times.

"Why do you always do that? Like pat, pat, pat, you're a cute little fella?"

"Jacob, I have a glass of wine in my hand, hello?" I smiled at him. "And you are a cute fella." Jacob had striking wild red hair and was about 5 feet 5 inches of cosmic folklore—he was eccentric, the rotors were always turning.

"Where is Trey? Who is watching him?" he asked.

"His mother." I smiled. He laughed and escorted me into the kitchen to get a plate of food.

I saw other friends. Their hugs and kind words comforted me. Even though I felt so rattled inside, I faked it. I partook in casual and lighthearted conversations, like, I love your shoes! Where did you get them? Or, do you prefer smoked or baked salmon?

I did not dare share with anyone the recent Trey-pisode. I thought, he still may come to his senses; we could still work things out.

PHYLLIS'S FAKE NEWS

CHAPTER 4

"Faith, what did you do last night?"

"Mom, what is going on?" I responded, sleepy and irritated.

"Phyllis sent me another email. She said you partied all night and then drove home drunk with the kids. She said she was terrified for the children's safety."

"Seriously? Her son cheats on his wife and leaves his family, and I am the evildoer? Perhaps, Trey is manipulating her into attacking me. This all seems so irrational."

"Were you driving drunk with the kids?"

"No! What the hell is wrong with you? I will not be attacked by all three of you with crazy stories!"

"Calm down, Faith. The email is hateful. I will forward it to you. She said again she was getting an attorney."

"An attorney, for what? Block her. I will handle this."

I have seen Phyllis do this tango before, mostly with Lonnie. She made up cruel stories, then pretended to have heard them from other people so she could portray herself as the innocent messenger, who coincidentally happened to hear the nasty truth about you. She thought her strategy was clever, jumping in and out of realities as it suited her arguments. It was difficult for a logical person to reason with her. The strategy worked quite well on Lonnie, whom she relished keeping in an unbalanced state of mind and with a feeling of inferiority, but I was not Lonnie. I refused to vacation in her alternate reality and battle from a place of made-up lies and delusions. That was not my playground.

I had to be careful with my next move. Emails and text were good, but I needed a record. I needed proof that she was a liar; otherwise, her tales would proliferate and go unchecked. She was counting on me spending so much time defending myself against her wild stories that I would become oblivious to Trey's real machinations. The only conceivable way I could successfully defend myself was to record everything that happened. So then, when they tried to turn my children against me, I would have a record. No "he said, she said," but solid proof—straight from the horses' mouth. I downloaded a recording app on my phone called *TapeACall.* Every lie they told, they would have to own. I would deliver it back to them, neatly, nicely, in an mp3 file.

I called Ralph. "Phyllis accused me of driving drunk with the kids last night," I said. He laughed. At first, I thought he was laughing at me.

"Oh, Phyllis, why does she do these things? No, you were not driving drunk. Tell her to call me, and I will clear it up for her." Ralph said this as if he too had also danced, or at least witnessed the Hamilton tango.

"Thank you for saying that. Trey and I are having a hard time in our marriage. He has been having an affair. He moved in with his mother, and now, she is attacking me. What's a girl got to do to have some peace and quiet while her husband has an affair?" I chuckled. It was my main coping mechanism. No matter what shitty thing was going on, I always managed to squeeze a laugh out of it.

"Oh, so sorry to hear that…I called to invite you to our Halloween Party. Would you like to come?" Ralph said.

"Oh, my gosh, yes! Thank you for thinking of us; we always enjoy your parties."

"We like having all of you over." Dead air ensued.

I rolled my eyes. Trey was always glued to his phone; he never socialized with the other men. He was a turd on a sofa. I tried to let it go, but I could not. They had attacked me as a mother, and even my own mother had fallen for the big Phyllis con.

Ralph continued, "I am sorry about the affair. I hope you and Trey work it out. I like him."

"What? You like Trey? Really?"

"I do," said Ralph, the great, benevolent diplomat, and champion of the philandering husband. It made me sick but alerted me to the reactions I could expect from other people, particularly men. Did they think that when another man was having an affair, he was only "doing his thing"? That it should be overlooked, and things should progress normally within the marital home?

"I suppose he has a good quality or two," I said, trying to find a balanced approach.

Ralph laughed again. "My good friend is going through a similar situation; how about I introduce you two sometime."

"I would like that. Thanks."

There was my first recording, disputing Phyllis's claim that I was driving drunk with my kids. Also, proof that Ralph knew I was not driving drunk. Just in case someone got to him and he changed his story. I had seen a Hamilton flip a bitch before. I saved the recording to my zip drive. Then I texted Phyllis and Simon on a joint thread.

Me: *Leave my mother alone. She has nothing to do with Trey's affair, and she has a heart condition. How thoughtless of you.*

Phyllis: *Jacob said you were drunk and driving with the children. You should be careful; you could get a DUI and lose the kids*

Me: *I talked to Ralph about your concern over my well-being, and he can verify that I was not drunk and driving and, furthermore, he said you are welcome to call him anytime.*

Phyllis: *When you were in California you told Jane you wanted a divorce and you disliked me and Simon. Be patient you will get what you want.*

Me: *Jane? Trey's stepmother? That is a lie. I am done with all the lies; leave my mother alone.*

Phyllis: *She isn't lying; it's true; you have been planning this all along.*

Me: *You always accuse people of things you are plotting. Well news flash, Trey left me; it's only a matter of time before he leaves you. He hates working at St. Mary's.*

Phyllis: *Now you're being mean. Trey will never leave me. He worships me.*

I wondered if she enjoyed making enemies, she had so many—real and imagined. She was rude to me, Simon was ill, and Trey was no longer on the path to success. I could not be sidetracked, running on her hamster wheel, trying to decipher her lies from the truth. I had to put the kids' needs first, and that meant, at a minimum, taking care of my emotional health the best way I could. I decided to ignore her text and block her.

Simon (on a separate thread): *I told Phyllis to let you and Trey work it out. I am sorry she did that to your mother. She promised me she would stop interfering. I think you need to talk to Jane; she told the whole family you said you wanted a divorce.*

Me: *Simon, I am sorry you are having to deal with this; your health should come first. You are right. This is between Trey and me, and regardless of what was said or not said to Jane, Trey is the one having the affair.*

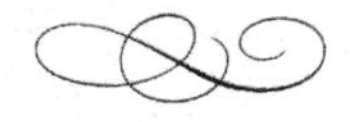

A few months ago, Trey and I had visited Dick and Jane in California. At best, the trip was strained. While we were there, a hysterical Phyllis called Trey. He put her on speakerphone; she was crying, having a jealous fit.

"Jane can't have my children!" we heard her declare. Trey had to pledge his allegiance to her, repeatedly, to calm her down. I was irritated. She was making our entire trip to see Dick about herself. When, in my view, the entire trip was about Dick getting to know his grandchildren. Dick was not a monster in my eyes. Yet, Phyllis hated him, so we all felt pressured to hate him too.

Trey and his dad were trying to rebuild their relationship. When Trey was an active drug user, Dick, being a psychiatrist, knew the best way to help him was by cutting him off and allowing him to hit rock bottom. As a result, Trey was closer to Phyllis and had to play by her rule book. That included Dick being an enemy of the state of Hamilton. Every time Trey saw Dick, it was a punishable offense. My attitude was that Trey was in his forties, and if he wanted to have a relationship with his dad, it was okay. The custody battle over Trey had long ended, right?

After the hysterical phone call, Jane wanted to know what was going on. I told her about Phyllis being jealous and trying to make Trey feel guilty over being at their house. Why not tell? It was the truth. And Phyllis had started it, shit.

Jane took it further than I anticipated. "I can sense your marriage is in trouble. Is someone meddling?"

"I am sure. We went on an anniversary trip for five days, and he packed one outfit. Something is wrong," I said to her with a tone of, What an idiot, right?

"You have taken care of him for so long with his addiction. He doesn't need you to do that anymore.

You are suffocating him," she said as if she had some intuitive sense of the true nature of our union.

I wanted to scream at Jane and then drown myself in her pool. Instead, I said, "We don't spend a great deal of time together. He is consumed with the Center and... his mother."

Trey and Phyllis were needy, psychic vampires draining me of my energy. He, with his bad boy, catch-me-if-you-can act, and she with her celebrity delusions of grandeur. All the while, Simon was in desperate need of medical care, and no one was stepping up to take care of him the way he needed. Phyllis wanted me to take care of Simon during the day and keep his medical issues a secret, especially from Lonnie. She was fearful that if people knew he was sick, they would lose their position in the community. They would be supplanted by a younger up and comer. Simon was the bulldog that moved mountains, and she was the power hungry chihuahua that paraded in designer clothes yipping and yapping. Power, vanity, and addiction were the family plagues. And I was exhausted.

After revisiting the chain of events during our California trip, I decided I should cover all my bases. I activated my recording app and called Jane. "I have bad news. Trey has been having an affair. Somehow, something you said is at the center of his adultery."

"Me? Why would a Hamilton care about anything I said?"

"I don't know. Phyllis said that you said I wanted a divorce during our trip."

"Oh no, you didn't say that. You were upset that he packed one outfit for your anniversary trip, and that he was consumed with St. Mary's. Oh, Faith, I am so sorry about this."

"Thank you for clearing that up. I am so devastated."

"Remember when I told you to put you and Maggie first, all those years ago?"

"Yes, I know you were right then, but I was unable to receive the message. I thought I had to save him."

"The only person who can save him is himself. It was never your responsibility, even though others made you feel as if it was. I always knew you would smarten up, and this was not a forever marriage."

"I am trying to smarten up. I am still puzzled about a bunch of things."

"Remember when Phyllis called me white trash? And what she did to Dick with Thorn? She's going to attack you."

"Well, it's a good thing I've seen her treatment of Lonnie. I know what to expect."

It was 8am, and I was already tinkering in the space of feeling high on adrenaline and emotionally drained. The kids were still sleeping. I walked upstairs into Maggie's room. I crawled into her upholstered cream bed frame. Her paisley pink sheets snugged her face. I watched her sleep. I didn't know how I was going to protect her.

BEAUTY FOR ASHES

CHAPTER 5

October 31 finally arrived, along with the first snowfall of the winter season. Nearly eleven days had passed with no word from Trey. He had not seen his children, nor called to check on them, nor expressed any interest in doing so. I supposed he was living it up in his parents' river front home, with maid service, parties, and dining at the best restaurants. Why should he express interest in his kids? Kids required selfless devotion, consistency, and hard work. That kind of responsibility and commitment had to pale in comparison to partying it up, Hamilton style. Besides, he knew I would sacrifice my life to take care of Maggie and Alex. Why should he have a care in the world?

I drove safely to the local Fred Meyer grocery store before picking up the kids from school. The first snowfall yielded the slipperiest roads. I was wearing navy uggs, grey sweatpants, no makeup, with my dark hair in a sloppy bun. Definitely the defeated-mom look. I unenthusiastically picked out two costumes for them. I normally ordered costumes from Pottery Barn Kids, but it had not been that kind of year.

In the bakery department, all shapes and sizes of spooky desserts were on display in the case. I was a sucker for edible art. Looking at the cheery tiny pumpkin-shaped cakes made me smile. They made me feel cozy and warm. Perhaps they reminded me of my childhood, trick-or-treating, or the anticipation of the unknown, going from house to house in search of sweets and treasures. I decided to buy two orange pumpkin-shaped cakes—one each for Maggie and Alex. Halloween was the beginning of the holiday season. This year mine had the promise of being truly unforgettable.

Picking the kids up from school, I could see that they were visibly excited about Halloween. They had been celebrating all day in their classrooms. As soon as they got in the car, I felt the energy shift.

"What am I going to be tonight? Is daddy coming home?" Maggie asked while scooting in the backseat.

"Yeah, what about me? I want to be a ninja!" Alex asked as he scooted in next to her.

"I haven't heard from your dad, I think he is working overtime at St. Mary's. Anyway, Maggie, I heard you say you wanted to be a witch, and Alex, you said you wanted to be a vampire, remember?"

"Yeah, I am going to be the scariest ninja vampire. Grrr grrr!"

Maggie pushed Alex on the shoulder lightly. "A vampire doesn't growl Alex. Everybody knows that." She flipped her hair at him with disdain.

Alex shoved her back. "Yes, they do, ugh, Maggie. You don't know everything! Mom, can I be the witch and Maggie be the vampire?"

"No, you can't have my costume! Mom tell him, he can't have it!" Maggie emphatically screamed. Alex cupped his hand over his mouth smirking.

I laughed. Nothing like sibling rivalry to keep things in perspective. At home, I showed them their pumpkin cakes and costumes. They were overjoyed with excitement, and I enjoyed watching them scarf down their treats.

Maggie, made me feel like I should reach out to Trey... at least for her sake. I texted him. "Trey, would you like to meet us for trick or treating tonight?"

"Mom, can we have some milk?"

I got up from the black and walnut dining room table to walk into my beautiful white recently remodeled kitchen. I opened the cabinet doors, using our new sparkly silver handles. I remembered briefly picking these handles out with Trey, not even a year ago. Next to the stainless steel refrigerator, that we had argued over, sat a beautiful amethyst crystal he had given me for my birthday. I felt ghost punched in the gut.

"Where is my milk?"

I pulled out two small blue plastic sized toddler cups. I poured the kids some milk, about half-way full. I deliver it to them nicely.

"Oh, really? I am almost eight years old, this is unacceptable. I want a large glass of milk." Maggie glared at me.

"Ya, I ain't no baby." Alex backed her up, puffing out his chest with pumpkin frosting drizzled down his white shirt.

I stood and admired this rare moment of unification. If only it had been directed at someone else, would I have appreciated it. "Portion control is important, it saves us money and its less to clean-up for whenever you spill it." I gave them a half smile of sarcasm and comforting love.

"Portion control? You gave us each a whole cake to eat. I would like a glass of milk to match the size of this cake." Maggie nodded her head at me, pointing to the cake.

"No," I said.

Ding. A text message. I picked up my phone off the dining room table.

Trey: *My paper is due tomorrow. Is it ready?*

Me: *Are you crazy? No, I am not doing your homework anymore. Ask Eve to write your papers.* My heart started palpitating. I walked back into the kitchen.

What was I? His doormat? I got no respect. Even the sister wives of TLC are treated better than this.

Trey: *You better have my paper ready tomorrow, or I will turn off the lights in the house.*

Me: *Do you think hurting me somehow doesn't hurt your children? What about your kids? I guess we can all learn to do homework in the dark and navigate the house with flashlights.*

I was rattled to my core. His threat showed no natural, protective instinct toward the kids. The more I was away from him, the more I saw the kind of person he was and what he valued in life: himself. Still, I would be damned and living without electricity before I wrote that paper.

"Oh no!" I heard a squeal from the dining room. I walked back in, Alex had spilt milk on the table, it was now dripping on my beloved pink greek marble floor.

"Mom, I am sorry," I looked at Alex, who wore most of his ghoulish snack on his face.

"It's okay, I will clean it up. Kids, go put your costumes on. We are going to Ralph's house soon. Let me know if you need any help!" The kids ran up the stairs.

As I was cleaning up the spilt milk with hot water and a wad of paper towels, I wondered, How could Trey not be here for the kids' Halloween? How could his paper supersede his own kids' special day? He didn't even acknowledge that in the kid world, this is a big day!

I felt tears rising, stinging my eyes. I pressed the warm saturated paper towels against my face. I sat down deflated on the marble floor in the family dining room, my legs out stretched in front of me. I looked around the vacant room. There, I felt the loneliness and isolation pulsating the quietness of the air and I realized, no one is here for me, and no one is coming. I was all alone. Suddenly, I was a single mother, being brutalized by the one person who had promised to protect me, help me, lift me up, and it sucked. It always sucks when someone changes for the worse.

Ralph's house was lavishly decorated for Halloween. It was party central, after all. Kids were everywhere, dressed in costumes, running up and down the slippery street in a foot of snow. There was a big inflated Grim Reaper on the lawn, carved pumpkins that were aligned to each step up to the double-door front entryway, four skeletons suspended from the top of his porch ceiling, and a smoky mist that exuded from the home. Inside, his spooky mansion's decorations only got better. I was greeted by a decently-clad French maid, serving misting purple martinis, and another one serving poisonous green candied apples. His wife had a huge assortment of food laid out on the buffet table. Ralph was behind the bar, as usual, making drinks to order for all his friends. Such warm, loving people, I thought. Maggie and Alex took off downstairs to the activity room where some of the other kids were playing. Lonnie greeted me with a hiss, dressed as Cat Woman.

"Hiss...Hello, sister. Nice costume. Hisss..." She was disappointed in my boring appearance—a white, form-fitting t-shirt, denim leggings, and cowboy boots.

"Sorry, I didn't dress up, again. You look so hot... meow,"

"Hissss...meow! Jacob is Batman." I looked over to the outside deck. Batman was having a martini and smoking a cigarette. "Let's go get a drink."

"Okay." I proceeded with caution.

Ralph came from behind the bar, he handed me a champagne glass. He was dressed as Shriek, green face and all. "Are you feeling better?" He put his arm around me and squeezed my shoulder. Yep, it was the sympathy squeeze.

"No. But I am doing my best to adjust and keep things as normal as possible for the kids. They are the most important." This sounded more pathetic spoken aloud than it had inside my head when I rehearsed it.

Lonnie heard me from ten feet away. "What are you talking about? What is going on?" She pried into our conversation, dying to know the gossip.

"I didn't want to tell you, but I kicked Trey out of the house. He is living with your dad and Phyllis. I caught him having an affair." I took a drink of sparkling champagne, I noticed an eyeball floating in the bottom of the glass.

"What? No! Jacob come over here!" Lonnie screamed from across the room and used her patent black leather cat tail as a motioning device.

"Okay, Cat Woman. I will take you now." Jacob seductively slid up to her, flipped his cape over his shoulder, dipped her and kissed her right on the mouth. I suspected tongue. We all stopped and stared. I thought, quite a dramatic display of affection. These two were either passionately in love, or fighting to the death. I preferred the latter.

"Faith, your costume sucks, what are you: a born-again virgin?"

Lonnie nudged him in the side. "Stop. Be nice. Faith told me that Trey is having an affair, and she kicked him out."

"Oh, Faith, I am so sorry. He is an idiot. A first-class idiot. What man would cheat on you?" Jacob said, now trying to comfort the born-again virgin.

I replied suspiciously, "Thanks, Jacob." I rolled my eyes slightly.

"I knew something was wrong. I didn't know what. Who is this tramp? I will claw her eyes out," Lonnie said, putting up her black fake nails in the air in an attack position.

"Trey told me her name was Eve. I don't know if that is true. He is protective of her." I took another drink.

"Well, I have your back, sister. I don't trust Trey. I worry about him living around my dad." Lonnie squinted her eyes at me, as to convey her mistrust of Trey.

"Your dad needs fulltime professional care."

"Phyllis said they were going to be hiring caregivers. We will see if that ever happens. She only cares about what the neighbors think."

"Luke, come over here. I want to introduce you to someone." Jacob motioned with his big cape toward a nice-looking man in the buffet line, sipping on a bottle of beer. Jacob leaned over and whispered in my ear, "Luke thinks you're hot."

I went from being distraught over Trey and Simon and Lonnie's reaction, to being on high alert.

"What? Jacob, no. I can't. I am still married. The born-again virgin isn't interested!" I tried to push the rewind button on Jacob's plotted course. Jacob gave me a devilish howl and a devious look. I knew the ratio of men to women in Alaska was high, but jeez, I had only been publicly separated for a few minutes.

Luke approached me. He was about five foot ten, with sandy blonde hair, green eyes, and boyish dimples, quirky and charming. He was not dressed up either. Thank God, because how do you get to know some weirdo adult wearing a costume anyway? Then I would judge him over the costume he had chosen—an unfair situation all the way around.

"Have we met?" I asked him while stepping away from him. Lonnie and Jacob were sizing up the situation. Jacob was probably thinking he was going to hook Luke up, while Lonnie was thinking about how she might use my affair to help her earn points with Phyllis.

"Like three times? Seriously, you don't remember me? That hurts my feelings." He had a pouty look on his face.

"No way. I totally remember you. You are Luke, Jacob's friend." I batted my eyes at him. I didn't know what I was doing. I felt awkward. I had not been in such a scenario in a decade. I asked myself if I was flirting or being bitchy, or maybe I am a bitchy flirt?

"That's not funny." Luke put his empty bottle of Alaskan Amber on the coffee table and walked off.

"Jeez, Faith, you're such a smart ass," Batman berated me. "If I was the real Batman, I would..."

Lonnie interrupted. "Give her time, honey. This is her first divorce." She stroked the back of his cape.

I felt ridden with anxiety. Picking up men with my kids downstairs, who does that? I asked myself, was that what single mothers do? What is going on? Was this my new normal? Weren't divorcees supposed to keep their kids away from potential mates until they were engaged, or something like that? Wasn't that written in the single-parent playbook? I flipped my hair at Jacob and gave him a look of disdain. "I am going to go check on my kids."

Downstairs, the kids were playing hide-and-seek. All the lights were off. I felt an overwhelming sense of urgency to find them. I saw Alex hiding under the pool table with candy stuffed in his mouth. "Naughty vampire," I whispered to him.

"Shhh," Alex quieted me.

I saw the seeker coming around the corner; it was a werewolf, crawling on its hands and knees. I watched Maggie sliding on her stomach from behind the theater chairs to the other side of the sofa. The familiar ding sounded: incoming text.

"Turn your phone off, you're going to blow my cover" Alex whispered.

Trey: *Bring my kids over to my parents' house, now*

What? Am I stupid? Do they think I would go over on their turf with my kids? I did not want to have to fight in front of my children, and all Phyllis wanted was a fight. She was desperate for control and using Trey to bait the hook, but I was not Lonnie. I had seen the bait, the rod, and the fisherman before.

Me: *They can come over to Ralph's house. The kids are playing hide-and-seek*

I knew that Phyllis disliked Ralph and his family and would never willingly come over to their house.

Trey: *You can't keep my kids from me. Bring them over here, now.*

Me: *What's the big deal? We will be here, waiting eagerly for your arrival*

Trey: *This means war bitch. I will destroy you.*

Who says stuff like that? He was going to destroy the mother of his children? Was he high on steroids? Had he been binge watching reruns of Hulk Hogan? Regardless, reconciliation seemed less and less likely. It was becoming clear that the children were a pawn in their game, another angle to leverage.

I left Alex and Maggie and went back upstairs. Lonnie and Jacob were at the bar, speaking in hushed tones, perhaps plotting. I was emotionally and physically exhausted, and all from just a few text messages. I tilted my head back to take the last sip of my champagne, making sucking noises trying not hard not to swallow the floating eyeball.

"Don't worry the eyeball is edible" Luke, again.

"Oh thanks, the last thing I need to do is to choke to death on an edible eyeball. Then it would be *'poor Faith she drank herself to death.'"* I cowered thinking how happy it would make Trey and Phyllis. I turned to Luke. "I am sorry about earlier. I can have a smart mouth. I apologize."

"It's okay. Jacob told me what's going on. I would like to take you out sometime. Here let me give you my card." He reached around to his back jean pocket, pulled out his wallet on a chain. He smiled at me and handed me his card.

I looked at the card. Luke was a realtor for Elite Realty. "I would enjoy that. Thank you for offering to cheer me up," I said, trying to keep it friendly. I heard people chanting, "Macarena!" Ugh, a group dance moment. Great. I began crunching on the eyeball.

I walked away from everyone and sat on the moss colored couch by myself. I told myself that I was content to be alone in a room full of people. I would enjoy a bit of solitude and observe everyone else's good time, or perhaps I was taking Trey's place as the turd on the sofa.

A woman sat down beside me. She seemed nice; she had long blonde hair and clear, beautiful skin. She was not wearing makeup nor a costume. "My name is Camille."

We shook hands. "Nice to meet you. Do you have children here?"

"Five! One of them is coming later; he is nineteen." She crossed her legs.

"Wow, you look amazing, I can't believe you have a nineteen-year-old. Are you married?" I smiled at here.

She yelled across the room, "Jimmy, come here."

I sighed despair. "My husband and I have been having problems; he isn't here. In fact, he threatened to destroy me."

Jimmy approached and broke our conversation. He was younger by at least ten years. He was wearing a yellow adidas jumpsuit and an eye patch over his left eye. Camille introduced us, and I congratulated him on his five children.

"Stepfather of five. I don't have any biological children." He moved the eye patch aside to scratch his face and sat down across from Camille.

"Stepfathers are often better role models than biological fathers. Good for you."

Camille smirked in agreement. "I had a difficult breakup with my ex. He built all the roads in this city, he had a lucrative business, but he was abusive. I left him, and when I did, I left everything. I had to start completely over. It was worth it, though, and I would do it again." She looked inquisitively at me.

"I don't know what is going to happen. I feel like I am constantly on high alert. I can't sleep. I don't know what is coming around the bend. We haven't hit our rock bottom. I don't know who I can trust." In the background, Cat Woman and Batman were doing the Macarena.

"I am a woman of faith. Let's pray." Camille uncrossed her legs and moved closer to me, she took my hands. "Dear God, you know Faith's situation. Please assist her with your infinite wisdom and love. Give her beauty for her ashes. Amen."

"Amen. Camille, I was listening to a Pastor whom promised me beauty for my ashes. How did you know that?" Had she staged a hidden camera in my car to watch me? The paranoia was contagious.

"I didn't know that." She laughed, "I just know it's true. God did the same for me, and God will do the same for you."

"Thank you." I felt the verity in her message.

"What do you do for work?

"I was taking care of Simon and helping Trey manage his life; now, I don't know. I am trying to press through to greener pastures, I suppose." Suddenly, I realized that I had been helping other people build their lives, and, in the process, I had not built one single thing for myself. I had nothing to declare as my own, not even the Master's degree I had been working on. I had sacrificed all of my time, energy, and talent for this marriage, for this family, and because of it I had no outside resources. A new level of panic set in. I nervously rubbed my eyes.

"I sell DoTerra oils for a living," Camille said. "Are you interested in getting into the oil business?"

"I don't know if I am in the right mind-frame to sell anything. I would probably use it as a therapy session and depress everyone."

Jimmy laughed. "Oh, come on, you will be fine. You're smart; you're cute; you are at the right party. Cheer up! Look at Luke. He is in love with you, and probably some others."

"Jimmy, maybe Faith doesn't want to date anyone. That's not the answer. She needs time to process and mourn the lost relationship."

"Listen, the best way to get over someone is to get under someone else." Jimmy raised his one eyebrow at me. I could see inside his head; he was chanting, "Do it, do it, do it."

I cringed at the vulgarity.

Jacob approached me. "I saw you talking to Luke. You guys going on a date?"

"You are such a wizard." Camille seemed mesmerized by Jacob as he spun around in his Batman cape.

"I thought he was Batman," I said.

"Jung's archetypes of different people. They highlight their basic human motivation towards others and the world around them. Jacob is a total wizard."

"Okay," I said, bewildered, acting as if I knew what the hell she was talking about.

I wondered what I was—caregiver or doormat for the mentally ill?

THE BIDDING WAR

CHAPTER 6

When my alarm sounded, I awakened from a vivid dream. I was in a large city in a bookstore. I was wearing a red mid-length dress, speaking to a crowd. There were copies of a book on a table nearby. When I finished speaking, I walked to a table and sat down. People, mostly women, approached me. There was a male energy by my side, a lover, a similar energy to the one in the yoga studio. Not Trey. I could tell this was a special dream. I had often had messenger dreams. I wondered what God was showing me—maybe hope, rebirth? That I will survive this nightmare and find a new love? At that moment, I felt so far away from that vision, and all I could think about was Trey.

It was mid-November. Weeks passed with no word from Trey. I was worried about him, but my pride kept me from reaching out. All I could do was stay determined to keep things as structured as possible for the kids. Whenever I felt unsteady, I visualized pushing all thoughts and emotions of Trey away from me. I told myself, *The kids cannot see me struggling; they cannot see me crying and out of control.* The future generation of my family was most important, not Trey's antics. He was an adult; he had had his time to shine. The kids had a right to a *somewhat* normal childhood. I minimized Trey's impact on my family by not allowing him to change the mother I was. In fact, my mothering duties were the same, since Trey was rarely at home anyway. When the kids were at school, I did have free time, but my mental state was so compromised, it was hardly enjoyable. Regardless, I tried to give the kids got the best of me, just like before.

When the kids were away, I tried to allow myself time to grieve -as much as someone can grieve in a state of suspension. Even grieving felt incomplete. I continuously hypothesized scenarios about what was really happening. I sought solutions to problems I did not fully understand. I was scrambled, trying to find a remedy to piece things back together. In my deepest desires, I wanted my family back. I had never been so isolated from Trey. I kept expecting him to come to his senses and try to negotiate a peace treaty, but time kept passing without any indication that he was ready to be a family man again.

It was the night of St. Joseph's school auction. We had bought a table months ago—well before I found out about Trey's affair. I had no desire to go but felt compelled to put on a good face for the kids. I did not recall sending out invitations, and I had to fill a table for ten. I verbally invited the PTO president, Chelsea, and her husband, as well as Kent and his wife Sandra, a couple from a well-known political activist group. I had not invited anyone else, though. I was going to have an empty table.

I panicked over the idea of hosting an empty table alone. I rationalized that Trey was also responsible; he should have to go with me. Perhaps we would have a good night, and he would realize what an idiot he had been. I was sick of living this way. I wanted my family back. In desperation I called Trey, only to be surprised when he answered.

"Hi, Faith. I have been thinking about you."

"Really?"

"Yes, we should talk."

"Okay. Good idea. Tonight is the St. Joseph's auction. I want you to go with me. Will you pick me up?"

"I will be there at six-thirty."

I got off the phone feeling positive. Trey wanted to talk, so he must have come to his senses. He must miss us and want his family back together. I only hoped he was willing to tell me the truth, so we could properly rebuild. The truth would provide a solid foundation. We could not rebuild on lies. We could not change or grow from what we failed to acknowledge—the sneaking around, the lying, the affair, it all had to come to light.

The nanny showed up at 6 p.m., right on time. Alex rushed to open the door in his green footy pajamas. Bea wore a red t-shirt and jeans, and had a yellow satchel of goodies thrown over her shoulder.

"Bethy, let's go build a snowman," Alex shouted at her, full of excitement.

"No, Bea, let's go downstairs and watch *Wreck-It Ralph,*" Maggie said aloofly, but still calmly combative brushing her dolls hair.

"Kids, I have a better idea. I brought all these crafts for us to do." Bea opened her big, yellow leather satchel—full of origami paper, paints, and Thanksgiving-themed projects.

"Yes!" Maggie said, jumping up and down. She threw her doll to the ground.

"I want to do mine first," Alex declared.

I looked at Bea. "The kids are in heavy competition for your affection."

"I love these guys." She hugged them both. Maggie squirmed away; she always shied from affection.

I went upstairs to change. In my closet was ugly dress after ugly dress. I debated if I should be slutty at my kids' schools auction, or classy and sophisticated. I was the vice president of the parent-teacher organization, and last year I had been the president. I needed to be a good example and dress the part of a picture-perfect matronly mother. I found a knee-length, white, turtleneck Vera Wang dress. I thought it was appropriate, and slipped into silver heels.

I heard Trey arrive, and peeked over the balcony to see Bea open the black wooden door. He did not even acknowledge her, just breezed past her to the kids. Bea and I had a solid relationship, but I thought, If you are leaving your kids in someone's care, shouldn't you treat them like royalty?

"Hi, babies. I have missed you," In the foyer Trey was squatting in his black suit.

Maggie asked, "Daddy, daddy, daddy, when are you coming home?" Maggie lept into his arms. Alex followed.

I rushed downstairs to interject before Trey blew his own cover. "He is helping Papa Simon, and we are all doing our best to get him better." I stood near our giant gold wall mirror across from the front door. I exchanged looks with Trey.

"Yes, that is right," Trey stood up. He proudly agreed; he preferred being cast as the noble hero.

"Is that what you are wearing?" He looked up and down at me with judgment in his eyes.

I felt unattractive and hurt by the tone of his voice. "No, I guess not." I went back upstairs to change. I rifled through my closet, again, in search of something less motherly, and more slutty.

He wanted me to feel like I was not good enough for him. After all these years of marriage, I was suddenly not good enough. Tears started to bubble up in my eyes. I sat on my closet floor. I talked myself out of crying and ruining my make-up. Instead, I took several deep breaths and prayed, "Please, God, give me strength, give me clarity, and please give me patience. Amen."

I kept praying until I felt more centered in my own skin, and God's reboot kicked in. I found a hot pink peplum Nicole Miller dress; it was about an eight on the slutty scale. I was either going to be the matronly mother who had given up, or the slutty, hot mama still fighting. I walked back down the stairs.

"That looks good." His eyes roamed all over my body. He enjoyed turning his wife into a trollop at his kids' school auction.

Trey was driving Simon's new red Mercedes. "Nice car."

"Yeah, I wonder if my mom will give it to me when..." He paused.

"When what?" Please, God, do not tell me he was going to say, 'When Simon dies.'

"When I trade in my car," he self-corrected.

"Your car is great, a classic," I said to him, trying to be encouraging.

"No, it's old."

"It's a 2011; it was like seventy thousand dollars!"

"It's old."

"Anyway, you look good, Trey. I like your suit," I said, trying to be normal and positive.

"It's Armani. I think the sleeves are short. My mom liked it, though."

Silence ensued. I looked out the passenger side window and rolled my eyes. I thought, *Patience, God, patience.*

"Aren't you going to tell me I look nice?"

"I already did." Trey's face was stone cold as he rhythmically drove to the Gala.

I reminded myself again to be positive. Obviously, I had to handle Trey with kid gloves. I decided to try one final approach before I would give in and call him a fucker.

"Trey, I know in the past we have had bad things happen in our relationship, but this one seems to be the worst. Would you agree?"

"I guess so." He sounded disinterested.

"Well, I would like to get to the bottom of it and try to rebuild. You are missing the kids growing up; you missed Halloween. I don't want you to miss Thanksgiving."

"Okay." He responded without emotion.

"Good. Well then, who is Eve?"

"There is no Eve."

"Okay, who was the lady I talked to on the phone that started this chain of events?" I asked calmly, but with a tone of get-it-together-dumbass.

"Nobody. Let's get through the night." He shut down completely.

I was not accustomed to not being able to reach him. I felt powerless. The anger turned into tears of hopelessness, and I started to cry. "Trey, please tell me. I can't live like this. I need to know what is going on. We have eleven years of marriage and two children. I deserve more from you than this. Why are you so hateful? What have I done to make you hate me?"

"Stop crying. You are going to look like hell."

"Do you want a divorce?"

"No."

"I can divorce you at any point in time. Get that straight." My tears turned back to anger.

He pulled up to the valet at the Feldberg Hotel, parked the car, unbuckled his seatbelt from the tan leather seats, and then unbuckled mine. He turned his head toward me. "You will be homeless. You need me."

"I don't need you like this. I don't need anyone," I yelled at him. The valet opened my car door. I hurried past him, trying not to make eye contact.

I forced a "Thank you" out of my mouth and kept moving through the revolving doors.

Trey hustled around the car to me, put his arm around my shoulder and whispered in my right ear. "Let's pretend to be happy. It is the kids' night." I wiggled away from him.

What kind of psychological warfare was this? I thought, the kids' night? Now, he had an awareness of others? His estranged children? What was I, the wife of Bugsy Siegel? What the fuck was going on? I had not signed up for this kind of marriage. Trey, full of masculine energy, reached over to grab my hand. I snatched it away.

"Don't fucking touch me."

He leaned over to in a hushed tone "Go clean your face; you look terrible."

"Fucker."

I went to the lobby bathroom. I felt worthless. Trey wanted me to be his public wife and raise his kids while he did whatever the fuck he wanted with whomever he wanted. This was not a marriage. This is not the mother, wife, or human being I envisioned myself to be. I was better than what Trey would have me believe about myself. I remembered what Joel had said, "I will have beauty for my ashes. I am not what people say I am. I am what God says I am." I prayed to God there in the pepto bismol colored stall of the Feldberg bathroom.

"Please, God, give me the courage to fight this battle and harden my heart to Trey. Let all things that no longer serve me fall away."

I took a few deep breaths and with their cheap toilet paper I cleaned up my face the best

I could. I told myself I was beautiful, and I just looked hungover from the night before, not like a hysterical mess crying in a ladies' bathroom stall. To Catholics, looking hungover was preferable to looking like an emotionally tormented wife.

Back in the full golden and light blue ballroom, Trey was giving a credit card to the auction ladies. He was getting our bid number 113. I felt a streak of revenge, disguised as empowerment, ignite inside of me. I gave him a look like, *Let's be charitable, bitch.* I found our table. Thankfully, all four of our guests had arrived for our ten-topper table.

Chelsea was wearing a long, yellow gown. We locked eyes. "You look beautiful." I gave her a hug and a social double-cheek kiss.

"So do you, Faith. How are you?" She curiously examined my face.

I suggested a drink and steered her to the bar.

"What is wrong? We have to present the auction chairs soon."

"Yes, on stage in front of all these lovely people."

"Are you okay?" she asked and handed me a glass of red wine.

"I fucking hate him." I took a big gulp, not like a refined lady, but like a woman wearing cutoffs at a monster truck rally.

"Oh... dear," Chelsea retorted. She stepped back, looking at me with her big, blue eyes inflated. Chelsea had not seen this side of me. She had not seen the veil lifted, where words like "Fuck you, eat a dick," and "Cocksucker" existed. You know—the unfiltered underneath.

"Let's go look at the auction items." Chelsea redirected the conversation that was going nowhere pleasant fast. She walked me over to the ballroom wall, where the majority of the auction items were on top of pale blue table cloths on display. There were jewelry, china, paintings, gift certificates, vacations, and countless other items to choose.

I simmered down. I tilted my head back and drank the rest of my wine, put down the empty glass by a planter, and grabbed another one off a random table. "Look at this beautiful mink coat! I will take it." I placed my bid number down at $3,000.

"What about the gloves and matching hat?" Chelsea was amused picking them up.

"Definitely. I need the whole ensemble. For sure." I put my number down again.

"Look at this painting. I think it is by Sydney Laurence."

"Not my style, but it would make a great gift." I put my bid number down. I took a sip wine.

"Uh-oh, somebody's coming over here," Chelsea warned me, snickering.

I looked behind me. Trey was coming. I turned my back to him and downed the rest of the wine. I put the glass down on the pale blue table cloth. "Hi, Trey. I was bidding on this beautiful, timeless piece of art." I motioned with my hand to welcome his gaze upon this lovely piece of creative expression. "Don't you love it?" I smiled at him, extending an invitation to launch back into the fire-breathing dragon I had encountered in the car. He grabbed my arm firmly and escorted me outside the ballroom into the less occupied hallway.

"What the fuck do you think you are doing?" he asked in a low-tone whisper but with force.

"You told me to pretend to be happy, and I was thinking, art curator -that would make me happy." I continued to smile.

"You can't go around bidding like a high roller! Who do you think you are?" He talked down to me like I was a spineless servant trying to upgrade my lowly station in life.

"I think I am your main bitch, so I should be able to indulge myself. Your side bitches can eat the crumbs." I walked away from him in haste.

It was a shame. The night had started out with such promise. I had intended to have an elevated, high-minded conversation with him, but he only understood depravity and words such as main bitch, side bitch, you-a-bitch, and son-of-a-bitch.

Back at the table, Chelsea was seated next to her husband and our friends, Kent and Sandra. They were wearing matching ensembles—navy and white pinstripes. I said hello to each of them and asked Chelsea to sit next to me.

"I bought wine for the table; please have some." Chelsea poured me a glass. She leaned over and whispered, "Are you okay? Where is he?" She seemed intrigued by the drama.

"I don't know, probably trying to undo all my bidding. What a jackass." I said it too loudly, and everyone around the table stopped to look at me.

"I am sorry. I hope you are all enjoying yourself," I back-pedaled politely.

Kent respected me as a lady, and here I was, at my kid's school auction, yelling "Jackass" across the table—not my best moment. I regrouped. I thought, *I can't allow Trey to do this to me. I must avoid and deflect all his negativity and maintain my dignity. That is the path to success, maintaining self-respect and dignity. I can't allow myself to swoop down to that level again.*

After some silent self-soothing, I felt grounded.

"Thank you for inviting us," Kent said. "Next weekend, the mayor is hosting a dinner. Would you and Trey like to be our guests?" He looked so sweetly into my eyes.

"Yes, of course. That sounds amazing. Also, I love your matching outfits."

"She made me do it" Kent said. Sandra shook her head irritated.

"Well you did it and that's adorable. Good idea Sandra." I looked at her.

"Pinstripes are so sophisticated," Sandra retorted.

"Where is Trey?" Kent asked.

"I don't know. I think he may have a little gas," I said, pointing to my stomach, and covering for him again.

"Oh, no! Here he comes!" Chelsea sounded as if she was about to witness a 1990's episode of Jerry Springer. Trey stomped to the table and threw his gigantic body into the chair next to me. I rolled my eyes. He folded his arms and looked away.

"We have to go introduce the auction ladies. Let's go," Chelsea pulled me up. I noticed Aunt Denali in the audience. She was at the head table with Uncle Peter. I smiled at her; she gave me a warm look and wave of recognition.

Chelsea spoke into the microphone, greeting the attendees and thanking them. Then, introducing herself and me. I stood in front of hundreds of people, and as I looked out at all of them I wondered how many other people were pretending like me. How many people were barely keeping it together, balancing a double life, an affair, an illness, a betrayal. Surely, I could not be the only one.

LUKE

CHAPTER 7

"Maybe Eve is a realtor," Chelsea said as she plopped down on my sofa wearing a matching lululemon camo workout suit. Chelsea had been running errands for St. Josephs and had come by to deliver the mink coat, gloves, and hat I had won at the auction.

A moment of silence ensued until I jumped up with great enthusiasm. It was an ah-ha moment, like the one Oprah talks about, except less positive in context.

"Yes, Chelsea! That explains it! That way, if Eve sells the house for Trey, they will both get a payday." I felt as if I had discovered the lost city of Atlantis.

"We don't know for sure," Chelsea said, her hand pressed under her chin, now rethinking her assessment.

"Nope, that is it. I am going to text this realtor I met a while ago. Luke. I am sure he'll know her."

At times, the state of limbo Trey had put me by withholding Eve's identity was worse than the actual affair. I thought Eve was the root of our problem, and if I brought who she was to light, I could regain control over this situation and end it, for better or worse.

Me: *Hi Luke, this is Faith from Ralph's Halloween Party.*

Chelsea was looking at me like I had lost my mind. But I was determined to make this the long-awaited remedy to all my restless nights.

Luke: *Nice to hear from you.*

Me: *Do you know a realtor named Eve?*

Luke: *No, I do not know an Eve. Lunch next week?*

I showed Chelsea the text. She said, "Fairbanks is small; everyone knows everyone. God will reveal the truth to you when he thinks you are ready. In his divine time."

Her words fell on vacant ears. I continued to text Luke some emojis.

"You already know so many truths," she went on. "You know he is having an affair; you know he is choosing her over you and the kids; you know he is checked out on being a family man. Does it matter who she is? He wants another life. Hell, he has already been living one behind your back, for God only knows how long. That is not what a husband and a father does. Fuck him." She grabbed my phone and set it on the stained glass coffee table in front of the bookcase.

My mood shifted from Nancy Drew to parrot without a voice box. My circumstances, and my need to put everything neatly and tightly in a little box with a big bow, made me feel defenseless. It was my own mental illness glaring back at me. My thought pattern, over time, had deteriorated to: Here, look at this; it is a piece of smelly poo, but it has such a nice, pretty, big, red bow, doesn't it? And here, just add a little Chanel No5, and it will smell all right, too. The evidence was clear—Trey was the smelly piece of poo, and I was a certifiable control freak.

Chelsea's words rattled me; they rattled to the point that I thought I hated her for a slight second. But the truth was the truth and some messes you just could not clean up no matter how many times you sprayed it with high-end perfume. I put my head down into my hands and began to sob. "I have been a good wife—the best wife. You would not believe the things I have gone through with Trey. The things I have done to help him. Above and beyond and above and beyond and above and beyond," I said to her, I wiped the tears streaming from my eyes with my shirt sleeve.

"Faith, to sacrifice yourself for another person is a beautiful thing to do. But there comes a time when forgiveness means letting go and walking away. God does not want you to keep hurting. God will give you beauty for your ashes." She reached across the coffee table to hold my hands.

"Beauty for my ashes." I looked up at her with tears still fresh in my eyes. I felt the truth in her words like before, but instead of anguish rushing over me, I felt a settled peace set in. I felt a tiny spark of hope.

Carter ran down the stairs. "Alex isn't sharing!"

I continued to wipe the wet tears from my cheeks, looked at the boys, and smiled at her. "Then, there's this."

We laughed.

Soon after Chelsea and her children left, the denial set back in, and I found myself reeling, thinking about Eve. I had unfinished business. All the breakthroughs that I'd had on the sofa with Chelsea were gone, and I was back in investigative mode, ready to fight. I googled *Eve, real estate, Fairbanks, AK* and *Eve, realtor, Fairbanks Alaska,* and *Eve listing house, Fairbanks, Alaska.* The only hit I got was an 80-year-old lady named Eve, and I was certain Trey thought he was too good for her.

My thoughts were on a loop: Eve, the harlot, who was going to sell my house. I couldn't stop myself. I was on a one-way street going the wrong direction and headed for a head-on collision. I texted Trey in a fit of rage.

Me: *You and your tramp will not sell my house, where my kids live, for a payday.*

Trey: *Yes, we will*

Had he confessed that Eve was a realtor? I could not believe anything he said. Fuck it. If Trey had forgotten that I was a sexy, desirable lady, I would just have to make him remember. If anyone was selling my house, it was not going to be Eve, the hooker, but Luke, the man-boy with dimples. I called him.

"I think we should go to the Mayor's dinner together. Would you be my date?"

"That sounds wonderful."

"Pick me up around seven."

My first real counter-attack was underway. If I took Luke to the Mayor's dinner, gossip would spread like wildfire. I knew that after Trey heard about me with another man, he would go insane with jealousy and demand to have me back.

For this to work, I had to prepare properly. I had to be a hot, sexy lioness for Luke, my targeted prey animal. I walked into my closet. I looked at my uninspiring, middle-aged mother clothing. So frustrating! No hot, sexy lioness clothes for me to bedazzle Luke. There was a pair of black, shiny, leathery pants. I recalled wearing them at a KISS concert ten years ago. I thought they were hot, and they'd protect me better from the cool night air than a dress, anyway. I tried them on; they looked good. I found a golden, shimmery knit sweater to match, and three-inch, red, patent leather heels. I felt as shiny as a Las Vegas prostitute on New Year's Eve, and I looked great. At least, that is what I told myself.

The doorbell rang. Alex answered; it was Bea.

"Where are you going?" She looked at me up and down, perhaps uncertain about my attire. It was the season to be merry, not scary.

I whispered, "Show stopping, right? There is man coming over named Luke, to take me to a dinner party. It's not a date. I promise; we're friends." I asked myself whether this was what separated people did. It was so uncomfortable and rather jarring.

"Good for you." Bea did not care, she stretched out at the kitchen bar in her reindeer inspired onesie. I was freaking out. Still, I could not shake the feeling that I was sinning, walking a fine line between honorable mother and lady of the night. I was consumed with nerves and regret. The doorbell rang. I thought, *Oh shit, what have I done?* Instantly, I wanted him to leave. I wanted to cancel and hide in my wardrobe closet with a blanket over my face.

Bea opened the door. It was Luke. "Come on in." She smiled at me like I was a naughty, naughty whore mother. I wondered if she could sense my fear.

"Hi. Luke Parker." He extended his hand, and they shook. The kids came over and ogled the strange man at the door.

"Who are you?" Alex asked walking right up to him.

"Hey, buddy. I am Luke. Who are you?" Luke bent down in his navy suit to make eye contact with Alex.

"I am Alex. Do you want to play *Skylanders*?"

"Maybe another time," I said. "Luke and I have a meeting to go to, and we are running late. Oh, Luke, that is Maggie, by the way." I pointed to Maggie, who had her back against the wall and a twisted look on her face. "It takes her a while to warm up to people."

"Yuk," Maggie said timidly, stepping from around the corner of the formal dining room.

"She looks like you," Luke said, smiling at her.

I marshaled Luke outside. He was driving a new silver Audi sedan. All realtors had nice cars. Big whoop, I thought. I wondered if Eve had a nice car or a rattletrap. Probably a rattletrap. "You must be a great real estate agent."

"This is the most luxe thing I've ever bought for myself." He walked around to open the door for me. Trey would never have done that.

"So, are you from Fairbanks?" I asked.

"Kenai. My parents own a building supply company there, and they wanted me to take it over, but I am not ready for that. I like Fairbanks better."

"Have we really met before?" I was surprised I did not remember him; he was so kind and easy on the eyes. I wondered how I could've overlooked him.

"Three times, like I said. The last time I was with my then girlfriend, she was so jealous of you. She thought I liked you. Can you believe that?" He looked over at me and winked. Hmm...man-boy dimples and a winker...that's a red flag.

"And how do you know Jacob?" I asked, trying to gauge how much I could potentially trust him.

"Jacob, Lonnie, and I have been hanging out for a while. They're cool people."

I figured they must have met on the party circuit. I determined it was a superficial friendship. "Are you sure you don't know anyone named Eve?"

"What is it with this Eve?" Luke looked exasperated.

"Trey told me his girlfriend was named Eve, and they wanted to sell my house," I said dramatically, hoping it would joggle some memory into him.

"Trey is bad news and has been that way long before he met you. You can do better. Everybody thinks so."

"You're right. I can do better. I would like to surround myself with real, honest people who have good intentions. Is that too much to ask?" I felt annoyed that the simplicity of my request was beyond foreseeable obtainment, and my world was upside down. I envied people like Luke, who I imagined lived an honest life. People who had the luxury of being unburdened by the darkness of their known and unknown.

"Probably. You're married into one of the richest families in Alaska. People are always going to be fighting over that money. God forbid Simon dies; it'll be like blood in the water surrounded by hungry sharks."

My eyes bulged, my throat tightened. "I guess I better learn how to swim with the sharks, or at least have a killer doggy paddle..." I giggled in sheer terror.

Luke's perspective helped me to see past Trey's betrayal. I was focused on the deterioration of my own family unit. It had not occurred to me that people were genuinely that money-hungry. Who would fight over someone else's money? The family had anticipated a Phyllis and Lonnie showdown, but that would be family fighting over family money. I was unaware of any outside interests at play. Then I recalled a higher-up from another, longer established state owned medical center telling me they were going to purchase St. Mary's after Simon retired. I wondered if that was what Luke was referring to. Phyllis always bragged about how St. Mary's was her great legacy. I did not know who Eve was, but I told myself that she was not in love with Trey. She only wanted money, especially, with that rattletrap she drove around.

"People are greedy and power-hungry. Are you unaware of that? We can put a man on the moon, but here on planet Earth, people are starving to death." He looked at me like he was talking to a twenty-five-year-old about puberty.

"If only feeding people were a glamorous endeavor." I thought I would fight for money to feed my children, but I would not fight for money, just for money's sake. "I am struggling to understand all the different dynamics orbiting around me. Simon always tells me that I believe the best in people to my own detriment. He says, 'Faith, not everyone believes or thinks the way you do.' I have been very naïve."

My worldview regarding money was simple. There was lots of money in the world. Money is replaceable, a renewable resource. People are not, at least to me. I felt sadness consume me.

Luke reached for my hand. "It's all right, Faith. I didn't mean to be hard on you."

At the dimly lit Petroleum Club, Kent and Sandra were dressed in matching green gingham outfits. Their six topper table was decorated with candles, red roses, and chocolates. I greeted them with a smile, a hug, and a kiss like the refined lady I was projecting.

"Where is Trey?" Kent asked, perplexed, looking at Luke.

"He is busy with the Center and taking care of Simon, so he sent his good buddy, Luke, to take his place. He is so noble..." I said, with a smile painted on my face.

Luke shook Kent's hand. "I dig the outfits bro." Kent ignored him.

I looked around the room. People were staring. For one, I was super shiny. I was probably blinding everyone within a one-mile radius. For two, I was not with Trey. I was with an unrecognizable, good-looking stranger with dimples. Scandal was a-brewing at the Mayor's Dinner. To calm my nerves, I told myself that, for all they knew, Luke was my brother, or cousin, or some version of a male relative.

Kent introduced his father, an elderly man dressed in a cobalt blue suit with stark white hair. "You're a good-looking couple," he said. We stood to greet him.

His words sent an SOS signal into the pit of my stomach. Danger, danger, damage control, damage control. "Oh, no, we aren't dating, we're friends. He is like a brother to me" I said patting Luke on the back.

He looked over to Luke. "You poor son-of-bitch; you're in the friend zone. My wife tried to do that to me. But I was relentless. On our honeymoon, we went to Argentina and made love on the beach every day. Best years of my life."

Luke laughed. "Are you still married?" We sat down.

"Coming up on 60 years."

"Congratulations!" I said.

"Thank you. Every day is the best day with her."

I felt myself becoming emotional over his lovely sentiment about his wife. Would a man ever feel that way about me? I had to make a choice. I could engage these feelings and become a blubbering mess at the Mayor's Revenge Dinner, or I could push these feelings away from me and maintain the façade of refined, contained lady, with no emotional trauma to display. I chose the latter course of action.

I pretended to listen to the mayor's speech, but my mind anxiously wondered about the circumstance I had put myself in. It was like the little, white angel over my right shoulder saying, "You have gone too far; you need to find yourself and pray about what you are doing," and the little devil over my left shoulder saying, "Forget Trey. Flirt with Luke."

Amid this inner dialogue, Luke leaned over and whispered in my ear, "Of all the women here, you are the most beautiful."

His words tingled up my spine and started a flutter in my heart. I could not remember the last time a man told me I was beautiful. I felt validated. I knew I still had it. I thought, *I am only thirty-three years old. I am not as repulsive as Trey would have me believe. Even in this costume attire, Luke thinks I am beautiful.*

He complimented me all night and made me feel like a princess vying for my affections. We left the dinner early. When we arrived back at my house,

Luke parked in my driveway, turned off the lights on his car, grabbed my arm, and pulled me towards him. We were only inches away from locking lips, "You know, you're really dangerous to me."

I felt intrigued. I wanted to be dangerous. I wanted to feel dangerously sexy in a come-hither sort of way. Unlike Trey, who was dangerous in a 'are you going to steal my wallet or give me the clap sort of way.'

"How so?" I asked with an air of innocence and a tone of tell-me-more.

"A damsel in distress, that is my weakness," he whispered, coyly closing his eyes and inviting me in for a kiss.

I froze.

Really? Damsel in distress? I didn't know this was a real thing for guys. He should have seen me in a cold sweat, crying on the bathroom floor a few nights ago. His weakness would have given him the strength to run for the hills. I guessed it was a very particular kind of damsel in a very particular kind of distress that men found sexy—you know, just marginally pitiful, but not too damned pitiful. Nobody wanted too damn pitiful.

He opened his eyes. We were still three inches apart, face to face. I continued to stare at him, curiously.

"Do you want to go to a comedy show on Friday night?" he asked awkwardly.

"Sure."

"I will text you."

"Great." I moved to get out of the car. This time he grabbed my face and kissed me with fury. I felt fearful and reluctant. The little angel over my right shoulder said, "You're a whore mother, now. What would the PTO moms think?"

I felt the Catholic guilt and pulled away. I put my hand up to imitate the traffic sign stop signal. "Stop. I can't. I am still married. I can't."

Luke looked at me as if I were challenging him rather than denying his advances. He kissed me again—this time with more fervor than before. This time, I kissed back.

It turned out that my concern over the wrong deed simply required me to acknowledge that it *was* a wrong deed. Once I did so, I was able to plow forward guiltless, like the hungry lioness I was dying to be.

We made out a little, maybe ten minutes. I pulled away, finally, and found myself grappling to maintain my dignity. I got out of Luke's car. Inspired by the PTO moms, I pointed my finger at him and said, "I have to go, and don't tell anyone that happened. Oh, my gosh, I am mother." I slammed his car door shut. He smirked. I refused to look back at him as he drove off. Luke had crossed the line. I imagined that he was extremely proud of himself. He probably had a big mouth too.

On the way up my front steps, I reflected on the larger implications of what had happened. This was the new trajectory of my life. This was what single mothers did; they sneaked around and made out with grown men in their driveways. I had not kissed another man since I was twenty-two years old. I told myself Trey had probably impregnated at least half of Alaska by now. If

I wanted to kiss someone, big deal, right? Why should he get to go around impregnating people, while I was left at home, pining, playing the role of the poor forgotten wife and mother?

Bea opened the door from the inside, startling me. "Welcome home." She was smirking underneath her onesie reindeer antlers.

"Take that hoodie off jeez, you scared me! How are the kids?"

"Sleeping. I saw Luke's car in the driveway. I've been watching from inside the house." Her eyebrows were raised.

"Oh, I lost my earring, but all is well. I found it." I showed her both my ears. She giggled like I was a panty-flashing school girl.

"What? Nothing inappropriate happened!" I used my strong mother-voice to convey that I was a refined lady, and how dare she question me on lewdness.

"I know what was happening. I *am* seventeen years old."

"I am an adult, for Christ sake."

I handed her a check. It was depressing that I found myself relating more to my seventeen-year-old nanny than to the PTO moms I had held in such high esteem.

I could not deny that Luke made a part of me feel alive again. He revealed a yearning inside of me that had not awakened for years. Luke had made this old, broken, battered wife feel attractive, desirable, and lustful. He also assured me that there were men in the world willing to date and woo a single mom. Suddenly, I had a new perspective of my circumstance, and it was positive and exciting. I had thought the next chapter of my life might be sad, lonely, and depressing, but perhaps it could also be thrilling, romantic, and full of endless opportunities for me to rebuild myself, just the way I wanted.

THE BROKE HOUSEWIFE

CHAPTER 8

I woke up with excitement the day I was to attend the comedy club with Luke. After dropping the kid's off at school, I planned on picking out my outfit for our next meeting. I was completely enamored thinking about what I was going to wear, who was going to be there, what Luke could possibly say or do to next win my heart, and if we would share another kiss. I had butterflies in my stomach; it was a welcome distraction from the usual ball of anxiety that I had become accustomed to.

I riffled through my closet. Again, ugly dress after ugly dress. I did not have any hot, sexy clothes. Judging by this closet, I had become a conservative, stodgy mother. I needed to go shopping, and stop dressing for the Catholics. Ugh! My cell phone dinged.

Bea: *Faith, is everything financially okay?*

Me: *Yes, what's up?*

Bea: *The check you wrote me bounced.*

I felt a rush of panic. Me: *That is impossible.*

Bea: *No, something is wrong.*

I played it cool. Me: *I will go by the bank. I promise you'll get paid. You are one of my top five favorite people. I was going shopping this afternoon anyway.*

I hurriedly got dressed in fuzzy black pullover and jeans. I threw my hair in a ponytail on the way to the garage. The butterflies and carefree daydreaming had morphed back into anxiety. I told myself to focus on action, like getting to the bottom of my potentially bounced check before reacting to "what ifs".

At Bank of America, the glare of the black porcelain tile floors reminded me of Trey's words '*You can't survive without me. I will destroy you.*' I took a deep breath and walked right up to the teller. "Hi, Sarah. Can I have a balance, please?" I asked extra-sweetly to hide the trepidation I was feeling.

"I need your I.D.," she replied, seeming annoyed by my cheeriness, or rather my attempt at fake cheeriness.

I handed her my driver's license. She labored with her computer for several minutes. The clock was ticking ever so slowly, and my anxiety was rising from my gut to my throat. I felt as if I were trembling from the inside-out.

"It says you are overdrawn by three hundred and seventeen dollars. How would you like to settle your account today?" she asked, as if I were another one of her irresponsible, loser customers she confronted regularly.

"That's impossible! I know months ago there was plenty of money in that account."

"It looks like you have been steadily withdrawing money over the course of the last month or so. Yesterday you wired a large sum to another account, and that transfer put this account into default once the checks cleared. Have you written any other checks? You could owe more if you have. Is there anyone else on the account?"

I gasped. "My estranged husband. Can he do that? Legally? I want my money back! How will I feed my children? How will I get gas?"

I felt lightheaded as my anguish rose to a level my brain waves could not fathom. I was strangled by own breath, and the room was growing dark. I could not keep my eyes open; everything was closing in on me. My heartbeat pounded in my throat. My eyes began to flutter.

"Miss, are you alright?" I heard the teller distantly ask.

Bam. I fell onto the tile floor of the Bank of America lobby. I awoke seconds to people gathered around me. I heard voices, but could not discern any particular face.

"Are you alright?" "How many fingers am I holding up?" We are calling an ambulance." "Are you a diabetic?" "Do you have low blood pressure?" "She is thin; maybe she is dehydrated." The questions kept coming from different directions.

As my vision cleared and my energy returned, I wanted to leave. I got up, resynched my ponytail, and picked up my black purse. "I am fine. Thank you for your concern. I am fine." I stood with my hands out as if to gesture to everyone to back up and stand away from me.

"Sorry, I haven't eaten today. Everything is fine. I am leaving now. Thank you for your help." I walked toward the doors.

The teller raced after me. "Mrs. Nathaniel, here is your I.D. back. Let me know if there is any way I can help you." She spoke with compassion this time, as if she were witnessing the collapse of someone's world, and it was too ugly to bear without offering help, even if it was a fake offer.

"Thank you." I looked away from her as I grabbed my I.D. without slowing my pace.

I needed to get to my car. Each step I took, I felt more and more helpless. If only rolling around in the bank parking lot, screaming wildly, were a viable solution. There were no tears to spare amid such utter shock and disbelief. Was Trey going to destroy me? How could he leave his family is this situation? He was trying to delete us from his life.

I sat down in the driver's seat. I opened a package of snacks one of the kids had left in the car. I began to eat the crackers. I called my mother on the car's bluetooth.

"I have been praying for you and Trey. I hope you have good news."

I felt like a lifeless puppet, that someone had just cut my strings. "Trey drained our bank account."

"What? He can't do that. He still has an obligation to you and his children. Has he seen the kids?"

"He wanted to see them on Halloween, but he refused to drive a few houses over, so then he threatened to destroy me. Then we went to Maggie's school auction, where he said he wanted to keep me as his wife, but continue to have girlfriends and party and do whatever the hell he wants. Now, he has left me destitute." I was numb.

"This is illegal. It's financial abuse. This is no longer a game. Now he is hurting the children. You've got to fight for the kids. Call him right now and call me back."

"Okay." I hung up the phone, deflated, defeated, and unmotivated to confront Trey.

I did what my mom said and called him anyway.

"Hello, slut," he barked.

Immediately, I was on the defensive. "You're the one screwing Eve, and whoever. How am I the slut?"

He shrilled, "Everyone saw you with that guy at the Mayor's Dinner. It's all over town. You're fucking somebody."

"Not true. I have been nothing but one hundred percent faithful to you since we've been married. What is true is that you actually *are* fucking somebody. Are you ready to tell me about that?" I asked, still taking the bait and not working toward a solution. Maybe he needed to release these emotions to ascend to a place of real communication. At least, I hoped.

"No, I will not tell you anything, whore."

"Where is our money? It's illegal and financially abusive for you to take our money and leave me unable to care for the kids. I consider this an attack on the children as well."

"You stupid bitch! Soon you will be broke and homeless." He hung up.

I realized he did not want to play the knight in shining armor, riding in with the wads of cash he had stolen. He wanted to play the bully and beat me into the ground and then watch me beg for mercy. I kept holding out hope for him to turn things around, but things kept going from bad to worse. I was unable to grasp the insanity of his cruel thought process. What had I ever done to make him hate me so much that he would hurt his own children to punish me?

I called my mom back. "It's not good. He drained our account because I went to the Mayor's Dinner with a...." I paused, hoping that if I said it superfast, it would not sound as bad. "male friend." I waited, expecting another round of punishment.

"Why would you do that? That is so inappropriate. You're a mother! What will the Catholics think?"

"Trey is fucking a harem of women like an Arabian Prince, and he expects me to accept it while I stay home crying over him! This is not me. This is all him. I refuse to chase after him and clean up this mess; he is on his own. I've served my prison sentence. I want out!"

"Do you have any other money?"

I remembered an account that had been set up in my name only. I thought it might contain several thousand dollars. I told her I had to go check.

I drove over to KeyBank, all the while praying for God's mercy, and for God to supernaturally give me the money to survive this disaster with Trey. I briefly thought about going inside the bank, but decided against it. I told myself I was better suited to pass out in the driver's seat with the car in park than collapsing on the KeyBank's lobby floor. I did not want to get a reputation. I could hear the water cooler talk. "Oh yeah, that lady, she was in here the other day and passed out in our bank, too."

I pulled right up to the drive-through teller. I put my car in park. I took out the pneumatic tube, I put in my I.D., and pressed send. The tube went up the portal and disappeared from view. Minutes passed. Then a lady's voice came over the speaker.

"How can I help you today?" she asked, with cheeriness.

"I need an account balance," I asked with dread.

I watched her play with my I.D. and then look at her computer screen. I watched her answer a phone call, text on her phone, straighten the pens on her desk, share a giggle with a co-worker, and riffle with the keyboard. It was taking an extraordinary amount of time to pull a simple account balance. I was becoming less shocked over Trey and more agitated watching this nitwit color-code pen caps. I said aloud to myself, "Hurry up, bitch."

I heard her voice over the intercom again. "I am going to send this back to you. Is there anything else I can help you with?"

"No, thank you."

"Have a good day, and for future reference, I can hear everything you're saying."

I was shamefaced. I looked around the pneumatic tube station to see her. She was looking at me, mouthing, "Bye-bye" as she waved with her right hand. I do not know if she was being sincere, but it felt sarcastic. I was confused, so I waved back. I thought, *no one has any privacy anymore.* Then I felt as if all my prayers had been revoked because I had called this seemingly nice, but slow, lady a bitch. I sat in the drive-through and prayed.

"Father God, please forgive me for calling the teller a bitch. I know what is happening to me is not her fault. I ask for forgiveness for projecting my frustration onto her. Also, if she is listening now, I ask for her forgiveness, directly. Father, forgive me for all of my sins, please give me the money I need to care for my family."

I pulled the capsule out of the machine. I opened it and saw the account balance, oh, thank God! This would last a while, at least, I thought. I prayed again with gratitude, "Dear God, I know I am not perfect, but please give me the power and wisdom to fight this battle. Give my family holy protection. Help me to multiply this money, to stretch this money to take care of my family as long as needed. Give me beauty for my ashes. Amen."

I drove away from the bank parking lot and headed home. After spiraling up so quickly in the early morning hours, I had to mindfully try to wind back down to a more even emotional state, a state better suited to take care of one's self and one's children. I texted Luke.

Me: *I can't see you again. My life is complicated.*

On my drive home, I attempted to re-balance myself, my motivations, and my goals on how to survive in the short term. I did a self-health update. My reality was as follows: I was living in a home I could not afford. My kids were going to a private school that I could not afford. I had a lifestyle that I could not afford. Trey had abandoned us—emotionally, physically, and at last, financially.

He lived in his mother's beautifully appointed home, replete with maid service and fancy dinners. He had a girlfriend. He had seen his kids once since November 6, and it was nearly Thanksgiving. I was on the cusp of a complete life change, from the roots up. I had tried to salvage the relationship. As of that day, it was no longer fixable.

How could I ever slightly trust Trey again? How could I reconcile all these horrendous behaviors to see him in a normal, human, light, to ever recognize the divine being he was underneath all the darkness he had welcomed into our lives?.

This perfect picture I had been trying to project onto the world was as phony as Grandma Phyllis's cheeks, and I was over it. I had to stop protecting people who wished to destroy me. I had to think of my kids and myself first. I had to admit, I had a problem, bigger than my ability to fix, and I needed outside help.

I needed an attorney. I pondered over my circle of friends, the ones I could trust, the ones who loved me, the ones who have been divorced. I thought of Aunt Denali. She was a real person, and she had a heart the size of Alaska. To add to her street cred, she had been divorced twice before. She had her own marketing firm. I knew she was not only a survivor but a conqueror. I called her on my car's Bluetooth.

"Faith! I haven't seen you since the St. Joseph's auction, and we didn't get to talk. What's going on?"

"Trey's been having an affair, and I don't know what I am going to do." I spit the words out, no going back now, I thought. Every time I said it out loud, it felt like the first time all over again. I wondered if that was how trauma patients felt.

After the usual I'm sorries, she came right to the point. "Are you going to work things out, or do you need an attorney?"

"I believe so. He has threatened to sell our home, he won't tell me anything about this lady he has named Eve, and he has drained our bank account. I hardly have any money." I started to cry again. I never thought I would be having this conversation.

"Come down to my office, right now. I will call my daughter-in-law, Ava. She's an attorney. Everything is going to be okay. I promise."

I thanked her profusely and got off the phone. I turned my car around.

A new wave of shock came over me. I could not believe I was going to meet with an attorney. I could not believe this was happening to me, to us, to our family. My brain was still trying to process all these horrific events, and I could not press myself over the top of the hill to get an accurate view of what was really happening in my life. I was breathing through each moment, and each moment was happening in tiny steps. I felt overwhelmed with grief, confusion, bereavement. I prayed.

"Father God, please give me a peace that surpasses all understanding. Please walk with me on this day and every day as I fight battles I see, and do not see. Amen."

I drove downtown and, luckily, found a spot immediately next to Denali's work. I walked into the multistory red bricked building through the double glass doors. The receptionist's name tag read Daisy. She wore black, nerdy glasses and a short tweed skirt. She had jet-black hair with bangs cut straight across her forehead. Pretty retro, I thought. I resynched my ponytail.

"How can I help you?"

"I am here to see Aunt Denali." I blurted it out like a moron. Daisy stared at me through her black rimmed glasses, perplexed. I wanted to say, Yes, Aunt Denali for the horse and pony show at 1p.m. I cleared my throat. "Denali Hamilton, please. She is expecting me." I repeated myself, this time with an air of pretension.

"Are you Faith?" Daisy looked at me like I was a child, not a grown woman, mother of two. "She is expecting you. Follow me."

She led me down a short blue carpeted hallway. "First door on the left." She pointed.

Aunt Denali sat behind her desk, working on the computer, with mounds of paperwork scattered in various piles. Her auburn hair glowed in the sunlight, and I thought I heard hymns from the angels. She looked that angelic. I walked around to hug her.

"Everything is going to be okay, Faith. Have you seen Tray's rap sheet? He's fucked." She swiveled her computer screen around toward me. She was on *CourtView*, a website where you could look up people's criminal offenses. Apparently, she had jumpstarted the investigation on Trey. I was not accustomed to this type of angelic support.

"Yes, the background check from St. Mary's is thirty-two pages long," I said, disappointed and defeated because all my efforts to help Trey had proved to be in vain.

"How the hell did he get hired in a management position at St. Mary's, overseeing people's care, with a rap sheet like this?"

"When the owners tell you to fire someone to hire their son, what can you do?" I shrugged. "The head of human resources hates him."

"I am sure he has a big fan club going over there." She chuckled. "How the hell did a nice girl like you end up with Trey?" she asked, putting me on the hot seat for poor past judgment.

"I was young and naïve. I loved him. I thought I had to save him, that I could save him. He had some good qualities or... he knew what to say to string me along. Who knows? You know, he even had his mother threaten me and my mother, and she lives in Washington."

"Huh...Phyllis? She doesn't like me or Peter because we aren't rich enough for her," Denali said with frank annoyance.

"She likes to play games with people, that is for certain. She would rather have fake enemies than real friends, and that is a sad way to live. But right now, I think she's being manipulated by Trey or vice versa. I can never tell—peas in a pod. I don't care. It doesn't matter anymore," I said sadly, looking down at the blue commercial grade carpet.

I thought about the last years of my life and how I had been too nice for far too long, pedaling back from their insanity and trying to cover it with grace and forgiveness. I had allowed them to manipulate me to keep the peace, and by doing so,

I had created monsters who had no accountability or boundaries—monsters who had now turned against me for some reason that I had not yet been able to grasp.

"Ava will be here any minute. My ex was crazy, pulled a gun on me. That son-of-a-bitch. I slam-dunked his ass, and you are going to slam-dunk Trey. You have rights. I can see it now. Trey walking into the courtroom in a five thousand dollar suit, looking all smug. Judges hate that shit."

I laughed because I could also see phony bologna Trey swaggering into the courtroom in an Armani suit his mama had bought, in an attempt to balance out the thirty-two-page rap sheet trailing behind him. It was an art the Hamilton's had mastered—using money to distract and shield bad behavior. Still, I had not considered slam-dunking Trey in the confines of a courtroom. The more I thought about it, the more I liked it. Aunt Denali showed me a new lens to look through, a new scenario to focus on—one where I was not a victim, but a victor. A scenario where I win and take back control over this situation and my life, without relying on Trey's mercy, but on my own intellect, strength, and prowess.

Then the catholic guilt nudged me. Was it Godly to seek revenge? To want justice? To want a little payback? To slam-dunk an ass? Up to this point, on my faith journey, I just thought God wanted us to love each other with kindness and generosity. Aunt Denali helped me to realize that I had to switch into a different mind-frame to avoid being pummeled to death. I tried to reason with myself and with God, to accept this new identity "Faith, Warrior Princess." I told myself that God wanted us to own our power through him, not consent to be a victim to anyone. God created all humans. God did not institute a monetary hierarchy upon us; we did that to ourselves. Regardless of assigned social status and paper dollar bills, our spiritual essence remained the same beyond all space and time. I argued with myself that there was righteous justice, and Trey had offended me at a spiritual level, a level at which he had no authority to operate. I remembered that all the people I admired most in the world were the people who had overcome great injustice, like Viktor Frankl or Sir Nicholas Winton.

I recalled a quote from Martin Luther King: "Injustice anywhere is a threat to justice everywhere." His words were biblical to me. He was one of the greatest fighters to have ever lived. Fighters were not silent. Fighters traded comfort and predictability for the higher good, for the higher calling on their lives. Still, I wondered where wanting to do what is right intersect with seeking revenge?

At this point, it seemed like a toss-up, but the idea of slam-dunking some ass was starting to feel good. I tried to meld the high-minded element of fighting a holy war with the raw human emotion of wanting to see Trey suffering, lying naked on the courtroom floor, hollering in a fetal position.

"Yes, Aunt Denali, I am going to slam-dunk his ass!" I pounded my fist on her desk. She nodded her head, like, 'Atta girl.'

Ava walked in, dressed in full business attire, including stilettos and a briefcase in tow. With her blond hair neatly tucked behind her in a French twist, she looked serious. “I apologize. I am late.”

“We were talking about how Faith is going to slam-dunk Trey’s ass,” Aunt Denali said. Ava sat down next to me.

“Yeah, totally.” I spilled the dirt to Ava.

Ava waited for me to finish. “Divorces are mathematical in nature,” she said. “Legally speaking, affairs aren’t recognized by the courts. He will endure no consequences for having an affair. No one cares about who did what to whom. Unless there has been DV.”

“DV?”

“Domestic violence. Has he hit you?”

“The night I found out about his girlfriend, there was a tussle in front of the bookcase. He typically is not a physically violent person. It would be unfair to say that it is an issue in the relationship.”

Aunt Denali chimed in. “What about drugs? He’s a known druggie.”

“Not to my knowledge. He’s been sober for six, close to seven years.”

“If he’s using drugs, he will not get custody of the children. He can’t leave you destitute. How much money do you have?” Ava asked.

“Almost none, now. I am freaking out.”

“I could give you 2k.” Denali offered.

“An attorney is going to cost you at least five thousand on retainer. You’re entitled to half the proceeds from the house if it sells. Is your name on the title?”

"Only Trey's. And I'm keeping the house."

"Still, as a married couple, you're entitled to half. Most likely, you'll be able to keep the house and the kids. Are you working?"

I was panicking. I had seen the Hamiltons bend the rules in their favor before. Trey could sell the house without me. He didn't need my signature to list it.

"No, not for money. I was offered pay to take care of my father-in-law, but I refused because it felt wrong." I felt defeated, like I was the one who had just been slam-dunked for being a dumbass.

Ava smirked, "Sounds like a case of rich housewife."

"What? Rich housewife? I could be homeless with my children!"

I had been broken in every way imaginable. I was in tears prior to walking into this office, but no one had sympathy for the perceived rich housewife going through a divorce. I did not meet the criterion of "pathetic enough" to garner true sympathy. Money dehumanized people, good people and bad people alike. Withstanding verbal abuse, financial abuse, abandonment, and adultery was tragic for the poor, but for someone with perceived wealth, it was thrilling. Everyone wanted to label it, pull up a chair, and watch the show. *"Who is going to win? Who is going to get what? Who is going to slam dunk an ass?"* But this was my life, and my pain was real, as real as a poor person's, as real as a rich person's. Pain was pain, and no one, not even innocent children, could get out of this unfettered and undamaged.

"Oh, Faith, Phyllis won't allow having her grandchildren out on the streets. It wouldn't be glitzy," Aunt Denali said while passing me a tissue box.

"I guess, you're right," I said, wiping my eyes, still fiercely offended by Ava's lawyer-ish, manufactured approach.

"I am sorry. I didn't mean to downplay your feelings, but you have to understand everyone has a certain perception of your family."

"Why? Because they're rich? That doesn't make them less cruel or buy them a special pass for their behavior."

"Well, it kind of does. I mean... you're sweet; you go to all the Galas. You have a nice life. What do you expect? People to shed a tear because your husband cheats on you? Lots of people's husbands cheat on them, and they're average."

"That's fake. I have been through things in this marriage that a weaker person would have vigorously run away from. I am not shallow. I am not heartless. I am not a less feeling sort of human; I am a broken housewife!"

HAPPY FUCKING THANKSGIVING

CHAPTER 9

It was 6 a.m. on Thanksgiving morning, and I was enjoying a cup of Peet's coffee before the kids woke up. I was on my sofa, peering out the window into my backyard, watching the snow fall gently to the ground. Nature moved in such perfect synchronicity; so many seen and unseen forces had worked in harmony to create that moment. I thought of people who had been hurt by other people, causing them to scoff at God's beauty and endless creativity. They chose to overlook his imprints, or they destroyed them as fit their needs. They gave their hearts to worldly things because it was safer, because giving your heart to Godly things required vulnerability and the inner work of unconditional love and faith. At that moment, I prayed for God to heal me so that I may always recognize the unexpected beauty of the world and be grateful.

I tried to reconnect to nature, the divine energy that had brought me here, attempting to recharge, re-boot, to have a deeper insight into what was happening in my life. After all, the energy that had brought me here was the same energy that was, on that day, clothing the earth in gently falling snow. The natural world waxed from chaotic to peaceful and swung in gradations between. If I could learn anything from nature, it was that life was about the balancing act between the dark and light, the creators and destroyers, the predators, and the prey. The physical beauty of the unseen world was only paralleled by the physical destruction it could create. The duality of nature and the duality of man—they raged.

But honestly, sitting on my sofa, bullshitting over the deeper meaning of life was preferable to mustering the psychological strength to cook a full Thanksgiving meal. We had an invitation to Ralph's house, but I just could not expend the energy to go over there and smile at everyone like everything was just fucking fantastic. While, at the same time, they all whispered about my separation, Trey's affair, and my pitiful single-mother status. Also, I was fearful of the consequences of celebrating Thanksgiving with friends and Trey finding out. What would he do next? Have the repo man confiscate my car while I was sleeping?

My phone rang. Who the hell would be calling me so early? I hoped it was someone kind, someone who wanted to wish me a Happy Thanksgiving. My buzzing phone sat on top of the white kitchen bar. I picked it up. It was Trey. My body trembled. I had not spoken to him since he had threatened to have the children and me thrown out onto the arctic streets.

"Hello."

"Simon is being flown to L.A.; he has lost all movement in his arms. I need your help." Trey sounded panicked.

My body tremors morphed into concern over Simon. I threw caution to the wind. "Yes, of course. What can I do?"

"Go by Bubba's and pick up his medicine and meet me at my parents' house. They need his medicine before they leave."

"Wait, I'll meet you at the Shell station on the corner. I can't go over to your parents'."

"Yes, okay. See you in an hour."

Bubba's was located in one of Simon's medical buildings. It was the same building in which he had his doctor's office and surgery center. Everyone at Bubba's knew my face; I had been in there about a thousand times picking up medications for Trey, Phyllis, and Simon. Still, I was apprehensive. I called Lonnie; she didn't answer. I sent her a text.

In a frenzy, I woke the kids up. They were wearing matching tan and white turkey pajamas. I told them to come downstairs for a quick breakfast.

"Mommy, it's Thanksgiving. When are we going to eat turkey? Is Daddy coming?" Maggie asked with wishful eyes.

"Turkey day; it's time for turkey." Alex patted the turkey imprinted on his belly.

"First, we are going to eat cereal. We will eat Turkey for dinner. Promise. We have to hurry up, though, because we have to help Daddy and Papa Simon." The kids sat down at the bar.

"I love Papa Simon. I miss him. Are we having Thanksgiving with him?" Maggie asked.

I served them Red Berry Special K cereal.

"I don't want to eat this! Where is the Captain Crunch or, at least... Frosted Flake" Alex said pushing the cereal away from him.

"Then don't eat it." I grabbed the bowl and tossed it into the kitchen sink.

I turned to Maggie, "We may be able to tell Papa Simon Happy Thanksgiving. I don't think we'll be able to share a meal with him; he's rather sick."

I loaded them into the SUV, still in pajamas with snow boots on their feet and big winter coats covering their small bodies. We drove through the snow over to Bubba's Pharmacy. My phone rang. It was Lonnie.

"What's going on?" she asked, panicked.

"Trey called me and said they are taking your dad on the jet to L.A.. He's ill."

"I didn't know. No one tells me anything," Lonnie said and began to cry.

"Call them now." I hung up the phone.

I pulled into the Bubba's parking lot. The kids sluggishly got out of the car. Inside the building, the big neon green sign said, "Bubbas." The pharmacy was still closed; it would not open for another ten minutes. But someone was inside. I knocked on the door. It was a man wearing a white pharmacy coat, with his dark hair pulled back in a man bun. He looked up at me with recognition and unlocked the door.

"I am Simon Hamilton's daughter-in-law, and I desperately need his medication. He's not doing well."

The man introduced himself as Ralphela and asked us inside. I introduced the kids, and we waited in the lobby while Ralphela walked behind the pharmacy counter. He shuffled around the stainless steel shelves. The kids started to whine.

"Mrs. Hamilton?"

I walked over toward the register.

"This is a large amount of pain medication for one person. I am going to have to verify this with Dr. Stella, since he recently picked up a similar script five days ago."

"Okay, you should do what you think is best. All I can tell you is that he is being flown to L.A. once I deliver these meds. I have no idea if the other meds were lost or what. He owns this building, you know. I don't think anything unscrupulous is afoot."

He paused, thinking about the consequences, I supposed. "All right, I'll fill this for you. I hope he feels better," he said with a tight smile. He gazed at me suspiciously while cautiously handing me the pills.

At the Shell gas station, I texted Trey.

Me: *Trey, I am at the gas station.*

Five minutes go by, then ten, then twenty. The kids were becoming restless.

"I want to go home I am hungry. I want to play *Skylanders*," Alex said.

"I want to go home, too. I am bored," echoed Maggie.

"Well, who knows what Thanksgiving is about?"

"It's about Indians eating turkeys," Alex shouted while unzipping his enormous blue winter coat.

"No, it's not Alex. It's about America and the Mayflower and people giving thanks for their families," Maggie said, always in the mood to autocorrect.

"Well, you are both right. It is about a group of people that wanted a different life, so they sailed across the sea to America. The people were met by the Indians who the land already belonged to. The Indians could have been mean and uninviting to the Pilgrims, but instead, they shared ideas and information that enabled the newcomers to survive on their land. After a great harvest and a season of growing food together, they joined hands and dinner tables to show gratitude for each other. Now look at us; we are all here because of them. Life is about helping others. Now, we are helping Papa Simon by remaining patient," I said, proud of my 'mom' answer.

"Blah blah blah... lets go NOW!" Alex screamed. He took his brown boot off and threw it to the floor.

"They had one nice meal. Then the pilgrims killed the Indians and stole their land," Maggie chimed in.

"Huh, well history is written by the winners. Let me call your dad," I barked back, irritated that Trey, like the pilgrims, was full of shit. I called Trey. No answer. I called Trey again. No answer. I did not want the pain medicine in my possession. Fuck it, I thought. I could drive over there and leave it on the doorstep or in the mailbox.

I pulled past the tiger statues into the Hamiltons' circular driveway. The lights were turned off in the house, and it was still snowing. The front doors were wide open. I wondered what kind of Stephen King movie this reminded me of. *The Shining*?

Rose Red? I looked back at the kids, pouting in the backseat. "Promise me you won't get out of the car."

Maggie exchanged looks of concern with Alex. "We promise. Hurry up."

I grabbed the white paper bag of pills and locked the kids inside the car. I walked through the perfect white, double-doors of the vacant house. I called out, "Hello? Anyone home?" Silence.

It felt eerie and dark. I thought I might discover a bloody body on the floor or perhaps a pentagram outlined with candles and a decapitated chicken head. On my way to the dark brown kitchen, I passed the white travertine staircase leading to Trey's room. I thought, Oh my God! What if he's dead? I dumped the bag of pills on the gold granite countertop and rushed up the stairs to his bedroom. Trey's black leather Tumi bag was knocked over, and everything was spilled out onto the floor. He had a disposable cell phone, a rubber band arm tie, needles, a spoon, and a bottle of Suboxone. I felt a new, but familiar, layer of hopelessness overcome my being. Trey was back on drugs.

I panicked, I didn't want Trey to use drugs. So, I gathered all the items and put them back into the bag, then ran out of the house with it. I threw the bag on the passenger's seat of my car and quickly started the ignition.

"I want to go in and see Papa Simon!" Maggie said.

"He isn't there; no one is home."

"What's in the bag? A present?" Alex asked, peeking around to the front seat.

"Definitely not. Do not touch this bag."

I had to tell Lonnie about the bizarre situation unfolding at her dad's home; she had a right to know. I called her as I drove. "Trey had me pick up your dad's pain pills from Bubbas, but no one is home."

"Those pills aren't for daddy. Trey can't take care of my dad." Lonnie said disgusted.

"I talked to Sabra," Lonnie said. Sabra was the Hamiltons' Secretary. She kept the financial side of their lives running smoothly and managed the Hamiltons' personalities well. "She said Phyllis and Simon have already left for L.A. Oh sister, this is awful. It's my dad, my only dad. Phyllis won't tell me anything!"

Upon arriving home, I hid Trey's drug bag under my bed upstairs. I was determined to normalize Thanksgiving for the kids. I plunged forth with preparing a full Thanksgiving meal on Thanksgiving Day. The turkey was pre-cooked, from *Harry and David.* I only had to warm it up. I set the oven temperature to 350 degrees and placed the turkey inside the oven. The kids were on the sofa in the family room, watching *Harry Potter.*

"Who wants to help Mommy make sweet potato soufflé?"

Oddly, there were no takers. I prepared all the side dishes—turkey dressing, broccoli casserole, rolls, cranberry sauce, and pumpkin pie. The kids did not bother getting dressed for the day. I allowed it. I thought we could have a free day binge-eating turkey. Perhaps we would watch a Christmas movie together, afterward.

I set the table and called the kids into the dining room after everything was prepared. "Maggie, would you like to say the blessing?"

"Thank you for the food we eat,
Thank you for the world so sweet,
Thank you for the birds that sing,
Thank you, God, for everything. Amen"

"That was beautiful, sister Maggie," Alex said.

"Yes, good job. Let's eat, and then tomorrow, we can unpack the Christmas decorations from the outside shed," I said, faking excitement about the beginning of the Christmas season.

"I love Christmas! Presents!" Alex.

"Christmas is about the birth of Jesus, who was also killed," Maggie remarked.

"Yepper...well...um..."

"Ugh, Maggie, you're just so perfect!" Alex waved his arms in the air. We all laughed.

As I was about to take my first bite after the long two-and-a-half-hour meal preparation, the phone rang. I had thought about turning it off, but I could not do it. I guess I was like a storm chaser on *NatGeo*. I could not turn away from the magnificent destruction of the storm.

The call was from William, Phyllis's former best-friend and butler, who I had not heard from him in over a year. Phyllis had fired him on the pretext that he had stolen a *Versace* ski suit, Simon's Patek Philippe watch, and an heirloom emerald ring. She also claimed he was a substance abuser, and he could not be trusted. Once Simon, in jest, had told me that he had William on camera parading around in their home wearing Phyllis's panties and lingerie.

Prior to his firing, I had found William to be a delightfully charming, fashionable young man, but Phyllis had turned me against him with her stories of his deceit and thievery. I ignored the call. I told myself I was not interested in William's drama. My phone rang again. This time it was Simon. I could not believe he was calling, with paralyzed arms no less. I answered.

"Simon, are you okay? How are you?" I got up from the table and walked into the kitchen.

"I have you on camera, breaking into our house and stealing Trey's medication. It is illegal to take someone's medication, and I will call the police if you don't take it to him right now," he said, trying to sound forceful and powerful through his weak, cracking voice. His threat did not frighten me; it deeply saddened me.

"Call the police!" That was Phyllis, faint in the background.

"Simon, I am so sorry that Phyllis is making you call me from your hospital bed. You are obviously on speakerphone. You should be focusing one hundred percent on your health, not Trey's drug addiction. You know I am not dragging my children to whatever sordid location he is at. I trust Trey knows where he used to live. You take care of yourself, now. Goodbye."

I hung up. I felt so depressed by Simon's threat and the fact that now he, too, had developed Stockholm syndrome with Phyllis—just like

Lonnie. I thought about calling him back and telling him about the oxy, but it could have been used against me since I was the dumbass who had begged the pharmacist for the medications. Besides, Simon was probably living in complete hell. The man was on his deathbed and had been reduced to calling me over a Trey-pisode. God Bless him.

I thought about how last year, everyone had come over to our house for Thanksgiving. My kitchen had been newly remodeled—white quartz countertops, white cabinets, new Wolf appliances. I was excited to make all the food. The Hamiltons breezed in and out in a timely fashion. Now, I was trying to press through the waves of assault, keep the kids safe, and their lives normal. The phone rang again; now, I was getting irritated. I looked at the number. I did not recognize it. I answered, thinking it might be Trey.

"This is Helga, from St. Mary's." I sat down at the bar.

I pictured Helga, with her short blond hair and pointy, scrunched-up face like an elf's, and reptilian eyes that always freaked me out. She had a dark, uninviting energy around her. She was Phyllis's current best friend and employee. Although Phyllis tried to make me like her, I was unable to warm to her.

"Oh, hi," I said flatly.

"Phyllis asked me to call you. I need to pick up Trey's medication. I don't want any trouble. I am with my kids." She sounded victimized.

"Listen, Helga, I am going to be frank with you. I know you are beholden to Phyllis because she has arranged for the Center to pay for your medication, but what she is asking you to get involved in is highly unprofessional and probably illegal. For your family's sake, say, no," I said, trying to protect her. I might not like her, but she was a mother, after all.

"I am doing a favor for Phyllis. I don't want any trouble."

"If Phyllis were your true friend, she would not allow you to get involved in such affairs," I said, trying to help her see the light and the true unbalanced nature of what her employer was asking her to do.

She continued to argue with me. Her mind was made up. Her boss had given her an assignment, and she was sticking with it. I gave up. Her loyalty had been well paid for, even if to her own detriment. Some people have to learn the hard way. Like me, I thought. "Fine. I will put Trey's medication on my front doorstep. Happy Thanksgiving."

I walked upstairs to my bedroom. I grabbed the Suboxone out of Trey's bag and threw it out on the porch. I slammed the door and locked it. I was disgusted with how the Hamiltons were choosing to handle their personal and business affairs. Now, they had an employee pulling their son from drug dens and feeding him opiate suppressors. So very far from where we were last year.

We finished our dinner. I cleaned up; it seemed to take me longer to clean than to cook. The kids were watching TV again. I took the opportunity to plunder through Trey's drug bag. I looked through the numbers on the disposable cell phone. There were two. One, I immediately recognized as Helga. Why was Helga texting Trey? None of the texts were inappropriate in nature, but it was odd, nonetheless. She was ten years older than he was, married, with six children—she could not be Eve. She was definitely not Eve. Trey was too shallow to bone Helga. She must be a mother figure to him. Still, I was unsettled. I called Aunt Denali. She asked me how I was holding up.

"I could be better. Simon is in L.A., paralyzed... so the story goes. Lonnie is pissed no one is giving her updates on her dad. Trey is back on drugs and, oddly, this lady from the Center—Phyllis's BFF—has been texting him on his disposable drug phone, which I found along with a spoon and a rubber-band arm tie. She isn't texting anything inappropriate. I think she is Phyllis's pawn, you know," I said, matter-of-factly.

"What? Simon is paralyzed? I will have Peter tell all his brothers and sisters. This is bullshit. Phyllis can't keep things like that from his family. If my sister's husband was doing that, I would kill him. Who is this lady, this employee?"

I told her about the interaction with Helga. "And this was right after Simon called me and threatened to have me arrested," I said, still processing the whirlwind Holiday celebrations that the universe had blessed me with that snowy Thanksgiving Day.

"Well, Happy fucking Thanksgiving. Arrested for what? This lady, she's Eve."

"No, she's not his type. Trey is so vain; he would not be seen in public with Helga."

"Come on, Faith, a man would cheat with a watermelon. Pull it together. She probably thinks she is going to be the princess of St. Mary's, and she and Trey will someday be the reigning king and queen." Aunt Denali gave a robust laugh.

"She's not queen material."

"Dammit, wake up! She's Eve!"

"Gross. I need solid proof. He's on drugs, now, so unless she's also a drug user, how could that even work? She's someone he and Phyllis can suck dry in the meantime," I said standing firm.

"That's true. You have bigger problems than his girlfriend. He can't be around the kids. Is he still working at the Center? Maybe he can get a family discount?"

"I do not know anything about his job. I do know that Phyllis will not allow him to be admitted to St. Mary's, bad PR."

We got off of the phone, and I reassessed my self-health update. I was living in a home that I could not afford. My kids were going to a private school that I could not afford. I had a lifestyle that I could not afford. Trey had abandoned us—emotionally, physically, and financially. He now lived in his mother's house, with maid service, and fancy dinners. He had a girlfriend. He was on drugs. He was going to lose his job. He would be kicked out of his parents' home, eventually. He would be shipped somewhere, discreet—to the lower 48 for rehab. I would either have to take him back and try to piece him back together for the sake of keeping our home and the kids in their school, or I could divorce him and potentially lose everything that I know.

It was time for the big question: was I willing to possibly lose my entire way of life and start over from scratch to keep my kids safely away from a drug user? Or did I want to do this game of cat-and-mouse with Trey for the rest of my life, under Phyllis's thumb, setting a bad example for my kids, and allowing them to be exposed to dysfunction at the highest levels? Did I want their childhood to be one of inherited, generational drug, mental, and emotional abuse? Or one of divorce, change, and uncertainty, but also, survival and overcoming?

It was a sleepless night for me. Trey was using drugs again; that meant he had new criminal associates from the underworld. Those types would kill their own mothers for drugs or money or just because. Drug dealers had no soul. It was only a matter of time before they would come by my house, where my children live, to collect Trey's drug debts. I decided to act proactively and called the other number in Trey's drug phone.

"What up?" a man answered.

"Word."

"Who dat?" he asked.

"Who dat?"

"Jay," he said.

"Where's Trey? I am having him and you investigated for drug trafficking. You better check yourself before you wreck yourself," I said in a deeper, threatening voice.

"Wrong number," he said.

"Jay, I know your real name. Stay away from Trey or you'll be sorry."

He hung up.

I felt better. Now Jay, the drug dealer, knew I would not be trifled with. I had put him on notice, or at least, that's what I told myself. Maybe he would even stop selling drugs to Trey. I felt a seething hate in my heart for Jay, the drug dealer. I knew him by occupation alone, and I hated him. I knew it was not Christian to hate. I tried to find grace for Jay. I told myself that Jay had had a hard life and was raised in a toxic environment that groomed him to be a drug dealer. He probably did not have a good role model or anyone to show him unconditional love.

Still, at some point into adulthood, did we not all have to put that childhood trauma behind us, own our behaviors, and decide the outcome of our own lives? Everyone was responsible for themselves, given good tools in childhood or not. He could have chosen to be an agent of light, not a dark Lord doling out poisonous, mind-controlling substances to self-destructive people. He could have chosen to dole out Bibles and blessings. Likewise, I had to own the place I was at in my life, and yes, at that moment, I hated Jay—the drug dealer, life-ruiner, soul crusher, family destroyer, liar, thief, killer.

RAT SHIT

CHAPTER 10

The following day I woke with a renewed sense of adventure. I thought, *Damn it, today we are going to press the reset button and have fun. Non-negotiable fun.* The kids were sitting at the bar, finishing breakfast. I was still in my pink fleece pj's.

"Get your snowsuits on; we're going to the shed for the Christmas decorations!"

"Hooray! Christmas!" Alex shouted.

"What about shopping? Don't people go shopping today?" Maggie.

"Why yes, let's go to the mall and watch hoards of people fistfight over LCDs and other trinkets in honor of Black Friday." My patience had thinned over the last twenty-four hours. Only my idea of fun was allowed. I briefly pondered whether exposing the kids to the mental illness of society would make me look better or worse in their eyes? Seemed like a toss-up.

"I want to put the first ornament on the tree." Alex stood pushing in his barstool, ready for action.

"Alex, we will do it together as a family." I began to load up the dishwasher.

"Does that mean Daddy is coming over?" Alex asked.

"Where's Daddy?"

I felt instant anger, followed by a deep sadness. I bit my tongue. "Maggie, he's helping Grandma Phyllis and Papa Simon. Meet me downstairs in the theater room in ten minutes."

The snow had continued to fall throughout the night; there was over three feet of it in the driveway alone. Each of us dressed in a full snowsuit, boots, hats, and gloves. I shoveled a trail from the sliding glass backdoor of our house to the white shingled shed, while the kids played in the snow. They grabbed their wooden flexible flyer sleds from the shed and took advantage of a small hill in our backyard.

In the shed, I moved cardboard boxes around, trying to find our Christmas decorations. I put the relevant boxes outside, including our ten-foot-tall tree.

"Kids, help me move these boxes into the house."

"Ugh, I don't want to move boxes," Alex said. His sled was tethered to his red snowsuit and he was dragging it back up the hill.

"Come on, Alex; you have to help." Maggie put her sled down. She pushed Alex as she walked past.

Collectively, we dragged all the boxes into the house, along with the snow. I didn't care that there was snow all over our new grey hardwood flooring. I just wanted the spirit of Christmas to lighten the mood.

As I started to unpack the boxes, I noticed tiny black pebbles everywhere. I took more and more decorations out—lights, bells, stuffed Santas, handmade wreaths, as I unpacked, more and more black pebbles fell to floor. I was perplexed. "What *is* that?"

Maggie's eyes got really big. "Rat poop!"

"Oh, my God! Rat shit! Kids, go take a bath, right now. Use lots of soap. People get diseases from rat shit. Oh, my God!" I was hysterical, screaming.

"AGAHAHAHAHA!" Maggie frightfully ran up the stairs. Alex laughed. I ran him up the stairs after her and into the shower.

I opened box after box, and discovered...rat shit. My entire Christmas had been infested. I was distraught. Ornaments, blankets, pillows, stuffies from my childhood, completely covered in rat shit. My life had turned into a form of rat shit, and here materialized in front of me, tiny black pebbles, rat shit. I had to piece Christmas together for the kids around rat shit. At least detergent and bleach would disinfect and clean the keepsakes. If only it were as easy to clean up the emotional rat shit.

I had awoken with plans to make Christmas wishes come true. Yet here I was again, feeling defeated, mourning the loss of a lifetime of Christmas decorations, and it wasn't even noon. I pressed the rewind button and thought of the drugs, the rat shit, poor suffering paralyzed Papa Simon threatening to call the cops—I heard Aunt Denali's voice in my head: "Merry Fucking Christmas." My phone rang. Unknown number—welcome to crazy town.

"I messed up." It was Trey. He had his conman voice on.

"Well, no kidding. Did you have me scam the pharmacy so you could steal Simon's medication?" I put him on speaker so I could take off my snow gear.

"I don't know what you're talking about."

"I am sure you don't. What's going on? You have amnesia again?" I screamed into the phone.

"I used drugs. I am stranded at the Icicle Inn." He said it with self-pity in his voice.

Typical. Trey always chose seedy hotels to hide in to do drugs. Often, he would buy a hotel room for himself and another for the drug dealer, to keep the dealer close.

"Helga came by and got your Suboxone, so you should call her. The kids and I are not a resource for you any longer." I threw my gloves to the floor.

"I don't want anything to do with that bitch!" he yelled.

"Well, Trey, why don't you call your girlfriend then." I kicked off my purple Sorel boots.

"I don't have a girlfriend, Faith."

"You're right. I never kicked you out for having an affair. I kicked you out for folding the laundry incorrectly. I remember now." I took my black snow pants off.

"Come on, Faith. I miss you. Please pick me up."

"No!" I screamed and hung up.

What a wonderful adventure for the kids to partake in. Let's pick up smelly, gross Daddy from a drug den and go shopping at the Walmart on Black Friday. No, Helga could take her kids, since she wanted to play the fool. Or he could call Eve; she could have him.

The phone rang again; it was William. Again. Why had he come back into my life? What the fuck were the Hamiltons up to now? "What's going on?"

"Hi Faith, how are you?" he asked, voice extra-sweet and feminine.

"I'm dealing with the rat shit that has taken over my life!" I yelled, looking at my chewed hand-made wreath scattered about the floor.

"Oh, hmm...sorrrrry. Phyllis called me to look after Trey. You have his medicine, and I need it," Will said like he was a man of great honor, riding in to save the day on his white pony.

I laughed—another pawn sent by the wicked queen. "Listen here, ya little fucker, Helga beat ya to the punch; she came by with her children already. I will not be tied up with drugs. Keep this crap away from us." I threw my black Patagonia jacket to the floor.

"I do not appreciate being called a 'little fucker.' He retorted.

"Of course, I am sorry. Now, why are you involved in this mess?"

"Phyllis is paying me to take care of Trey and the kids, as needed. So you can call me anytime for help with anything," he said, cheery in his high-pitched tone.

I rolled my eyes. "I am so sorry that you have been saddled with the unsavory task of caretaking for Trey. Meanwhile, who is taking care of Simon? He's sick!"

"I am in charge of Trey." Will cleared his throat.

"How nice. And how long have you been sober?" I probed.

"Eight months. I am attending meetings with a sponsor. I've lost my driving license, but Phyllis has hired a chauffeur for me, which is helpful in getting me to my job and back home," Will said proudly.

"Well, perhaps, you can connect to him on a level I haven't been able to. Where are you working?"

"Ruby's Chandeliers & Home Decor."

I wondered if this was the best Phyllis could do, she must be struggling. "Good for you, Will. I do have an issue maybe you can help with."

"Anything to help the family. I am all for families staying together." He sounded gallant.

"Trey took a large sum of money out of our joint bank account. Can you get that back for me?"

"Let me call you back about that..."

"I have two children and bills to pay. If Trey wants to be a party boy while you spotlight him, that's his choice, but he has to take care of his family. That's non-negotiable."

"Gotta go. Cheerio!"

Phony Bologna Will the show pony. Of course he had to go. What could he really do? I guess he needed the extra money. How was Will supposed to put Trey the Train Wreck back together again? He was in complete destruct mode now. There was no stopping him. My phone rang again. It was Lonnie, and she was sobbing.

"Oh my God, sister. Thank you for telling me about Daddy. She won't tell me anything. She's always trying to keep us apart."

I sat down on the last stair of the staircase. "It's true. You're not crazy. Ten years ago, I was warned to stay away from you. You've always been perceived as an enemy."

"What?" She asked. She sounded shocked as if someone had finally confirmed a long-held truth she had harbored in her heart.

"Yes, Lonnie. Trey said Phyllis hated you more than anyone else on earth. Your dad knows. We've talked about it numerous times. To quote him, he said once, "A man will love another man's child, but a woman will always see the other bitch."

"I know she has always hated me. My dad will only admit it when he has been drinking. He's either defending her or talking about divorcing her every time I see him. What can I do?"

"Start telling people about it. Record your conversations. Once it gets back to her, she will warm to you because her foremost concern is over what the neighbors will think. In the meantime, call Aunt Denali and Uncle Peter for help. Phyllis, over time, will delete you from her life. Unless you can figure out how to be valuable to her..."

"No one has ever spoken to me like this before. I hate this. Thank you, sister."

We got off the phone. I thought, "Fuck it. Let the truth be your shield. If I am losing everything, if people are trying to destroy me and hurt my family—fuck it!" I got to choose the role I played here at the end of Simon's life and at the end of my marriage, and I chose the role of truth-teller, shooting double birds on both hands as I orbit in and out of their sphere of insanity. I chose the role of protector of my children. I chose the role of keeping Trey away from Simon, and keeping Uncle

Peter and Lonnie close to Simon. The last eleven years had been a rugged affair, trying to keep Trey stable and a joyful family intact. Needless to say, I did a lot of smoke blowing. I vowed on this Black Friday; I shall blow smoke no more.

Knock knock...Someone was at the door. I thought, drug dealer? Was I safe? I was still in my pjs. I walked up the stairs. I peeped out of the door window. It was my mom! I opened up and hugged her. "Mom! How long are you staying?"

"Until the end. Whatever that may look like." She was dressed in a navy velour tracksuit, a brown suitcase in her left hand, her shoulder length dark hair tucked behind her ears.

It felt like I was in the movie *The Lord of the Rings: The Two Towers,* about to be defeated by the orcs, when Gandalf the White appears, holding his bright staff upon the mountaintop, dispelling the darkness below.

Alex and Maggie, half-dressed, came running down the stairs from their bedrooms, filled with excitement. The Christmas joy I was trying to manifest was now plainly in front of me in the form of Grandma Kate.

"Grandma, Grandma, Grandma!"

"This is the best Christmas ever!" Alex hugged her legs.

"It's not Christmas, Alex." Maggie.

I felt such relief and gratitude. Being in the presence of my mother's unconditional love and having an in-house support person was a Christmas miracle. Now I could act with heightened clarity and focus. She took the children into the family room. I sat on the sofa by myself. I could break down for a bit, release some emotions. I sat in silence, processing all the rat shit and pondering how the hell I was going to clean it all up.

THE FAMILY MEETING

CHAPTER 11

The Monday morning after Thanksgiving brought additional delights. My mother had gotten the kids up and ready for school. I lay in the bed in a state of immobilized depression. Trey had texted me in the early morning hours to call him. I didn't want to respond, but I thought I needed to stay abreast of his mental faculties to best understand the right ways to navigate this unpredictable situation. My fate was still largely tied to Trey's, and I felt he was hell-bent on taking us all down with him. I used my *TapeACall* app and called him back.

"How are you feeling, Trey? Are you still at the Puffin Palace?" I sat up in my bed, gold Euro pillows stacked behind me.

"No. My mom and Simon are coming home tomorrow. We need to have a family meeting."

"What's going on?" I looked out the beveled windows to see if it was snowing.

"I am not feeling well. A nurse from St. Mary's is coming over to give me a Vancomycin drip."

"Is that legal?"

"I don't know. My mom wanted Jana to do a PICC line because we could not locate any veins in my arms for the drip. I think they're going to have to go in through my neck again." The poor-me tone was nauseating.

"Yikes! Sounds dangerous. Is it the flu? I heard it was going around."

"No, I have developed an infection. My foot is fucking rotting off. Does that make you happy?" He was screaming, annoyed by my refusal to acknowledge his illness the way he wanted me to.

"Oh no. I guess you haven't been going to work, huh?"

"I'm sick. I haven't been able to work."

"Trey, you've never been a functioning drug user. It's all or nothing with you. Also, it's dangerous to work at a rehabilitation center and be an active user. Did they ever catch the person who was stealing pain medication from the pharmacy?"

"I don't know, Faith. It was probably Edgar or someone in supplies. I am in pain."

"I don't think it's legal for the Center to send employees outside the building to administer care. Who's the doctor ordering these at-home treatments?"

"Faith, stop it! I could lose my foot! And my mom is no better than me. She takes pills!"

"Your mom can still function in society. You can't. You have to stick to the treatment plan. I don't know what kind of fight you're having with her, but I am sure it is because you've relapsed and are not showing up for work. Is your girlfriend a drug addict?"

"I will work when I feel like it. My parents own the motherfucking Center. They can't fire me, and I don't have a girlfriend!"

"You're going to get fired. Your mom is sending employees with their kids to our house to pick up your Suboxone and to pick you up from drug hotels. Now, she is sending employees to her home to give you IV drips. This is fucked up. You took all our money. I need it back. We have children. You need to keep your job."

"Yeah, I know, Faith. We need to have a meeting about the money. Right now, a nurse is coming over here to give me Vancomycin. I have the flu. I don't want to talk about this. I know I fucked up!" he hung up.

I realized that Trey had told me at least three different stories during our conversation. Something was not adding up. I decided to call Will.

"Trey's developed cellulitis from shooting black tar heroin. He is in terrible shape—like Simon," Will told me.

Not like Simon. Poor Will was so terribly misled. Simon had built an empire and was now ailing from a legitimate series of illnesses beyond his control. Trey was a spoiled brat who had led a tremendously privileged life that was structured in such a way that it genuinely took more effort to fail than to succeed. Now, he was lying in the bedroom above Simon with a self-inflected wound from heroin, screaming for sympathy and understanding from us mere commoners. I suppose some were so common as to give it to him. Still, it was best to keep the lines of communication open with Will, even though he annoyed the fuck out of me. I made sympathetic noises.

Will said, "Phyllis and Simon would like you to come over for a family meeting once they've returned."

"I will bring my mom with me. I am happy everyone is on the road to recovery," I replied, trying to keep the sarcasm to a minimum.

I googled "cellulitis." The top threads read "Bacterial infection from dirty needles, black tar heroin." Downstairs, Mom was baking chocolate chip cookies. I told her the latest Trey-pisode.

"Don't have sex with him ever again. You need to get tested." She bent over to put a fresh batch of cookies into the oven.

I sat down at the bar. I felt sick to my stomach and on the verge of a vomit. "What would the PTO moms think?" I folded my arms and rested my head on the table.

"My Lord, don't tell them," she said, aghast, clasping her heart.

I broke into prayer. "Dear God, protect me and the children from all contagious diseases. St. Michael, please defend and protect us from all forces visible and invisible that wish us harm. Amen." I picked up my phone off the kitchen counter.

I called my OB's office.

"Good afternoon, Alaska Women's Health," the receptionist trilled.

"Hi, I need to make an appointment for a routine checkup and... Actually, lots of tests." I was panic-stricken.

"What are your symptoms?"

"An unfaithful husband."

Before I could even knock on the Hamiltons' door, Will opened it, energized and eager to assist. He was barefoot wearing jean shorts, and a pink polo shirt. My mom, handed Will a plate of chocolate chip cookies.

"Welcome, darlings. Delicious." He gave us each a fake, double-cheek kiss. "The family meeting will be upstairs. Hi, Maggie and Alex, please come with me to the kitchen." Will took the children's hands and walked away with them. I saw three maids in the background, dusting and disinfecting everything. Will looked back at me with his face pinched like a bow. "They're waiting for you in the white room." He pointed toward the stairs.

Oh shit, the white room. That room was completely white: floors, couches, furniture, drapes, walls—completely white as to mimic saintliness. Phyllis even hired someone to make matching white tiger couch throw's and pillows with the Greek God, Dionysus as the centerpiece. In reality, the white room was Simon's torture chamber for employees who misbehaved. Whenever someone received an invitation to the white room, it meant "Prepare for battle," not "Welcome to my angelic room full of spiritual gifts and treasures."

I looked over at my mom. "This should be interesting."

She followed me up to the third level, where the white room was distinguished by a separate staircase from the rest of the house. A balcony overlooked the floors below, and I often wondered how many people had been thrown over and how they got the blood out of the carpet?

Simon and Phyllis sat on the sofa next to each other. Simon was wearing grey and white striped pjs. Phyllis was wearing a cheetah print smock. Simon looked heavily medicated, with his walker close by. I felt empathy for him, instantly, and wished to whisk him away from this white, torture chamber he had once bent to his will. Now, strangely, it held each of us hostage in different ways. Phyllis was seething with anger; she looked like she had not bathed for several days, her *now* blonde greasy hair pulled back in a ponytail. She was not wearing any makeup except for the permanent makeup she could never take off.

Trey was shirtless; he stood by my mom near the staircase, ready to bolt, like a petulant child rather than a forty-year-old man. He was swollen, puffy, and angry, as if he were being forced into this meeting. He looked high or coming down from being high. His eyes were dark and vacant. “Faith, we’ve got to talk. This is outta control,” he said to me, as if I shared responsibility for his behavior.

I raised my eyebrows like *You crazy motherfucker*, but I said, “I agree.”

My mom remained silent.

“Hi, Phyllis. Hi, Simon,” I said flatly.

I quickly realized Simon was too sedated to speak. Phyllis ignored me, instead yelling at Trey. “Sit down right now!”

Trey sat down but huffed and puffed defiance with his body language. My mother chose not to stand by the drapes, in case we needed to make a quick exit.

Phyllis reached into a big manilla envelope that was sitting on the coffee table; she started pulling out bills—at least thirty of them. They were Trey’s bills and our household bills. “Here are several thousand dollars worth of monthly bills, plus private school. What’s your plan?” Phyllis tried using her eagle eyes to intimidate me.

“Ask Trey what his plan is,” I said.

Trey screamed, “You leave me outta this, you bitch! You ruined my master’s degree!” He stood up in fury like he was going to hit me. His ripped jeans sagged.

Phyllis piggybacked on Trey’s attack, “I could have your heat turned off in your house tomorrow, and you and the kids would freeze.”

Simon shuffled his walker around, trying to stand. I instinctively went to assist him. Phyllis screamed at me, “Don’t touch him! You are no longer family!” I saw drool slide down her chin.

Simon looked upset, unsteady, and on the brink of tears.

I said to her, “I worry he is going to fall. You need to help him.”

Phyllis glared at us. At that moment, I could not tell which one of us she hated more. I felt grateful that I could leave that awful house and circumstance and sad that he had to stay. Simon steadied himself and sat back down.

Trey was still standing, full of rage. He yelled, “Mom, stop! She’s a fucking bitch!” He hiked his jeans back up.

My mom said, “It’s time to leave.” She grabbed my arm and escorted me down the stairs.

Phyllis yelled after me, “I am taking the kids out of Catholic school! I am not paying for it. You’re not acting like a Christian!” I was astonished. I could handle someone coming after me, but when someone attacked my kids, things tended to go sideways.

“I don’t think it’s very Christian of you to have employees pick up your son from drug hotels with their children,” I told her. “I don’t think it is very Christian of you to have employees come over to your personal residence to administer IV medications to Trey for cellulitis from using black tar heroin while telling them it is from the common flu. You’re covering up his drug addiction and probably his affair, too. Perhaps I should talk to other Christians, and they can determine who is the better Christian.”

Phyllis’s eyes bulged. She yelled, “Trey and I are filing for divorce!”

"Take care of YOUR husband!" I yelled back at her.

"You take care of YOUR husband." She yelled back at me.

Will, along with the maids, carefully escorted the kids to the car. My mom and I followed their lead. I stomped out of there, leaving the Hamiltons' torture chamber for the last time. I felt adrenaline rushing through my body and cathartic relief from the emotional purge I had just vomited all over the white room.

I realized that all my efforts on Trey's account had been for nothing, but I had learned a holy truth. Each of us is responsible for our own life, and the things we create in our lives are the things we pay attention to—happiness, love, kindness, or the darkness of plots and schemes.

I had been unwise. I thought saving another human was the noblest act I could perform in my mortal life. In the process, I had lost my identity. I had allowed other people to tell me who I was, and they didn't tell me with a loving heart, they told me with green stacks of paper. I was an investment that had gone bust.

As we pulled out of the driveway, my mom looked impressed. "I don't think they will be arranging another family meeting."

"I think I slam-dunked her ass."

"What does that mean?" Alex asked.

"Nothing, honey. Do you want a happy meal? It makes everyone happy."

"Why was Grandma angry? And daddy looked mad. He didn't even say hi to me." Maggie asked.

Grandma Kate said, "Sometimes adults argue because everyone has different ideas about what's the best thing to do. Grandma Phyllis, Papa Simon, and Trey all love you very much."

CHRISTMAS CONFESSION

CHAPTER 12

"Merry Christmas!" It was the happiest time of the year! Hooray!

I wondered what would befall me this Christmas season—jail, death, gonorrhea? I had not heard from the Hamiltons since our family meeting in November. I had no idea what had been going on in their world, and I was relieved. The weeks of silence were welcome. All I could do was hope that Trey was back at work and sober and that Simon was being cared for by professionals.

While driving to my appointment with Dr. Smith, the OB, I prayed, "Dear God, please spare me from disease and filth; please protect me and help me to keep my health for my children. Amen."

I arrived ten minutes early. "I have an appointment with Dr. Smith," I said to the plump petite receptionist who was extra polite. Her smiling, positive energy caught me off guard. I thought to myself, "She must not have gonorrhea."

In the lobby waiting area, I pulled out my phone and looked through my calendar. The kids' Christmas Eve Pageant was coming up. The

Hamiltons had been telling everyone I was keeping the kids from them. They had not asked to see the kids since the family meeting. I sat down on the orange leather sofa. I texted Trey.

Me: *The kids' Christmas Pageant is December 24th at the church.*

Trey: *We will be there. Will has their Christmas presents in his car. He's not answering the phone. He's been missing for days.*

Me: *Why would you give him the kids' Christmas presents?*

Trey: *It's my mom; she's acting crazy.*

Me: *Well, no one's perfect. Are you going to see the kids for Christmas?*

Trey: *Yes. We need to talk.*

Me: *Come over at 5:00 pm, but I will see you at the pageant beforehand, right?*

Trey: *I would not miss it for the world.*

Great, I thought, now he's turning on his mother. His girlfriend must not be a suitable caretaker for him. Even though I didn't like Phyllis's recent decisions, a part of me thought Trey was manipulating her. Her life was hard. In addition to caring for Simon, now Phyllis had to care for Trey, too. Phyllis had to be ready for him to leave. This was the worst time of her life and Trey wouldn't stop putting her in unwinnable situations. Jeez, she must feel like she is losing everyone and everything?

"Faith?" A young nurse with bright green eyes and long dark hair called my name.

I stood to identify myself and followed her into a sterile, lifeless room. The exam table had uninviting cold steel stirrups protruding from it. Ugh. I remembered how I hated those things. On the counter sat a tray with three extra-large, distinguished Q-tips, a packet of gel, clamps, and a gigantic popsicle stick. Ugh again. I told myself to breathe. Just breathe. Just breathe. The nurse handed me a gown and left. It was hospital-grade, misty green, and more like an elongated paper towel made to clean up spills and other hazardous materials than an article of clothing. There was a knock on the door, and Dr. Smith entered. Her short silver hair reflected the ice blue of her eyes quite nicely. Her lab coat partially opened.

"I found out my husband has been having an affair, and I am sure there have been others. I am a mother. I want to be safe." I purged out the words without thinking, catching myself by surprise.

I felt embarrassed, but I knew from taking care of Trey that what you did not tell the doctor could hurt you; likewise, what you did tell her could hurt you. I chose not to share the story of the dirty needles because I did not know what implications that would have for my children. Was she legally required to have me investigated, or have the kids quarantined? My children were safe, and I did not need unnecessary drama.

"It's more common than you think. I am pleased you're here and are protecting yourself now. Go ahead and lay back." She zipped up her lab coat, washed her hands and put on blue gloves. She sat on a small swivel stool, and rolled on in.

Dr. Smith always had a compassionate and generous bedside manner. I usually sent her thank-you notes after each visit, but I was not sure that I wanted to revisit this memory with a thank you note. I could see it now: *Dear Dr. Smith, thank you ever so kindly for testing me for STDS. You're the best! XOXOXO Love, Faith Nathaniel*

She had me lie down and put my feet into the stirrups. I squinted as she performed a plethora of exams involving cotton swabs and vaginal clamps. It made me feel like such a loser. I was not good enough; that's why my husband cheated on me. There was something wrong with me. I felt such shame, having to endure not only the physical pain but the emotional pain of the attached broken promises and unanswered questions. How did I get to this place in my life?

"All done," she said at last. She scooted away from me. "You can get dressed and meet me outside." She stood, removed her gloves, washed her hands, and excused herself from the room.

I felt weepy and helpless, like I was the victim of a well-thought-out sex crime. As I took off my misty green hospital gown, I began to cry. I felt defeated, humiliated, off my divine life path. I grabbed the tissue box off the counter and sat with my paper towel gown on the hospital bed and cried. No one wanted to get checked for STDS because of an unfaithful husband and dirty needles. This was a hard day.

Still, I could not sit forever, feeling sorry for myself. I had children to raise.

I prayed, "Father God, please give me the strength to endure this day, protect me from suffering in this way again. Give me beauty for my ashes." I got dressed and wiped off the black mascara streaming down my face. I went out into the hallway to find Dr. Smith.

"I'm sorry you are going through this." I nodded my head. Dr. Smith rubbed my arm. "I won't have the results back for a week. Did you want to renew your birth control prescription while you're here?"

"No, thank you. I won't be needing that." Who would have sex with me? I probably had chlamydia. I was unclean. Trey had made me unclean.

I drove home, depressed. My pride had been wounded, my dignity and self-respect stripped from me. If I had been a serial slut, an unconscionable whore, a lady of the night, I would perhaps be able to rationalize my current situation. But I was married; I had been a faithful wife for eleven years. It was incomprehensible to me to not have control over such private matters.

Christmas Eve arrived with no word from Trey. I assumed he and his family would not be attending the kids' pageant this year. The play was about the Nativity. Maggie was playing a sheep, and she was looking forward to showing off her acting skills to her father.

"Daddy's going to be there, right?" Maggie asked. She was cute in her fluffy white outfit. We were all sitting in the living room killing time.

"I hope so. We'll see how Papa Simon feels."

"I miss Papa Simon. I want Daddy to see us," Alex said, dressed as a donkey.

"Grandma Kate and I will be there. We love you guys."

"We sure do! How about a cinnamon roll?"

I texted Trey. Me: *The play is starting in an hour; are you coming?*

Trey: *Of course, I'll be there.*

Me: *Good. It's important to the kids that their father is there. They only have one father.*

The building was full of happy parents. My mom and I sat in the back row of the church, saving a spot for Trey. The play began. We took pictures and waved to the kids. It became apparent that Trey was not coming. After the grand finale, I walked towards the stage to collect my lamb and donkey.

"Where's daddy?" Maggie asked.

"Daddy could not make it; he's sick." I avoided eye contact.

We went in search of the teachers to say our thank-yous before we left, and ran into one of Lonnie's friends. She had a small frame, but the curves were kicking, and tonight, she was spilling out of the top of her dress, but who am I to judge? I just got tested for STDs. Her hair color had recently changed to a golden blond. She hugged me tightly and patted the kids on the head.

"I like your hair. Although I do prefer you as a brunette." Mom walked off with Maggie.

She pulled me close to whisper in my ear. "I know what they're saying about you isn't true."

I whispered back, "What are they saying about me?"

"That you're having an affair with Vince Swalding, and you stole thirty thousand dollars from Dr. Hamilton." She stared to watch my reaction.

I pulled back, "What are you talking about? Who's saying these things about me?"

"Phyllis, but we know how she is." She winked and rotated her index finger around her ear, making the universal sign for crazy.

I was appalled. "I am having an affair with a married dog musher?"

"Shh... calm down. Lonnie's on your side. We all know Phyllis makes up stories. She has been doing it to Lonnie for decades."

"Did Lonnie send you here to tell me this?" I watched her closely.

"No. I have a niece in the play; she's a third-grader. Anyway, are you going to Senator Murkowski's Luncheon next week?"

I stared at her. I was no longer in the mood for small talk. I took Alex's hand and walked away briskly. I felt like I had been assaulted. Down the hallway, I saw my mom talking with Maggie's teacher. I gave her the universal symbol for, let's get the fuck out of here. I rushed to the parking lot with my little donkey. I sat in the car with my head down on the steering wheel, waiting for her. I heard a bang on the window. Chelsea.

"You bolted out of there so fast! I was calling your name; you didn't hear me, huh? Where's Trey?" Chelsea was wearing a bright pink overcoat, chewing a wad of gum.

"He's sick with the flu," Alex offered.

I turned back to Chelsea and whispered, "He didn't show up. And this lady I barely know—Lonnie's friend—tell me that I have been having an affair with a dog musher and that I stole thirty thou from Simon."

"Who started that rumor? Cruella Deville?"

"It's her style."

"No one will believe that; it's crazy. Besides, Trey is the one not showing up for the kids' Christmas Pageant. Everyone noticed. And where was Cruella? Skinning puppies for her fur coat?"

Mom and Maggie, got into the car. We bid Chelsea *Merry Christmas*.

Back home, the kids and Grandma Kate began discussing Santa's arrival. Grandma Kate and Maggie decided to bake cookies to leave out for Santa and his reindeer. Alex decided he would eat the cookies and watch *The Grinch*.

"Someone needs to write Santa a thank-you note," I said from the formal living room putting the final touches on the tree—gold and silver tinsel.

"I'll do it!" Maggie volunteered.

"Ya, put my name on it will ya?" Alex asked stretched out on the sofa.

The kids were excited over Santa's anticipated arrival. They seemed to have recovered from their dad and other grandparents not showing up. I felt bad that their Christmas was not like any other they had ever had. They had half as many presents under the tree than usual.

Of course, Will was supposedly holding Maggie's and Alex's presents hostage in his trunk, somewhere in the valley. Several stories were circulating, but tonight was about the birth of Jesus, not presents.

I stood, staring at the Christmas tree. I thought about the power of Jesus' crucifixion, the betrayals he endured at every level, how it killed his human body, but fulfilled his spiritual purpose. Then I thought about Judas and how his betrayal pushed Jesus into his destiny. The resurrection changed history. Now we can receive grace. Now we can receive second chances.

The next morning, the kids eagerly rushed downstairs. They were wearing matching red and green pajamas. Santa had brought Maggie an *American Girl* Doll and Alex a *Fireman Sam* firetruck playhouse. The kids were excited over their Christmas presents and opened them all in less then an hour. In prior Christmases, it had taken them days. One thing was certain: Grandma Phyllis happily spoiled her grandchildren with material items. Surprisingly, the kids did not seem to notice the difference in the number of presents they received. Perhaps they were just as happy with less.

Grandma Kate began cooking. I sat at the bar, drinking coffee, watching the children play. Maggie looked over at me. "Is Daddy coming over?" She asked.

"Does he have presents for us?" Alex.

"I will text him, kids."

Mom gave me a foreboding look.

Me: *Trey, are you still coming at 5? You haven't seen the kids since around Thanksgiving.*

Trey: *I'll be there at 5:00.*

Me: *What happened to the Christmas pageant last night?*

Trey: *What are you talking about?*

Me: *The kids' Christmas pageant; you said you were going to go.*

Trey: *I don't remember that.*

Wonderful. Now Trey was suffering from drug-addict amnesia. It was so unfair. While the rest of us had to participate in society, work, and take care of others, Trey got to check out as he pleased, and claim drug-addict amnesia as a valid and proper excuse. In reality, he blew his kids off to party. How convenient it must be to pronounce yourself a drug addict and then not have to participate at a normal, functioning, human level. What a blanket excuse to behave any way you damn well pleased! Life, according to Trey, worked like this, "Sorry, I didn't get groceries to feed our starving children because I am a drug addict. I spent the money on drugs." To which I, the codependent, was presumably meant to say, "It's okay, honey. We'll starve because we understand your disease, and we want you to be comfortable."

Wake up and repeat. Wake up and repeat. Wake up and repeat.

Who the hell could live that way? Drugs were a more powerful mistress than whoever this Eve chick was; she must be reeling, that her golden goose is out of control.

Thanks to Grandma Kate, we enjoyed a lavish Christmas dinner, with turkey, stuffing, sweet potato soufflé, and chocolate cake. By the time we were done eating, it was 5:30; there was no sign of Trey. I thought he must have had drug-addict amnesia again and got lost on the way to our house.

My mom kept saying, "He's not coming."

I believed he was not coming, but I wished that he would, to say hello to the kids. Maggie and Alex were still too young to have an awareness that they were being abandoned, but abandonment by their father would haunt them throughout their lives. One day, they would have to reconcile their own identity and reflect on this moment in time. Trey was hurting their emotional development, and there was nothing I could do to stop it. My message to Maggie, Alex and myself for the rest of my life would be:

"God is your one creator. Your true Father. Not me or Trey. As parents, we are entrusted with your care. I take that divine mandate seriously. Trey is incapable. Humans in all forms are imperfect; do not take it personally. You are well-loved or you would not be here. Each person must learn to be responsible for themselves, for their own happiness, for their own identity. Don't give your power away to other people, not even your parents. God says who you are, not people, not me, not

Trey. Life is about loving yourself and everyone you meet unconditionally, in a healthy way."

At 8:30 p.m. on Christmas Day, there was a knock at the door. I thought, Drug dealer.

"It's Daddy! It's Daddy!" Maggie shouted from the living room. She ran out in her elf onesie.

"Daddy!" Alex repeated as he slid across the floor, in his Jedi costume.

"Oh, great. Trey's here and we just put our pajamas back on" Kate said, irritated. Her arms folded and back against the wall.

Trey slithered through the door, and the kids rushed to him. "Merry Christmas, guys!" He looked unclean in black sweatpants and a black hoodie that read "*Trialblazer.*"

"Merry Christmas!" Maggie said jumping up and down.

"Presents! I want to open presents!" Alex.

"Let's go sit by the tree." I offered.

Trey was carrying unwrapped presents in paper bags from Walgreens. I guessed that Walgreens was open on Christmas Day, and it was the one-stop shopping place for dead-beat dads across the country. The kids did not care; they made a big deal over his arrival, and over the trinkets he brought them. It felt sweet and pitiful at the same time. Trey was driving Simon's brand-new Mercedes, but this was the best he could do for his own children. Maggie and Alex tore through the Walgreen bags.

"I love you guys," Trey said, then pointed at framed photos of the kids and me from Aunt Denali's wedding. "Why aren't I in the pictures?"

"Probably because of recent events." I studied his face.

"Can we go to the theater room and talk?"

"Sure Trey," I said. I could tell he was being plot-full Trey, manipulative Trey, sneaky-snaky Trey. I wondered what outlandish story he would assault me with next.

Mom glared. She could tell a Trey-pisode was afoot.

We walked downstairs together and sat on the loveseat next to each other. I felt his defenses go down. He was vulnerable. Maybe finally I would be able to get the truth out of him. I activated my *TapeACall* App on the phone. He gave me the "I love you" look. Old Faith would have fallen for it, but it just sent creepy chills down new Faith's spine. I saw the transparency of his desperation, his deceitfulness, and his manipulations as a last resort to salvage a life he had so easily thrown away months ago. He shifted around on the sofa, uncomfortable in his own skin.

"I don't want to do this on Christmas day," he said, starting with an apology.

Given past experiences, I had learned that when someone as unstable as Trey was ready to confess, take advantage of the moment because it was fleeting. I could tell that he needed to be babied along and made to feel safe.

"It's okay; let's clear the air and try to start fresh. Who is Eve?" I patted his leg lightly.

"There is no Eve." He put his head between his hands like he had been a bad boy.

I rephrased the question to make it easier for him. After all, he was pretending to be fragile. "Who was the lady you programmed into your phone as Pichaard?"

"It's Helga. It's always been Helga."

"Helga? She's married with six children, with chronic IBS, and your mother's BFF. No fucking way. You're lying." I stood up and pointed my finger at him as to say 'off with his head!'

"Helga has been stalking me. She might be stalking you, too. She's so jealous of you. She wants your life. She told my mom that I was her next husband." Trey accused her as if he were the prey of Helga, the middle-aged, European seductress.

I was disgusted. I felt sick to my stomach. Not that long ago, he had been protecting her from me. Now, the tide had turned; she was stalking him, and he—a mere victim of Helga's poon-tang.

"Does your mom know?"

"Yes, but she only cares about money," Trey said, tearfully.

"How did the affair start?" I sat back down on the sofa next to him.

"Helga came to get me out of my office one day to check on my mom. Mom was nodding off at her desk; she had been taking morphine or shooting up Demerol, I don't know which. She was obviously under the influence. Helga and I escorted her home. We started talking about getting mom into the Betty Ford Clinic. She was nice to me, she flattered me, and soon she was texting me all the time. I got carried away. She started telling me she was in love with me. When you read that text, nothing had even happened yet."

"Then why hide her name in your phone under Pichaard? Why did she say she knew you very well?"

"Weeks before you found out, Sue, the CEO of Saint Mary's, pulled me and my mom into her office. She said her assistant had noticed a high amount of data usage on Helga's phone; she looked into it and saw by the number of text messages that we were having an affair. She said if it didn't stop, she was going to fire Helga, and it would be on me."

"Wait. Hold up. Are you telling me that your mom knew about your affair weeks before I even found out?" I said, trying to contain the wild anger growing inside.

"And then Helga started telling me she was in love with me. She would not leave me alone. She told me her husband had moved his gay lover into their house, and they were having problems. The night you kicked me out, she left her family. She came to work with a neck brace and told Sue that her husband was beating her. It was a lie; she's a psychopath. Sue gave her a St. Mary's apartment. Helga thought we were going to live together in that crummy apartment. My mom is pissed at Helga over that one," Trey said, scoffing as if living in an apartment with Helga was beneath him.

"What about Simon? Did he know?"

"He didn't at first; he knows now, and he's pissed. He wants me out of the house. Can you believe that?"

"Those apartments are for traveling medical professionals, not employee mistresses. You have been threatening me, my children, my home—to have our heat turned off in the dead of winter. Meanwhile, St. Mary's is putting up a married employees in an apartment for the owner's son to screw? There are eight real children involved. I can't believe the lack of conscience and morals from people who own a wellness center. I think you're better suited to own a brothel."

"What about Vince and Luke? You fucked somebody! We're even."

"I can't believe you are trying to redirect my dinner with Luke to justify all the shit you've done to the children and me over the last several months. Even Grandma Phyllis—a whole-family betrayal!" I stood, I put my hands over my face. I paced the floor full of rage, sorrow, and disgust.

"All she cares about is money. It's her fault. She needed Helga to help run the Center. She can't do it alone, and Helga knows our secrets," Trey said as if he was the victim yet again, this time of his mother.

"Trey, you're a man in charge of your own fate." I glanced at his sweatshirt. "A real *trailblazer*. If your mom did encourage you to have an affair, you still had a choice. You chose the affair. You chose the drugs. You chose to lie and cover these things up from me. To abandon your kids. Do you know I had to get tested for STDs because of you?"

"Because you're fucking Luke," Trey said, he stood in a defensive posture now, as if he had manufactured some sort of ground to stand on.

"I did not fuck Luke, but soon, I'll be fucking somebody—my Christmas gift to you. Now get the fuck out of my house," I screamed, enraged.

"I love you. I am sorry. Can I live in the basement?" Trey dropped to his knees, grabbed my hands, defeated and obviously out of resources.

"Hell no! Get out!" I ushered him up the stairs and out of the door.

"You are a stupid bitch," Trey slammed the door behind him.

I opened it back up "No, you are a stupid bitch!" I looked across the street, our neighbor was walking their dog. "Merry Christmas Fred! Apologies." I waved and shut the door. Trey sped off.

"Where is daddy going? He didn't say bye." Maggie came running downstairs.

I wrapped my arms around her, "I know pumpkin, there is a medical emergency, he had to leave. He told me to tell you that he loves you." I hugged her. "Okay," she muttered. "Do you want to come sit with me by the tree?" She walked off into the kitchen.

I was so angry. This was a new low for the Hamiltons. Without Simon guiding the ship, Phyllis's and Trey's mental illnesses were on full display. I had so much to process. Helga, what was wrong with this lady? She had a debilitating disease and six children. Was she fucking crazy, leaving her kids? If I had a debilitating disease, I would be so wrapped up in my kids and family. What did she think—this was her last opportunity to make it to the big leagues? Dragging her children around to drug hotels after Trey...sad.

I wanted nothing to do with her. If I'd had a fight in me before, to duke it out with "Eve" over Trey, I surely did not now. I refused to lower myself to Helga's level. I recalled her smug words, "I know him very well." If she thought Trey, the most selfish man alive, would care for her in her old age and with her IBS, she didn't know him very well at all! He was not cleaning up anyone's shit.

As for Grandma Phyllis—was she really the drug user Trey had portrayed her to be? Was it true that Trey and Helga had caught her under the influence and then bonded over her addiction? I wondered if Helga was the person Grandma Phyllis sent over to their residence to give Trey that IV drip. I wondered if Phyllis had set this whole debacle in motion, trying to cover her own drug use or perhaps just trying to keep St. Mary's together. I didn't think she was so depraved that she would hurt her own grandchildren, but who knew? If Trey was telling the truth, what was she thinking now? That her BFF, Helga, had turned out to be a poor substitute caretaker for Trey, and she needed me back? Did she send Trey here tonight to reconcile? I could see her—wearing a black satin robe, sitting in a red velvet chair, in a dimly lit room, twiddling her thumbs with resting bitch face, "Trey summon Faith. I hold her livelihood in my hands; (cackle, cackle) … I have a big purse."

I went into the kitchen.

"Where's daddy?" Alex asked. His eyes full of confusion.

"Daddy had to leave suddenly." I avoided him.

"What's wrong with him? Is it the flu?"

I wanted to say, Listen, your daddy is a real crazy motherfucker. Get used to it, kids. Instead, I gritted my teeth as if a gun were being held to my head. "Papa Simon needed him back. Why don't you guys go play with Alex's fire truck, while I talk to Grandma Kate."

Maggie said, "Okay, fine. Let's go, Alex. It's another secret meeting we can't hear."

I told my mother what Trey had told me. My voice was breaking. It surprised me how quickly anger could morph into despair. I started crying.

"Helga? Isn't she a grandmother? I can't believe it. And Phyllis! What is she thinking?" My mom hugged me. "It's okay, baby. They're living in a glass house; it's a stack of cards, and it will crumble. People can't lead a sinful life like this and expect to come out clean. Karma is a b.i.t.c.h," Kate said, spelling the last word, and wiping the tears from my eyes. "You can't let them break you. Get angry. Stay angry if you have to, but you must keep moving forward."

I knew she was worried I would fall into a black hole of paralyzing depression. "I'll stay strong for my children. I think Helga is dangerous. Trey said Helga is jealous of me and wants my life. That's so creepy."

"I say we should give her Trey if he is even telling the truth? Hell, let's give him to her anyway. What do you think?" Mom offered me a cookie.

I looked away. I wasn't ready to confront that.

"Sorry, too soon, I suppose." She put her arms around my shoulders again. "How about some hot cocoa. We have miniature marshmallows?"

HELGA'S GOT DRUGS

CHAPTER 13

Ralph invited us to his New Year's Eve party. He said he had a friend he wanted me to meet. A new year, but not a new beginning yet.

The kids were excited about the party, and the promise of fireworks further fueled their enthusiasm. Maggie put on a sparkly grey dress, and Alex wore a top hat that lit up every time he moved. It read, "Happy New Year." I wore jeans and a silky black blouse. Grandma Kate chose to stay at the house. I think she needed a break from all the drama.

The roads were icy; I drove slowly. There were so many people in attendance that I could not find a close parking spot. We had to leave the car two streets over. I was wearing two-and-a-half-inch heels of bravery; only an Alaskan girl could understand the tightrope of walking on the ice in stilettos, while managing small children no less.

Ralph's home was dimly lit, the only source of illumination for the room was the gigantic log fireplace and the several candles strategically placed in the grand entrance, the living room, bar, and kitchen. A table by the front door was littered with party favors: Happy New Year 2017 hats, balloons, wine glasses, bubbles, party horns. Glitter was sprinkled about the table. Maggie grabbed a purple fur boa scarf and wrapped it around her neck. Alex took one of each. Some of the other kids they knew from previous parties were there, and they wanted to go downstairs with them. One of the kids was playing with a guinea pig.

"I am going to get that hamster," Alex said, eyeing the helpless rodent.

"You have to take turns, Alex," Maggie replied, mothering him.

"Wait. Stop," I said, making eye contact. "Listen to me. Stay inside. Do not leave this house without telling me. The ice on the water is unsafe. I'll be in the living room or the kitchen. I am staying on this level. Do you understand me?"

"Yes, mom. Come on! He's leaving with the hamster!" They dashed off.

Lonnie and Jacob were by the bar, speaking with another guest. Lonnie was wearing a gold sequin dress, with a matching headpiece, like Cleopatra. Jacob was wearing black, shiny, patent jeans, and a white button-down shirt that was barely buttoned. His chest was exposed, and I had a feeling he was just getting started. I made my way over there.

"Have some Champs," Lonnie said, handing me a glass of champagne.

I took the glass, afraid to drink it after being accused of driving drunk by Phyllis.

"How have you been?" Jacob asked.

"I found out who Eve is." Ralph popped up from behind the bar, interrupting our conversation. I shushed.

"How are you doing, Faith?" Ralph turned and yelled across the crowded room. "Harry, come on over here!" A nice-looking man of average height, dark hair, and piercing brown eyes approached us. "Harry, this is Faith. I've been meaning to introduce you two. I believe you are both going through a similar life event."

Suddenly, it occurred to me that Ralph was trying to hook his buddy up like Jacob had tried to do with Luke. In boy world, I guess everyone wanted some street cred for hooking a brother up, or perhaps it was the simple fact that the man to woman ratio in Alaska was so high. Men must have felt pressured to squeeze in face time early when a single female landed on the radar. Harry extended his hand. "Hi, Faith. Nice to meet you."

He had a gentleness about him that I found endearing. I sensed that he had been humbled by his circumstance. I said hello.

"I guess from what I hear you are going through a divorce."

"Oh, not yet, but soon, I would imagine. What about you Harry?"

"Yes, she filed. I caught her in the act with our neighbor. He was someone I considered a friend." He sounded defeated and broken-down by the memory of the experience. We sat down on the barstools next to each other.

"Like in the act?" Jacob piped in and started to dry-hump Lonnie from behind. Jeez. He was like a wind-up toy from the 1950s, just a few clicks to the right, and there he goes. Still, I admired his uninhibited approach to romance.

"Yep, I walked right in on them in our bedroom. I had left for work, forgot my laptop, had to turn around and drive back home. Heard a rustling noise upstairs. Walked up the stairs, opened the door, and there he was, butt-naked in the corner trying to hide underneath our sheer drapes," Harry said.

"Did you beat his ass?" Lonnie asked, pushing Jacob away.

"I charged him; he started begging. 'It doesn't have to be like this. I am sorry. I am sorry,'" Harry said, kind of laughing now, recalling the cowardly, naked lover of his soon-to-be ex-wife begging for mercy.

"What a pussy. You should have knocked his teeth in," Jacob said, his fist held high in the air.

"Did you catch yours in the act?" Harry looked at me.

"No, thank God! I'd be in prison right now. I caught Trey through a text message. He hid her identity from me for months, and then suddenly, on Jesus' birthday, he thought a confession was in order. My best Christmas to date! He told me it was Helga, a fellow employee."

Jacob made a face of disgust. "Wait. Helga? I have seen her at the Barre3 class with Phyllis; she looks like a troll. She's hideous." He gave himself devil horns with his index fingers.

"Thank you, Jacob, I appreciate your input." I reached around to pat him on the back.

"Wow, sister, I am disturbed. She's been at the house a lot, but I thought she was helping with daddy because she's an EMT, right? She was even at Christmas dinner with the rest of the family. Phyllis definitely knows," Lonnie said, her face stiffened.

"I guess Trey came over right after Christmas dinner and forgot to tell me that part. Wow! I am still processing everything. It's hard for me to believe that Phyllis would partake in something so slimy. It's counter-intuitive to what a loving mother or grandmother would do."

"No, No, No. It's Saint Mary's. She's protecting Saint Mary's."

A light bulb turned on in my head. "Oh, my God! That's what Trey said. Trey told me that his mom pushed him into Helga's arms. He said she needed help running the Center. Could she have thought that Helga was an upgrade from me because she has the added bonus of already knowing the inner workings of St. Mary's, and she can administer IVs?" I wondered if perhaps, for once, Trey was telling the truth.

"That's how she thinks. She told me to marry for advantage. You know: money, status, but I refused. I would only marry for love." Lonnie grabbed Jacob's hand while gazing deeply into his eyes.

"I love you, baby," Jacob said, holding her gaze, puckered up for a kiss. They had such a passionate union. Full of highs and lows, but Jacob was no slouch; he owned his own business and was Lonnie's intellectual equal. But Phyllis had stamped their relationship with the mark of disapproval. Why? Because Jacob was an outlier, he was an untamed wolf, and Phyllis knew she could not get him to fit into her perfect picture of glamour, sophistication, and indulging the little people.

"Do you think you'll reconcile?" Harry asked.

"No! I tried to pull deep and muster some feelings for him, for the kids' sake, even one I could not conjure. Now, I only want my kids and my house. How about you? Are you fighting for the kids, the house?"

Lonnie and Jacob walked off together.

"We have two homes, one child; we'll see. I am concerned about my daughter. My wife says she loves this guy." I saw myself reflected in his eyes. I felt like I needed to be strong for Harry. I patted him on the back.

"You know, Harry, Trey chose to cheat. I will not lower myself to fight over a man, especially with someone like Helga. I would rather be alone. The same is true for you; fighting with him is a downgrade for you. You deserve an amazing woman, not a tart that doesn't even have the decency to get a hotel room. My God! Let's put our kids first. I say let's both let go and let God guide us. We'll have beauty for our ashes."

Lonnie walked over to us and grabbed me by the arm. "Harry, I am so sorry to interrupt. Faith needs to say hi to someone." She pulled me away.

"Can I call you sometime?" Harry asked.

"Of course," I said and smiled, looking into his eyes and acknowledging our shared pain. I felt connected to him.

In the candlelit kitchen, Chloe, Simon's business associate at his medical practice, was standing by the sink in front of windows that overlooked the ocean. She had athletic gear on and was older than her looks would let you know. She had a stern energy about her, as if to project to the world that she was not to be trifled with. She seemed thoughtful and upset.

"Long time no see," I said.

She grabbed me by the waist, whirled me around like a ballroom dancer, and kissed me on the lips. It was uncomfortable but amusing. "I am so sorry. Phyllis is such a dreadful woman. She turns on everyone, eventually. She hates me, and I haven't done anything to her. I can't believe what they are doing to you."

I thanked her for her support, pondering if she would dip me next. I glanced over at Lonnie. What was she plotting?

Chloe said, "Simon has stopped paying me and his entire staff. I don't know what to do. I am going to have to find a new job."

According to Chloe, Simon hadn't been to the office in months. The last time he came in, he was slurring his words, and the patient refused to have him operate on her. Chloe canceled the rest of his appointments and sent him home. Bubba's Pharmacy had been complaining, about the medications going to Hamilton household.

"Phyllis has him all doped up." Chloe told me she had gone to their house, and Phyllis had slammed the door in her face. "She better watch out because Carl is pissed and ready to blow the whistle." Chloe paced. Carl, who worked in Dr. Hamilton's office too, had written Phyllis's graduate papers. By law, to be an administrator at St. Mary's you had to have a master's degree.

Wow, I thought. Carl and I have something in common.

"I have given him decades of my life, and this is how I am being treated." Chloe huffed and puffed in anger.

"After what I learned about Trey's and Helga's affair, I am not surprised to learn about Carl. St. Mary's is a grand extension of her ego. I've always known she was a plotter. I just didn't realize her plotting had no limits," I said.

Lonnie piped in. "Finally, you see her true colors. And once you see it, you cannot unsee it. St. Mary's is the one place she can go where people have to worship her." Lonnie turned to Chloe, "Dad asked me to help sort things out with his practice. Somehow, Phyllis found out and he threw me under the bus. He's scared to stand up to her."

"I would like you to come by the office on Monday and speak with Carl," Chloe said to me, glancing at Lonnie.

"Yes, and maybe Dr. Stella about all of the medications being prescribed to them. Trey has been talking about his mother's drug use for years. I have largely discounted it, but it keeps coming up," I said.

"Dr. Stella is a drug doctor; it's all over town. Everyone at the office is talking about it. I knew someone who told me he got his aunt hooked on oxy. Not long afterward, she died of an overdose.

It's a matter of time before the FBI investigates him," Chloe said.

Lonnie said, "Kind of brilliant... Creating repeat clients by giving them an addiction, all while you are the one with the pen and pad... Anyway, at my urging, Phyllis has hired caregivers for my dad. Trey is no longer looking after him."

"Thank God. A drug addict does not make a good caregiver, especially when doling out OxyContin," I said.

We heard bangs and booms. Outside, fireworks were blasting in the sky. I saw the kids in the yard with Harry and Ralph. I smiled, watching them jump with excitement and then gaze up with wonder as the rockets combusted into the air above. We stopped talking about the insanity in our orbit for a bit to watch the light show from the kitchen windows. No matter what dissatisfactory thing was happening in our lives, the effect of flashing brilliant colors of light against the dark arctic night was bursting with magic, wonder, and promise. Sometimes, it's okay to enjoy the moment and all it has to offer.

The Lady Senator's Holiday Luncheon had arrived. I forced myself to go. I had to keep moving forward and showing up. Lonnie was out of town, and she had asked me to take her place at the head table, but I chose to sit near my dear friend, Maria. I had not seen her since the Saint Joseph's Auction, and that night I was not on my best behavior. I wore a grey sheath dress with low nude patent leather heels. My hair was pulled back in a bun.

The reception was being held in The Rentz's Ballroom. The ballroom was decorated in Christmas colors, gold table cloths, red napkins, and mistletoe sprinkled about the tables. There must have been about five hundred of the finest ladies in the whole state of Alaska in attendance. I saw Aunt Denali first; she was wearing a candy-apple-colored pantsuit, full of sass, and black sequin heels.

"How have you been, sugar?" she asked. "I hope you're taking care of yourself and those precious babies. Have you filed yet? I hope you kick his ass." She gave me the stare-down as if I had all the power in the world, and I was not caught between maintaining firm boundaries and starving to death.

"Not yet." I told her that she'd been right about Helga being Eve, and about Trey coming over on Christmas Day to confess. "Merry Christmas," I finished. "Personally, I prefer jewelry."

"No shit. I'm always right about men with little peckers. Narcissists are simple and should be treated as such. Inflate the ego when you want to negotiate, deflate when you want to escape." She raised her eyebrows at me, as if I needed to pause, find a pen, and write this down.

"There's more. According to Trey, Phyllis knew about the affair weeks before I found out and chose to cover it up. Then, Helga conned the CEO of Saint Mary's out of an apartment so she and Trey could play house."

"Sounds illegal. And like a Lifetime movie. Sometimes truth is stranger than fiction." "We're having our own issues. Simon called Peter the other day because he had fallen and could not get up. Peter had to rush over there to help him. When Peter arrived, no one was at the house. He was alone."

This didn't surprise me. Their gardener had called me over to the house a few times because she had found Simon on his back in the yard, unable to move. Once, he told her he had been stuck there for two hours, face down. I said, "Lonnie talked Phyllis into hiring caregivers who'll be there twenty-four hours a day. Let's pray Trey doesn't run them off or steal them for himself." I saw my friend Maria approaching from a distance.

"Listen, Aunt Denali; I have to go. Call me, okay?" I gave her a hug.

Maria was wearing a long, elegant, white dress that complemented her dark, curly hair and olive skin, but her real beauty lay within. She was one of the kindest and most intuitive women I knew. We greeted each other with a double cheek kiss. "I have been meaning to call you," she said, sounding concerned. "I've been hearing some strange things." We walked to our assigned table and sat down.

"Like what?" I was already exhausted by her potential response.

"Well, that the Hamiltons are drug addicts, and you're having an affair with that dog musher, and that Saint Mary's is tanking, badly."

"Wow! That's a lot to digest. Drugs, affairs, and bankruptcy, huh? That's my life. Still, I don't know why this dog musher was chosen for my torrid love affair? I suppose because it's more glamorous than Joe the plumber coming to the house to clean the pipes," I laughed at my own joke. She stared at me.

I filled her in on the drama. Maria continued to stare at me.

"I was concerned about Trey, actually. I don't know how to tell you this." Our waitress came by, poured us some water, and served us our first course. "Trey came by the house last week and asked my husband for money. Trey told him that drug dealers were going to come after you and the kids otherwise. My husband said someone from the St. Mary's liaison office kept calling Trey's phone, like incessantly. Trey said it was the drug dealer. My husband gave him two hundred bucks and told him to get his life together."

"Are you kidding me?" I felt two inches tall. "Maria, I am so sorry. The liaison is Helga, Trey's lover" I looked at the brown carpet, too ashamed to hold eye contact.

"He has used the 'give me money or drug dealers will kill my family' line before. One day, it may actually be true. Please forgive me?"

"You didn't do anything. I love you. You will always be my sister. This liaison is a whore." She hugged me, although she seemed surprised by my confirmation, as if she had been expecting to hear a more positive version of the 'give me money or the drug dealers will kill my family' story.

"Trey said his mother set up the love affair with Helga, and she is also abusing prescription drugs. I don't think he is a reliable source, though."

"What? This is unfixable. Trey is on drugs, possibly his mother? You have got to take your kids and get the hell out of here. This isn't a safe place for your kids, Faith."

I was unsettled by Maria's suggestion. I had not thought about moving. I had not thought about what my life would be like if I stayed here. But it was only a matter of time before Trey exhausted everyone's patience, and Phyllis shipped him off to rehab somewhere in the lower forty-eight. After all, Phyllis could not have her drug-addict son going around town, hitting up her friends and employees for two hundred dollar fixes. That was not the life of a glamorous celebrity son.

My phone rang. Simon. I apologized to Maria and found a secluded area before taking the call. Simon's speech was slurred; he sounded distressed. "Please take him back. He has to move back in with you. I can't take care of him. He took all my medication. Two-hundred and forty pills are missing. You have to find him. He may die."

"Trey's a survivor. The critical issue is that you're in pain, and you don't have any meds. Who should I call?"

"No, find Trey. I am going to start drinking."

"Bad idea! Don't worry about Trey; he's probably trading them on the black market for heroin." I had read an article saying you could get sixty dollars a pill on the streets for oxy. Then I added, "I'll check on him. Is he not at work?"

"He stopped going to work in November. I don't know why I am still paying him. Phyllis won't let me fire him."

"He can't be responsible for other people's care! Look what he's doing to you!" I yelled in frustration. "Where are your caregivers?"

"They don't start until Wednesday. Please, can he live in your basement?"

"No, Simon. I want to help you, and I wish I could fix Trey, but I cannot have an active drug user around my children. It's dangerous."

"I am paying your mortgage! I demand he live in the basement!"

"Trey's forty years old. His girlfriend can get them another St. Mary's apartment to live in." I heard a beep, beep—incoming call.

"Simon, Trey's calling me now. I'll call you back," I switched over. "Hello!" I shouted, still upset by the desperation in Simon's slurred speech. I grabbed my purse off the table and walked out of the ballroom, into the hallway.

"Faith, I need help," Trey said pitifully.

"No, Simon needs help. You took all his pain meds, and he's in legitimate pain, real pain, Trey. You can't do that to him. Take his meds back to him immediately!"

"Someone's trying to kill me," Trey said, trying to inspire sympathy now from a phony murder plot.

"What, like someone you owe drug money to? I don't appreciate you hitting Maria's family up for money, saying your drug friends were going to hurt my children."

"I owe money. They are coming after me. Someone tried to shoot me. I ran for cover!" Trey sounded hysterical.

"Call your girlfriend. She helped get you into this mess; she can help you out of it."

"She won't talk to me. She gave me her debit card and pin number. The dumb bitch," Trey said as if he had served her a little payback on my behalf.

"Seriously?" Had he drained her account? I couldn't believe it.

"Yes, she deserved it, look at what she's done to our family."

"She has six children! How could you? Do you only care about yourself?"

"Faith, pleeeeease. I'm so sorry. I don't care about her. She's stalking me. I need money. Meet me at the bank. I'll give you something you really want."

"Like what, Trey? Simon's medication?"

"Evidence. Simon's meds are long gone."

My curiosity got the best of me and Simon had asked me to check on him. "The bank downtown?"

"Yes, KeyBank, downtown."

Before I left, I told Maria where I was going to meet Trey, in case he killed me or took me hostage. He was on drugs and desperate; anything was possible. I drove to the bank, wondering what the hell he was going to give me in the parking lot, another confession? Definitely not jewelry.

Trey had parked his car length-wise, like an asshole, taking up two lanes. He was standing beside his Mercedes, which was freshly dented on the right-hand side. It was fifteen degrees outside, but he was wearing green short-sleeved hospital scrubs and flip-flops. It looked as if he had a long, hard night.

I pulled up next to him, locked my doors, and cracked the window a few inches.

His eyes were wild, like those of an untamed hyena. He looked high, and he had obviously been driving. He threw his phone through the crack of my window and screamed like a petrified, six-year-old girl, "Look at it!"

His text message exchanges with Phyllis were on the screen. Trey began to rock his feet back and forth.

Phyllis: *Trey, I have shot up all my Demerol. I am going to die. This is what you want. Me dead.*

Okay, I get it. Her life was hard right now, but what, was she in labor? Who would give her vials of Demerol? I checked the number to make sure it was from her. It was.

Phyllis: *Trey, call Faith or Helga. You need help. Helga's got drugs. I don't want you to end up like Johnny.*

I looked at Trey. "What's this? Your mom telling you to call her employee because she has the drugs you like over me, your wife?" I asked him.

"She set me up! She wants me to be with Helga. She forced me into it. I chose you. I love you. Do you have any money?"

"Where's your mother?"

"In Scottsdale."

"Who's watching Simon?"

"I am."

"Trey, he's alone and immobile. How could you?" What creature was inhabiting this human body in front of me?

He was slinking around my automobile like an arctic raven circling an old crusty cheeseburger from McDonalds. "Where's my money? Can I live in the basement? Give me back my phone."

I re-checked the number to make sure it actually belonged to Phyllis. I took a screenshot of the text messages and sent them to myself. Then, I threw his phone and some cash out of the window. "Call a cab," I said, flipped him the bird, and drove off.

Now I had proof. Phyllis had been trying to delete me from Trey's life all along, probably the first day he started working at the Center. She likely viewed the kids and me as competition for Trey's attention, and with Simon's failing health, she needed extra security. She was so delusional as to think Trey would give it to her. Phyllis and Trey were the exact same human being. Plotting and manipulating each other, each for their own distinct selfish ends. Now there ends are at odds—I called Lonnie and told her about Simon's situation. "He needs help, now."

"Can you take care of him? I am out of town."

I knew Lonnie had an important job, but she should have jumped into action instead of passing this on to me. Her dad was being neglected and in unimaginable pain. I was giving her every reason to get on the front lines of his care like she had told me she wanted to do all those months ago, but she was not following through. "I'll make sure he's okay," I said and hung up.

I called Aunt Denali—the only solid, morally-grounded female in the family.

"What a shit show," she said. "Peter's on his way."

TAKING A LOVER

CHAPTER 14

The relationship between the Hamiltons and me was at an all-time low. I could not imagine being in the same room with them. How could I ever look Phyllis in the eye again? How could a grandmother plot the dissolution of her son's marriage, knowing it would do irreparable damage to her grandchildren, not to mention her son, who needed a high-quality caretaker on high alert twenty-four seven? I could not fathom the full extent of all the calculating and scheming against me that had occurred during the last several months or years! I had to jolt myself out of this situation. I needed a new focus. I could not allow myself to go around in circles, retracing the steps of their plotting, trying to make sense of it all. I needed something to keep my mind occupied on something positive, something new, something fresh.

I decided to take a lover. Not a revenge screw, a lover. Someone who could ignite what was left of my womanly desires. Someone I would enjoy a fast and fleeting romance with. I liked Luke, but

I did not feel the sexual passion, sadly. I mean, I had met him three times before I remembered who he was, yikes! I liked Harry, but I did not feel the red-hot chemistry needed to take me to a different place. Rarely had I met someone and felt that instant chemistry zing. In fact, it had only happened a handful of times. Unfortunately, Trey had been a zinger, but obviously, he just ended up zapping me.

The last time it had happened had been five years before when I met Lonnie's then-boyfriend, Brad. She had dated him briefly before marrying Jacob. When I met Brad, he and Lonnie were acquainted through politics. Lonnie gathered the family to meet him at his place of business. He was her latest boy-toy after her most recent divorce. When we locked eyes, he gave me the *I love you* look. It was intense, and it took my mind to an altered state where I prophesied briefly that he was my next husband. Brad had left a memorable impression. He had greased my rusty old love engine.

It was obvious to everyone around us, too. Trey even took me aside and said, "You think you have problems with me? You'll have real, big problems with that guy." I remembered squinting my eyes at him and thinking, *How could our problems get any bigger? You are on the verge of being arrested for embezzlement!*

The last time I had seen Brad was a three years ago in Atlanta. We were celebrating Trey's cousin for earning his Ph.D. in psychotherapy. We were eating at Maestro's Steakhouse and Brad was Lonnie's guest. We sat next to each other. He still gave me that love-struck look, which I found rather intoxicating. I could feel his attraction towards me. His energy felt red-hot and inflamed with sexual desire. I was wearing a short orange cocktail dress, and he kept staring down at my legs, like the greatest treasure in the world lay a few inches away.

I had enjoyed the way he lusted after me, and I had occasionally fantasized about him. Brad was a big zinger. He also lived a several towns away, which was an added bonus in my decision-making process. In case he turned out to be a quack, I didn't have to worry about looking over my shoulder. And I liked that he knew the Hamiltons. I needed someone who understood the unique situation I was in and the psychosis that was at work.

After a short deliberation, I decided Brad had all the qualifications I needed to be a jovial distraction in my life. Someone I would enjoy getting to know and who would keep a part of me living, breathing, and feeling alive. I thought, *Brad Rosenbloom, my new lover, my guinea pig of desire.*

How would I establish communication, though? DUH! Maggie had a jump-roping competition in Brad's hometown, where he owned a property management company. I decided to move slowly. I emailed him about a room at one of his Airbnbs, just to take a toe-dip in what I hoped would be a pool of passionate kisses and quiet whispers.

Hi Brad, how are you? I hope life is treating you well. Maggie has a competition in Juneau January 20th, do you have any rooms available? Thanks, Faith.

I sent it on my way to Dr. Hamilton's building, where his office was located to meet Chloe.

As I walked into the office, I could feel something was off. The pewter and yellow accented lobby was cold, vacant, and empty. It felt like a funeral had just commenced. No one was in sight behind the receptionists' desk. I rang the bell. Still, no one came. Was I alone? Had somebody accidently left the office door unlocked? I was about to leave when Chloe walked into the lobby from the back rooms. She was wearing a light pink button-down shirt and green surgery scrubs. Her blond hair was neatly pulled back into a surgical hairnet. "Come on back," she said.

I followed her down the patient hallway, the lights were off and all the doors were shut. "I didn't think anyone was here."

She ushered me into a room. "I know. It's like a ghost town around here. This was Simon's office. Look at this place. He hasn't been here in months. Seriously, it's a mess. We're all about to walk out and leave in protest."

The office was, indeed, a disaster. Loose papers were scattered about in various piles on his mahogany desk. His filing cabinet was cracked open; his red leather chair was floating about in the middle of the floor. There were pictures of the grandchildren everywhere. It was heartwarming and heartbreaking. I wondered how many different people had come in here and rifled through his things.

"Simon is gravely ill. Trey stole his meds. Phyllis is in the desert. The whole family is in crisis, Chloe.

You need to put yourself and your family's needs first. I fear this ship is sinking."

She looked dissatisfied. "Well, he owes us money. Come over here, and I will introduce you to Carl."

I followed her further down the dark hallway. It felt like doomsday was upon us. The office employees that remained seemed to be in a severe depression. She took me into another office. An extremely fit, balding gentleman sat behind a dark wooden desk gnawing on a hotdog; he had a mustard stain on his face and was wearing a t-shirt two sizes too small to accentuate his physique. Carl saw me, and a look of horror fell upon his face. I could tell he knew who I was. He put the hotdog down. His discomfort was palpable. "I don't think we've met," I said, reaching my hand out to greet him.

He shook. "Nice to meet you," he said. He sounded shy.

"So, Carl, were you paid to write Phyllis's papers for her Master's degree? I was doing the same thing for Trey, so no worries on any judgment coming from me."

"Yes, I did, they paid me for that, but now they won't pay our salaries," Carl said, wiping his face with a brown paper napkin.

"I'm sorry. No one is thinking clearly right now or making healthy choices."

Chloe said, "Lonnie is no better. She was in here two days ago. She asked me to violate HIPAA and pull Phyllis's and Simon's prescription drug list. I said no. I don't trust her." She looked at me to gauge my response.

"You shouldn't trust her. I love her, and I know Phyllis has made her life hell, but she has some version of Stockholm syndrome. She doesn't have the courage, yet, to properly defend herself."

"I'd give the information to you," Chloe said placing her hands on her hips.

"Really? Sure I'll take it."

I followed Chloe down the hall into another office. She turned on the lights, put her eye glasses on and logged onto a computer. I sat down adjacent from her in a free standing chair. Chloe printed off multiple sheets, and handed them to me. Phyllis's script from Dr. Stella included morphine and Demerol vials bi-weekly, and one script for morphine, another script for Demerol from another doctor in the building. He was supposedly a 'good' Catholic. I wonder what she told him to get those? These prescriptions went back to October and it was January. And here was Simon's script for two hundred plus pills of OxyContin, bi-weekly, for months.

I was floored. Pain management following surgery typically requires less than a week of a narcotics like OxyContin, and then they put you on Ibuprofen. Perhaps he was in constant pain for other ailments. I was not a doctor but this didn't feel like any kind of pain management I had ever encountered. What was going on?

Simon, along with Dr. Stella and a four other doctors, owned the building. Simon had the largest ownership. Bubba's Pharmacy leased office space, and so did Dr. Stella, the gastroenterologist. This was abuse at the highest levels. Was Dr. Stella trying to off Simon, destroy the Hamilton family, or was he simply fearful of not doing what they demanded?

"My God, Chloe, they have a small pharmacy at their house. No wonder Simon hasn't been here in months. No wonder Trey relapsed. What the hell is Dr. Stella thinking?" I stood up to question her.

"The pharmacist at Bubba's has been complaining about all these scripts going to one household. They have threatened to go to the FBI. I've begged them not to." She readjusted her eyeglasses.

"Well, someone has to stop this. Simon is in real pain. I've seen him. I've seen Phyllis pop pills in his mouth at the dinner table, and I am not the only one. But Phyllis has no business injecting herself with Demerol. Why would Stella give her that? Is she in labor?"

"Perhaps they have a deal on the side?" Chloe said, winking at me.

I felt another lip-lock coming and stepped away from her. "Whaaaat do you mean?" I looked around nervously.

"Phyllis and Dr. Stella. They're sleeping together. Everyone knows that." She batted her eyes at me.

"Oh... gross! No thank you for the visual," I said, averting my eyes in disgust.

She laughed. "Phyllis is a swinger, don't ya know? I knew her when she was married to Mr. Nathaniel. Woo-hoo!" Chloe wiggled her body.

It was disturbing to think about Grandma Phyllis being sexual. However, Dr. Stella had some sex appeal.

"Can I have these sheets?" I asked her, changing the subject. It was none of my business if Grandma was a swinger, good God. I had plenty of bad memories to overcome. I did not need this one, too.

"Yes, take them. Help us all," Chloe said dramatically, imposing on me the responsibility of cleaning up this shit show. I wondered when I had become the shit show cleaner-upper.

"Ya, I'll do my best."

I was so disturbed. Dr. Stella had the whole family hooked on some form of bad juju. Trey was also seeing him for Suboxone, and God knew what else. What kind of doctor was this? I wondered about Jay, the drug dealer, and thought the only thing that separated these two professionally was a PhD. I could not believe drug doctors and dedicated users were running medical facilities. Without Sabra, the Hamiltons' secretary, guiding the ship like Magellan, I wondered where they would all be—stranded on Gilligan's Island?

As I was exiting the elevator of the medical building, my phone beeped to alert me of a new email. Brad! My heart skipped a beat in anticipation of our hot, steamy love affair.

> Hi Faith, good to hear from you. Lonnie told me you were going through a hard time. I am so sorry. You are such a kind woman and deserve only the best. If you ever need someone to talk to my number is 907.887.8331. We do have space available for your

> group. I'll comp your room. Hope to hear from you soon. Brad

I brain-swooned. Then I thought about Lonnie and what a big mouth she had. Ugh! I texted him.

Me: *Hi Brad, this is Faith. Thanks for being so gracious. Things have been hard, but I am keeping a positive attitude. Sometimes, everything has to fall apart for something better to fall together, right?*

I think, Good response! I was proud of myself. Then my phone rang. Oh, my God, it was Brad. Seriously? Why was he calling me? My generation doesn't talk on the phone. Shit! But I had to keep moving forward, even though phone convos were way out of my comfort zone. "Hello, Brad," I said and giggled. I got into my car. I switched the phone speaker to bluetooth. I began to drive home.

"Tell me what's going on with Trey? I want to help you."

Hmm, jumping right on in there, huh? I said, "Trey's been having an affair with his mother's best friend and employee, who is also married with six children." Ugh. That sounded so psychotic. When did I become an over-sharer? Dammit!

"Let me get this straight—Trey's mistress is his mother's best friend and an employee, where Trey also works. His mistress is also married with six children." He laughed obnoxiously. "Welcome to *Days of Our Lives*!"

I didn't respond. This wasn't the steamy hot love affair language I had anticipated. What an ass, I thought. Epic fail. Dead air ensued.

He tried a different approach. "How could he cheat on the most beautiful woman in the state of Alaska. What's wrong with him?"

I liked the smooth talk; I could do this. That's what I wanted—more fantasy and less laughable dysfunction. "I don't know; he's an idiot."

"Are you going to leave him?" He went straight on. "Whenever I have a tough decision to make, I use a decision tree." He seemed proud of his problem-solving strategy.

"What's that?" I asked, rolling my eyes as if the concept was not self-explanatory.

"You weigh the pros and cons of each possible outcome of the decision. You start at the bottom and write the decision to be made, then work your way out with branches of possible outcomes."

"What are you? My life coach?" I asked in jest.

He laughed. "Yes, I'll be your life coach and guide you through this difficult time," he said, proud of his new title.

"What are your assets?" he asked.

I felt annoyed. This was not romantic banter; this was not the making of a hot, steamy love affair. Buzz kill.

"We have the house; that, I am keeping."

"What? No cabins? Everyone has a cabin in Alaska. No other homes?"

"He does have bank accounts that I don't have access to, but I am pretty sure he's running out of money."

"Hmm...give me a minute. Let me think."

Huh, okay, maybe he is trying to come up with a proper solution on my behalf—what a nice guy.

"Okay, Faith, I have decided as your life coach, you are the most vulnerable. You're going to get screwed."

I swallowed hard. I felt deeply insulted. "What?" I asked in a threatening tone. I would twist him up like a pretzel for saying that.

"Sorry, in my experience, that is what usually happens. Is there anything else I should know?"

I thought, *no asshole.* I was certainly not going to tell him about the drugs, even though blabbermouth Lonnie probably already had. He was not my therapist or lawyer, and this was not romantic. Somehow our conversation was going terribly off course. I redirected. "Oh Rats... I got a message the Jump Rope Competition has been cancelled. Anyway, how are things going for you? How's business?"

"Alaska is in the middle of a recession, but my properties in Laguna Beach are making money."

"What kind of properties do you have?"

"I have five homes and a duplex. One home we are listing for fourteen million dollars. It will be the highest-selling home in the area if that's what we get for it. Do you mind if I come and see you on my way back from California, in a week or so?"

"That would be great. I could use some of your life coaching services."

I got off the phone with Brad. Although I found some of his questions slightly irritating, he was a different breed of human than Trey. Trey would never think of making a decision tree. Yet when he was twelve, he burned down a large forest in his neighborhood. That day he killed a lot of trees;

however, I doubted any good decisions were made. And while Brad wanted to be my life coach and help me make wise choices during this grim time, Trey was the very reason I needed a life coach.

Yin and yang. It is real.

THE PAGAN OR THE FATHER

CHAPTER 15

My discussion with Brad led me to call a priest. Perhaps I did need council from a holy man, someone who offered true healing and guidance, not a panty-chasing life coach.

I could not call on the kids' school priest; he was too close to home. I didn't want any awkward situations going down at St. Joseph's. So, I decided to reach out to Father Frank, the resident priest of Saint Mark's Cathedral.

I felt I knew him. Several years before, he had told my confession to Phyllis. Then, he and I had had a bit of a scuffle, but he had since apologized. He was human after all and was probably beguiled with Phyllis's money and prosthetic beauty. I had allowed him to counsel Maggie, as a good-faith effort to show all fences had been mended. Then, I recalled the latest throw-down between him and Phyllis.

Several years prior, Father Frank, along with other priests in Fairbanks, had decided every place of worship needed a quarter-million dollar statue of Jesus or some saint. They competed over who could get the largest donations for the biggest and most glorious statues for their respective churches. Personally, I liked the statues and thought they were incredible testimonies of human creativity and spirituality. The artist, Giovanni, was divinely talented. Other people felt the statues were a distraction from the mission of the church. Phyllis was one of those parishioners.

Father Frank claimed that she had promised him funds for some of the new statues he wanted to decorate the church with. When it was time to pay up, she had not followed through. She claimed he had called her a liar in an email, which Simon had been all too eager to show me. Simon believed organized religion was more about money and less about soul-saving. He loved prodding me with the hypocrisy of religion. Truly, the email could have been interpreted a few different ways; he had not flat-out called her a liar.

Since Father Frank knew the family best, I decided to contact him. He immediately emailed me back and invited me to come by his office. The kids were at school and I had time. So, I drove over to St. Mark's Cathedral, parked my car in the ice covered lot, and braced myself for the cold arctic air. I had not been to this particular church in a while. The outside was shaped like an A- frame, a large white cross stood atop the steeple. On my way to his office, I walked through a newly constructed church courtyard. First, I noticed a beautiful new memorial dedicated to Mother Mary. It was serene, peaceful, and angelic. I took the time to shiver by the lighted memorial and pray for healing, guidance, and strength.

I walked further toward Father's office, and I heard a crow, "kakakaka," I looked up. I noticed a huge statue of Jesus standing over me; it too was glorious. It reminded me of the Jesus-looking statue in Rio, Christ the Redeemer. There was even a newly-placed bench near other statues, for reflection. As I stared in awe at the magnificent statue garden, I wondered if I was a pagan. If it had not been ten degrees outside, I would have gladly taken the time to participate in this lovely prayerful exchange with each magnificent Saint. However, I had to meet Father Frank, and I was losing feeling in my fingers.

In the reception area of his office, I felt like I had stepped back in time to the 1970s. The secretary greeted me with a smile. Church secretaries are the kindest people. She instantly made me feel safe. "Father is expecting you; come on back."

I followed her to his new office. It looked nice. He had a brown leather sofa for counseling sessions, I imagined. There was a small oak desk, and a corduroy blue lazy boy, that looked perfect for mid-day naps. Father had not aged since the last time I had seen him; he still looked 60 years old, tall, with thinning black hair. "Thanks for seeing me on such short notice." We sat across from each other. Father Frank looked happy and ready to receive me. I spilled my guts on the floor to him about my current life path and began to cry hysterically.

"Oh, Faith, I am so sorry. You know I had an issue with Phyllis," Father Frank said, making my pain about him. Or perhaps he was trying to share in my victimhood; I did not know. He did not possess the warmth of a priest. Rather, he had this oddly detached intellectual approach to life's challenges. Maybe it was a strategy he adopted to survive the ups and downs of the priesthood.

Still, I was uneasy about his response to my circumstance. "She told me she wouldn't give you any money for the statutes. You called her a liar. She said money should be spent on people in need, not on statues." Father passed me a tissue box.

"I did not call her a liar like she claimed, but she did offer us money for the statues and we were counting on it. Then suddenly, she backed out. I sent her an email, explaining my disappointment." He leaned back in his lazy boy, interlocking his fingers.

"Well, she changed her mind, I guess..." I folded my arms.

"I could tell she had some interesting behaviors. She even made me second-guess my interpretation of reality. Do you need an attorney? I will give you names of people. Do you mind if I call my friend and ask him for recommendations?" Father offered eagerly.

This was not the holy counsel I came here for. I wanted to talk about my deep spiritual wounds, not about attorneys. It felt like he was hot on the gossip trail. "Thanks for your help. I need spiritual direction. There's also drugs involved." I pulled out the sheet that Chloe had given me from my purse. He took it, and I watched his face change. His eyes began to flash around the room. He stood up briefly, then sat back down in his chair. He seemed suddenly uncomfortable, as though he was venturing into unsafe territory. "I would not go around showing people this. You should focus on your kids. You may be carrying the cross now, but there is a new beginning for you, the sun is coming. I promise you'll make it through this and be stronger and wiser." Finally, he was being the spiritual healer that I had come here for, but his tone had changed. His words did not feel genuine, but like a staged rehearsal from the altar.

"Thank you, Father," I said, feeling vulnerable and less safe than before I had walked in there. I stood up.

"Before you leave, is it all right if I call my friend? He's a prominent business owner, a good Catholic, and he's been through a difficult divorce; he also knows the Hamiltons." Father pulled out his new iPhone, ready to dial.

I nodded my head yes. I sat back down. Jeez, this was weird. Was this someone he wanted to gossip with after I left? I did not care if it was. What did I have to lose at that point? I watched him curiously.

He put the call on speaker. It rang and rang. A man finally answered, and Father Frank launched right in. "I am here with Faith Nathaniel; she's married to Phyllis and Simon Hamilton's son. He's abandoned their family, and he's back on drugs.

Sorry Faith, Phyllis told me Trey's a heroin addict. Faith needs a good attorney."

I said, "Yes, I would appreciate that." Was he divulging Phyllis's confession to this strange man and me?

"Do you remember who your attorney was?" Father asked him.

"Yes, Abe Greggs. I think he's retired now. The Hamiltons are kooky clan, but they donate to the archdiocese and help underwrite the CSS Ball every year," he said. Father Frank looked nervous.

GETTING THE DIRT AT VITA'S HAIR SALON

CHAPTER 16

The day had arrived for my long-awaited rendezvous with Brad. We had been texting on and off the last couple of weeks. He had called me "the most beautiful woman in the state of Alaska"—that was a lot to live up to. I was sure the most beautiful woman in the state of Alaska who did not have a gray grow-out or a braidable mustache. Clearly, personal grooming had not been high on the priority list.

I needed some TLC at the beauty salon. I did not want to go to my regular salon because those beauticians expected me to be happy, perky, and fun, and I wasn't in the mood. I'd grown tired of pretending. On Facebook, I'd seen ads for Vita's Hair Salon. That was probably as good a place as any. I looked up the number and called, asking for an appointment for a root touch up, and lip and brow wax. The receptionist told me that the aesthetician had left for the day, but that they could do the touch-up. I gave her my name and said I'd be right down.

I debated over washing my hair before going. I had not washed it in days. But what was the point of doing it now? They would wash it for me, right?

I asked Kate to watch the kids. I grabbed a coke zero from the fridge. I drove two miles to the hair salon in sweat pants and no makeup. As I pulled into the vacant strip mall parking lot of Vita's Salon, my phone rang. Trey. I felt grief-stricken seeing his name. I parked the car. I took a swig of coke.

"My mom is back," he yelled. "She ambushed me with Will. They packed my stuff and told me I had to move in with him. He said he's in recovery and can help me. They can go fuck themselves!"

I began to choke cough on the cola. I was trying not to laugh. Sometimes the best strategy was to sit back and let things naturally unfold.

"Hey, what's wrong?"

I said, "Oh, Trey, I am so sorry. I hope you two can work it out. After all, you guys got into this mess together. Stay strong for each other. I am rooting for you. If you get a chance, ask Will what happened to the kids' Christmas presents."

"Oh yes, that's a great story. He got a DUI on an already suspended license. The police impounded his truck, and he was in jail in North Pole. The presents were locked inside his truck in at Jerry's tow yard. It's a joke. He isn't sober. He can't help me." Trey yelled in anguish.

"Sounds like an unhealthy living situation."

"My mom has some nerve, calling me a drug addict. She thinks because she gets her drugs from a doctor, she doesn't have a problem, and because I get mine off the streets, I am a trashy drug addict. She's the same as me." He was still yelling.

"That's right, Trey, drugs are drugs, and if you are misusing them, it doesn't matter where they came from. If I were you, I would call Dr. Stella and complain."

"He won't take me as a patient anymore. My mom's crazy. I can't believe she is kicking me out." He had calmed down, but his tone was full of righteous indignation. Then it turned to wheedling. "Can I come live in the basement? I love you."

"No. You cannot be on drugs around the children."

"Bitch!" Trey shouted and hung up.

So much for loving me. I decided to shed one tear and keep moving to my hair appointment. Oddly, Trey's distressed phone call had really picked up my spirits. I giggled to myself; now the animals were turning on each other. Now he feels what I feel. I giggled some more; it was a bit of karmic justice from the universe. God did love me.

Vita's Hair Salon was Parisian styled with black, hot pink, and white décor. It was hip.

The young dainty receptionist had blue shoulder-length hair. She led me to Vita's station. She must have been about nineteen years old. Spunky and carefree.

I took a seat. The joy from hearing Trey's plight quickly left me and was replaced with a sharp depression of hopelessness. If Trey was living with Will, that meant he was one shipment away from being sent to the Lower 48 for rehab. If that happened, I would have to communicate and negotiate with

Phyllis directly. I neither liked nor respect Trey, but he was a buffer between the Hamiltons and me. Once he left, what was I to do? How could this ever have a happy ending for anyone?

Vita was tall and thin like a gazelle, with long, blond hair and deep dark, brown eyes. She looked tough and confident. Her aura was that of a strong woman—the kind that had been through hell and slain dragons, like Aunt Denali.

"Is this your salon?" I asked.

She told me that it was with such pride that I thought, *She is definitely a survivor of something. Nobody gets that strong picking daisies and petting ponies.*

"Is everything okay?" she asked. "I feel like you need a hug."

I cracked a smile. Was it because I was wearing sweat pants and had let my roots grow out? Whatever the reason, I accepted. I liked hugs.

"That's better," she said, rubbing my back. "Are we covering the grays?" She swiveled me around to face the mirror.

"Yes, please. I need to look super-hot and sexy for a first date."

She laughed. "Who's the lucky fella?"

Call me paranoid; it felt safer to lie. "I don't know yet. I am just projecting positive energy into the future." I wiggled my fingers at her.

She laughed again. "Has it been a while since you had a date?" She stood behind me as she fastened the cape around my neck.

"Actually, I am separated from my husband." I gave her the briefest of summaries.

"The same thing happened to me," she said. "My husband was unfaithful with my sister. I was so broken. The only thing that kept me going was my children." It had taken her several years to feel halfway normal. Her husband had hidden money in the Cayman Islands. It had been a nasty, abusive divorce, and the post-divorce relationship was nasty, too. He had used their daughters to hurt her every chance he got.

"Now I have this salon; I am in a stable, happy relationship with a younger, better-looking man, and I don't have to talk to my ex at all. The girls talk to him, sometimes. One piece of advice? Don't have children with another man, even if you remarry. It'll be difficult on the kids." She began to squirt color into her black wax coated bowl.

"You seem like a strong, wise woman. Authentically strong." She swiveled my chair to face the back of the store.

"It took me a decade to get here," she said. "Have patience. Everyone you meet is either a lesson or blessing; coincidentally, your family is both! Try to stay positive." I laughed. "I recognized your last name. Are you related to Mr. Nathaniel?" She grabbed a paintbrush to mix the color.

"He's my father-in-law. Trey's biological dad. He is happily remarried and has moved to a sunnier climate."

I told her that Trey's stepfather owned Saint Mary's and that Trey worked there, along with his girlfriend, Helga.

"Helga, with a pixie haircut, blonde, and an elfish face?"

"Oh, my God, you know her?" I turned my head back to look at her.

Vita told me that Helga had broken up at least three marriages, even the marriage of the man she was currently married to, and her own first marriage. Every time with married men. "It must be her type. She comes in here sometimes, and I do her hair. She's such a troubled person. She must be so tormented inside," Vita said. As she began to paint the roots of my hair.

I couldn't muster understanding for Helga, the whore. "Wow! Three marriages? Hmm, I don't have sympathy for her. She has hurt people, big and small, with her brokenness. Instead of making victims, she could choose to be a real woman and heal herself." Vita walked around me with a bowl full of hair dye, stroking sections of my hair in between aluminum foil.

"Wayne Dyer says, evil is love going in the wrong direction. No one can act beyond their level of consciousness."

"I know and some people are soooo in love with their egos they don't have a conscious." I chuckled at my clever response.

"Try to see yourself in everyone you meet, and there you will find your compassion again. I know it's a journey. I spent several years being angry. I only hurt myself."

"You are so wise," I said to her. I felt my eyes roll. I didn't want to hear this shit; I didn't care about having compassion for Helga and her fool dickery! I briefly imagined taking the bowl full of hair dye and running out the door.

“I cut her ex-husband’s hair. He’s single and attractive. He has an excellent job as a project manager for Conoco. Derek is his name. I wish he could find a good woman.” Vita put the hair dye down on the vanity.

Apparently, Derek had come home from work one day to find Helga with her bags packed and their one-month-old baby in the car. She moved in with Alister, the man she was currently married to, that day. “He was devastated; it was completely out of the blue.” I silently thought, *wow hairdressers do get a lot dirt.*

“Ugh, what an odd way to start motherhood,” I commented.

“Meanwhile, Derek’s good-looking and well-off financially,” Vita reminded me, with a twinkle in her eye and an upbeat tone in her voice.

“Twenty minutes, I will give you a rinse okay?” I nodded my head.

About that time, I heard the bell of the salon door ring. A man walked in; he looked like a younger version of Benjamin Bratt. Vita bent down and whispered in my ear, “Shazam! He is here! That’s him sitting in the lobby.”

“What, who’s him? What are you talking about?” I whispered back like we were exchanging national security secrets.

“Derek! That’s him!” She pivoted my stool to face him. I felt like a turtle, trying to duck under the cap, “Turn me around, turn me around!” I quietly pleaded.

I wondered briefly whether we were on candid camera. By this time, my hair was covered in color, and I was looking like a space alien wrapped in aluminum foil. Vita went to Derek and talked to him. I could not hear what was being said, but I saw them both look over at me. I quickly averted my eyes. It was one thing to be in this position in full hair and makeup; it was quite another to be looking like a homeless person that Vita pulled off the street for an ambush makeover. Vita rushed back to me, a skip in her step.

"He thinks you're pretty; he wants to meet you!"

"Seriously? He must be desperate. I am hideous. I think I slept in these pants last night."

"I told him you're looking for a hot date." Vita laughed out loud. I chuckled and shuffled around in my seat. I had created this moment, and now I had to live through it. Karmic justice. God did not love me.

I gave him a gander, and wondered how Helga had captured such a stud. Her current husband was ordinary looking. Helga had told everyone that her ex-husband had been physically abusive to her, but this man didn't look like an Ike Turner to me. Also, I remembered that Trey had accused Helga of stalking him. Perhaps Derek could give me an insight into the inner workings of Helga-the-cheeseball.

"I'd love to meet him," I said as if he had a chance.

Vita turned Derek over to another stylist, saying, "These two need to be done at about the same time." She added for all to hear, "There's a coffee shop next door. You guys should have coffee." Now we were all on the same page. Vita enjoyed her role as a beautician/ matchmaker for Jezebel's wounded warriors.

"Okay," Derek said, looking at me wrapped in foil.

"That sounds great," I replied like a Stepford wife.

After we were both done, Vita officially introduced us to each other, her eyes beaming with potential.

Derek asked, "Would you like to join me next door for coffee?" I nodded and sheepishly smiled.

He held the door open for me, like a perfect gentleman.

Next door, the coffee shop felt industrial, made mostly of steel with ash concrete floors, with a cold draft wafting through. I walked to counter, ordered our coffee and paid. Derek had secured a small black iron table for us by the entrance. Easy exit, I thought. I liked his style. I sat down across from him. "So, Derek, you were married to Helga?" I tucked my hair behind my ears, ready to hear some more dirt.

"For five years. We've been divorced eight." He told me that she'd come to Alaska with an Austrian couple as an au-pair. "She broke up that family. Started sleeping with the husband. I should've run when I found out, but she was very persistent." Derek took a sip of his coffee. "I hope that makes you feel better. She is relentless when it comes to men. I am sure she pursued him."

"Were there other warning signs she was not operating with a full deck?" I tried to remain even toned. I imagined myself as an objective journalist, trying to get the facts.

"Back then, I traveled for work. Not long after our child was born, she started calling me, saying people were breaking into our home. I was in Barrow, Alaska, the first time it happened. I immediately flew home. Someone had written on the walls in red lipstick, 'You are all going to die.' I called the police; they staked out our home. A several days had passed with no activity, so I returned to Barrow. She called again, saying someone had broken into our home for a second time. I flew home again; this time, someone had written on the walls in red lipstick, 'I am watching you,' and had thrown a tire iron through our front door stained-glass window. I called the police again, and they called the FBI. They investigated. They concluded that Helga was breaking into her own home and writing cryptic messages on the wall. They recommended psychiatric counseling for her. Soon after that, she took off with Alister." Derek still seemed traumatized, eight years later.

Sitting across from him, I saw his scars so visibly. He wore them on his face, in his body language, and in his voice. Eight years later and he had made little progress toward healing. He had been wounded so long he didn't know any other way to be. Just talking about this experience made him relive it. It was clear he had not emotionally grown past this point.

I promised myself at that moment that I would not be like Derek. I would not allow Trey or his family to permanently traumatize me and take precious years away from my life. I told myself that I was going to move on and live my life out loud. I was going to surround myself with happy, productive, encouraging, God-loving people. Not people who used religion as a sport. I promised myself that I would dig until I found forgiveness for Trey and

Phyllis. They would not hold me captive for eternity as Helga had successfully done to Derek.

I felt the need to encourage him and comfort him. I reached for his hand. "Derek, you're smart and good-looking. You're going to meet your perfect mate. Normal people do not go around destroying other people. It's wasn't you, it's her."

"I don't want any additional drama. We're in a civil place now. And co-parenting rather well." Derek moved his hand away from me, and buried his head into his coffee mug. I wanted to shake him and yell, "Rise up! This woman is walking around with your balls in her purse. Go get your balls back!"

Instead, I suggested that he check on his kids. "Trey's a heroin addict. She went with your kids to a drug hotel to pick him up. And Helga gave him her debit card. He drained her account. Also, Trey said that Helga told him that Alister moved his gay lover in their house around the kids. Oh, and that he beat her up." I took a sip of my coffee. "You know coffee beans grow in the dirt?" I took another sip.

Derek's face dropped. "What? Alister's gay?" Derek now laughing. "No, she wouldn't let a man beat her. Bullshit!" He put the mug down, smiling from ear to ear.

"She probably did make up the stories about Alister to garner sympathy from the Hamiltons. I guess that's Alister's karma," I laughed. "Now she's turned him into a swinging wife beater. And she's the victim."

Derek looked unnerved and pale, "Ya, she accused me of that, too, after she took off with my newborn." His mood shifted again, his hands began to tremor.

"Well, I know for a fact she took your kids to a drug hotel to pick Trey up, and I do believe she gave Trey her debit card. I think Helga thinks if she helps Trey when he's down, he'll return the favor one day with marriage, and she'll be rich. Trey's manipulative. Sounds like they are working each other, each for their own selfish ends." I ran my fingers through my hair to fluff it up. "Just step in and do a welfare check on your kids."

"I will." He scooted his chair away from the table. He dug into his khaki pocket and put three bucks down. "I am sorry she's sleeping with your husband. But I don't want any drama from her. That relationship destroyed me." He stood to leave. He walked towards the door.

"I understand. Thank you for speaking with me." I looked in his eyes. He looked rattled.

"Let's have dinner sometime. Want to?"

"I'd love that." I wrote my number on the coffee receipt and handed it to him.

"Please keep the faith, Faith. Things are already looking up for you." He smiled, pointed to the sky, and walked out the door.

Poor Derek, I thought. I don't want to date a man whose balls are in another woman's purse. I don't want to be like him. I want to be like Aunt Denali and Vita. They're strong and wear their scars with dignity and use them to provide healing and counsel to others. Derek was scared to confront the darkness of his past. He was still hiding and pushing everything down, deep inside instead of lifting it up and out. You had to go into those dark places to rediscover yourself and rise up, stronger, wiser, full of more love and compassion, not less. If you did not take the time to heal properly, you risked becoming a dark, uninviting energy, someone who lived from a place of fear, ego-centered and victimizing others along the path of self-destruction. I wondered what a Godless person did when things fall apart. Indulge in the fleetingness of fleshy pleasures?

On my way to the car, I received a text from Brad, my fleshy pleasure. Instantly I was directed back to my new, light-hearted agenda: "Taking a lover."

Brad: *I am landing in an hour; can you pick me up at the airport?*

Me: *Yes!*

I wrote with an exclamation point because I was a happy bitch. I thought, *With Brad I can pretend to be happy and carefree, like the blue haired receptionist. I can check-out of this horrid cycle I'm in, at least for a few hours.*

I picked the kids up from school. Maggie got in the car first.

"Mama, when will see daddy again? Is Papa better yet?"

"What's going on with daddy?" Alex.

Their questions deflated my high, and my throat tightened. I was in an unwinnable situation. I could not tell them the truth now. But how long could I lie? "Your dad loves both of you and will always be in your life. Papa's sick right now, but everyone is working hard to get him better."

I felt like such a loser mom, for repeating the same lie to her time and time again. But what could I have done differently without traumatizing them? I was scared to fracture the illusion of the solid family unit she still thought she had.

At home, Grandma Kate met us at the door. She was wearing jeans, a white button down blouse, holding a giant serving fork in an aggressive manner. She was hysterical. "I was about to call you. Someone tried to break into the house!" She pointed the fork toward the front door.

I thought immediately, Helga? Or a drug dealer? Or maybe Helga, the drug dealer? "What happened?" I tossed my keys on the coffee table and sat down.

My mother told me that someone had pulled up in a purple sedan full of people. A blonde woman had got out, gone to the garage door, and started wiggling on the handle. When she hadn't been able to open it, she had tried the front door. It had been locked, so she'd started walking around to the back of the house. "I set off the house alarm, and she ran and jumped back into the car, and they drove off" Mom said, still upset.

I sent the kids to the kitchen for a snack.

"Mom, the cheeseball..." I winked at her, "has short blond hair and a purple sedan. I am sure it has to do with Trey." I told her about Trey's new living arrangements. "He's desperate. There's no telling what he's stashed in this house." I curiously looked around the room.

"Your dad wants us to make a police report," Mom said, and I did.

The dispatcher said there had been a string of break-ins on the hillside. She would make sure to send a patrol car through our area.

Mom sat next to me and put the fork down. "You've got to move. You can't stay here with the kids. It's unsafe. Every drug dealer knows who you are, and they will all come searching for you to find Trey."

"We have a house alarm. Let's keep it on. It could be random." I walked to the ADT device on our hallway wall. I double-checked to make sure it was on.

Mom approached me, two inches from my face "This means all that money you had is gone."

That was likely true. It would not be the first time. Trey had blown a huge sum of money in a matter of weeks. "We're rich, we're poor, we're rich, we're poor," I said, trailing off, deflated and numb to the insanity. I walked back into the living room.

"Snap out of it! What are we going to do? This is the worst-case scenario!" Mom yelled, her arms waving in the air, like she was stranded out at sea on a buoy.

I shrugged. "Money is replaceable. Who cares about money? A lot of what's happening right now is about money. I am over it. I am taking a lover." I leaned down into the couch cushions.

My mom looked at me like I was a three-headed fire breathing dragon. "Taking a lover?" Her hand cupped her heart as if she had seen the ghost of Christmas future, and it was a deep, dark, vacant grave with my name on it. "You can't take a lover! Remember what happened last time you were seen out with another man? Go on a nice date if you must, somewhere discreet. But don't sleep with anyone until after you're divorced. It's a sin." Mom pointed her finger at me to emphasize her stance on the matter.

"Soon, they will have nothing left to punish me with, and that will be a momentous day of liberation. As for sins, what about the sins against me?" I shot back.

"You're only responsible for yourself in this life," my mother said. "Trey, Phyllis, Helga will reap what they sow. God will take care of them. I am worried about your mortal soul, not theirs."

"You're right. I believe God will take care of each of us. God has given me a hot date tonight, and I am going." I put my feet up on the coffee table.

"What about the kids? You are not spending time with them."

I felt anxiety, guilt, emptiness overcome me. "Well..." I began to sniffle "if you must know, I don't know how to parent alone, it makes me feel like a loser mom. I feel like I have broken them in a way that can never be unbroken, and it hurts to the depths of my soul to smile in their faces and pretend things are okay." Hollowness filled my chest, my heart literally hurt. I closed my eyes, trying to fight back the emotional overload pressing down on me.

Mom put her hand on my knee. "Oh my doddle dumpling, you didn't do anything. Stop beating yourself up. One in three marriages ends in divorce. You have time to make things right. Stay home with us tonight?" She smiled warmly.

"No, I can't stay here all night with you. I have to get out of this house."

My mom stood up, rolled her eyes and walked out of the room. I interlocked my fingers behind my head. I exhaled. "Kids, come tell me about your day."

Kate interjected, "Faith, have you seen this?"

I was instantly annoyed, emotionally fatigued, but I went into the kitchen where she was. She had been rummaging through the mail, and now handed me an envelope addressed to Mr. and Mrs. Nathaniel. The words were written in yellow crayon.

Oh my God, this was beyond psychotic. Who addresses a letter in crayon?

"You better open it," she said eagerly.

"No. I can't deal with this shit today. It's probably an anthrax letter. It's going to have to wait. I need to get ready." I tossed the letter back on the counter.

"Where are you going? Can I come?" Alex tugged on my hand.

"NO! Mommy needs some alone time." I gave him a kiss and wiggled my hand loose.

How much of my life force could these people zap from me in one day? Whatever was in that letter might keep me from my hot date, and I was not going to allow that to happen.

In the bathroom, I cussed like a sailor, trying to scrub the dark hair dye off my face. I hated it when hairdressers stained my forehead with dye. It wasn't sexy. I looked like Eddie Munster. I changed into a cute outfit, beige heels, jeans, and a blush colored halter top. I put on extra makeup.

I kissed everyone goodbye and jetted out of there as quickly as possible.

On the way to the airport, I reflected on prescription drugs, FBI, Derek, burglary, and now, a crayon letter. What was next: a Molotov cocktail?

Five minutes from the airport, I began to get nervous, thinking about Brad. It was an excited redirection of energy. I put a romantic spin on it and thought maybe it was butterflies in my tummy. It was surreal to pursue a man that I had had occasional fantasies about. I never imagined I would be single and in this position.

I pulled up and parked outside of the Alaska Airlines arrivals station. In my rear-view mirror, I saw him approaching. He was wearing a blue North Face jacket, and jeans. He looked older than I remembered, too old for me. I wondered *how old is he?* He opened the passenger door and got in.

We hugged across the middle console. He did smell good.

"How was your flight?"

He looked at my hairline. I ruffled my bangs to try and cover the dye.

"Great. I was able to work the entire time." He sounded proud of himself, puffing out his chest. I liked a man who worked, but his energy felt nervous, and little eager; it was making me uncomfortable.

"Oh, are you a workaholic?" I began to drive.

"That's such a negative word. I take great pride in my accomplishments." He huffed. It felt like he had been accused of this before.

We decided on an Italian restaurant, and I asked him his age.

"Forty-nine. I will be fifty in August."

Oh, my God, fifty? What? I could not do fifty. Why would he be interested in a thirty-three-year-old? What was wrong with him? Was he normal? I interrogated further. "Have you ever been married?"

"No." he stared out the window.

Fifty-year-old male, never been married. Two red flags. "Kids?"

"No." He twiddled his thumbs.

A 50-year-old male, never been married, no children. Three red flags. Maybe he was sterile. So I gave him two red flags because I had sympathy for the infertile. I dug for additional clues. "Why has a man with your countless talents never been married? You're attractive, successful, you have great manners, and you work. Surely, there have been a ton of women after you." I said hoping flattery would make him spill his guts.

He declared, somewhat dramatically, that he had done something stupid in his thirties. "It changed my life forever."

"What was that?" I asked flatly. As if this day could deliver any more drama.

We got out of the car and walked into the restaurant, *Mambinos*.

"I went to L.A., looking for a Persian bride willing to relocate with me to Alaska. A member of the synagogue I was attending caught wind of the story. They contacted the media, and it took on a life of its own. I was even invited on the *Today*

Show. When the story fizzled, I moved back home. People in Juneau were unimpressed with me. People would come up to me and say things like, 'What, nobody in Juneau is good enough for ya?'

I laughed. The waitress approached us with menus and water.

"None of the ladies would date me. I started traveling to California. I've been unsuccessful with relationships there. Eventually, the miles become too taxing." Brad recited this like it was a familiar story in his repertoire of why he is mate-less.

I thought this narrative was bullshit, but I rolled with it. I was not interested in analyzing and fixing him. I just wanted to have a fun time.

"Wow" I opened my menu. "How come things didn't work out with Lonnie? Did you guys talk about marriage? I remember Simon asking you to marry her." I giggled.

He laughed nervously. "When Lonnie drinks, she can be mean." He opened his menu for a moment and sat it down.

"Well, I am glad you guys are still friends. I know she's had a hard time." I took a sip of water.

"Be careful with her. She is primarily concerned with herself and sustaining her lifestyle." He looked me dead in the eye.

I shrugged. "She loves her dad. And Phyllis has made things unnecessarily hard for her at times." I continued to turn the pages of the menu.

"Yes, I understand that." Brad sounded more thoughtful than before. "When I was eight, my dad left my mother for another woman. The break-up destroyed my mother; she never moved on. My mother died still in love with him. I took on the role of defender of my mother. My sister preferred my dad because he had money. It was hard growing up that way. We were treated poorly." Brad's face changed; he became emotional.

I put my menu down. "Oh, my gosh Brad, I am so sorry about your mother's passing. When did she go to heaven?"

"I was nineteen; she was terminally ill. I was alone with her when she passed. When I got home, I found my sister sleeping on the couch. I told her of mom's passing, and she ransacked the house, took mom's jewelry, and flew to Seattle to pawn it. I followed shortly behind her, trying to recover the jewelry." Brad straightened his back firmly against the booth.

I felt traumatized hearing the story. To face the passing of your mother virtually alone. To be so young and dealing with an absentee father and sister. How fucked up. It reminded me of Trey stealing Simon's medications and leaving him, handicapped, to fend for himself. I asked Brad whether his sister was a substance user.

"Not anymore. I am on good terms with her and dad now, and he's still married to my stepmother. They've been together for thirty years." Brad held up his glass. "All of that is water under the bridge now." He took a drink. "My dad's sick. I go to visit him as often as possible. My stepmom takes great care of him. It's hard being a caregiver." Brad sat the glass back down on the table. I was still watching him closely.

As Brad was speaking, I realized this was why he was a fifty-year-old bachelor. He knew betrayal at an early age and had to take on roles he wasn't yet mature enough to handle. He had scars that had not fully healed. Then I thought, *Maggie was seven. What if Brad is Maggie in forty years? Will she be permanently scarred? Would she never marry or have children? Would she live in fear of being vulnerable to love? Would Alex choose wealth over their poor mother and abandon me?* I felt strongly and soulfully connected to Brad. His pain mirrored my own in many ways. He had both the wisdom of a seven-year-old victim and a fifty-year-old survivor. I supposed he overcame by filling the spaces in his heart with the hustle and bustle of business. I supposed it protected him from getting too deep, from feeling too much with any one particular person.

I looked at him with compassion. "You're a good son, and I'm sure you're a good support system for your dad and your step-mom. Your mother would be proud of you." I reached for his hand.

"I told my mother at her gravesite that all I am and all I'll ever become is because of her." His eyes began to water.

He got me. I started to tear up, "How have you overcome? That's a lot at such a young age."

"I focused on work. I started my first business at nineteen. My roommate said, "Your mother is dying; your business is going to fail." I knew at that moment I had to move out of that environment. I could not be around any naysayers. I kept choosing positive people and positive environments, and kept working, pressing through all the roadblocks." He put his napkin in his lap. "What about you, Faith? Where does your strength come from? It is hard to imagine someone leaving all that money."

I felt puke rising in my mouth. It disturbed me, the various worldviews people had. "You know, God gives money to people and takes money away. All the money in the world can't make an addict stay sober, but God can. It's important to me that my children are raised in a healthy, stable environment than around an abhorrent amount of money. What will that teach them—how to buy things, but not be grateful, how to feel superior, but not confident?"

I ordered a glass of wine. Brad stared at me. "What?"

Brad gave me the love-look, as if he knew what I meant; he got it. "What I thought about you was right. You have Biblical beauty, a voice like honey, a gentle nature. You're so refreshing to be around. You have only begun to unlock your full potential on the world." He held my gaze from across the table.

Maybe he was a seasoned operator, but I didn't care. I thought I could get lost in his words forever.

We talked for hours over chicken piccata and a ribeye steak. I drove him back to the airport. We made plans to see each other again. Brad sure did provide a non-judgmental, loving space for me to be in. I thought he could be my best friend. Maybe all I needed was a best friend with a ding dong?

At home, my mother was sitting on the couch, with the lamp on. She had been reading an Agatha

Christie novel. She was in red pajamas with big white snowflake imprints down the sleeves and legs. Her pajamas were cheery and red, but her face was angry and red. “Where have you been, Faith? In case you are wondering, the kids are sleeping.” I shut the front door.

I was offended. What was I? A sixteen-year-old who had gotten busted for sneaking out of the house at three a.m.?

“I was with Brad Rosenbloom. You’ve met him. In Juneau.”

“I remember. Did you sleep with him?” She put the book beside her on the sofa.

“No, I am still a virgin!” I yelled behind me as I walked up the stairs to my bedroom.

Now she was livid. She shot straight up from the sofa. “You’re barely holding it together, Faith. Now is not the time to go on dates! You left us alone right after someone tried breaking into the house. How could you?”

I could not find the rationale to sincerely apologize. Being with Brad was a welcome relief. Listening to other people’s stories, like Brad’s, empowered me; it made me feel not so alone. I could see that there was life after divorce, after betrayal, and after deep loss, there was a rebirth. I walked back down the stairs. I stood in front of her.

“Mom, the police are patrolling the area. We have a house alarm. But you’re right; my life is falling apart. I can’t keep lying to the children. Their dad is not coming back. And who knows what Trey has done? I could have AIDS right now.” I tucked my hair behind my ears. I squinted to imply sincerity. "Brad's a friend. It's not a big deal."

My mom's anger softened to compassion; she wrapped her arms around me. "I know, baby. I love you. I'll be here for you as long as you need me. You will always have a home with me."

I calmed myself by slowing my breathing.

"What was your date like?" she asked, trying to keep the lines of communication open.

"It was less passionate than I thought and more soulful than I anticipated. I think I made a friend for life."

CRAYONS AND CODEPENDENCY

CHAPTER 17

We were lounging around the house, drinking coffee, when my mom whipped out the letter—the one addressed to the Nathaniels in crayon. The kid's were at school; we had the house to ourselves. Initially, we laughed at the insanity of the letter. It looked cartoon creepy. Really creepy. It had Trey's stink all over it.

"How far off the rails can we go?" I asked mom in jest, I pulled my pink sweater over my jeans.

"They aren't boring. I'll give them that." She slid the letter toward me across the dining room table.

I opened the envelope. There was a single sheet of white paper folded like a business letter. Whoever sent this had taken the time to individually cut each letter from a magazine or newspaper. They were glued together to construct the words, "Leave Helga alone; she has evidence." We exchanged looks of disbelief.

I pushed my back into my chair. "What the fuck's going on?" I asked her, as if she knew.

"Faith, have you been threatening that woman?" Mom scooted away from me. She folded her arms tightly, the threads of her cashmere gold sweater stretched across her chest.

I told mom about my coincidental meeting with Derek, and all the dirt he had spilled on Helga.

"Oh, my God. She's KGB. She's dangerous. We should preserve the letter... for fingerprints." Mom stood and went into the kitchen.

"No, she's Austrian, not Russian... I think." I looked up trying to recall the cheeseball's nationality.

"Well, this letter feels threatening. Do you think she's trying to sue Trey for sexual harassment?" Mom came back with a Ziploc bag.

"I don't know. I am sure she's the type, and I am sure she has a great case against St. Mary's. I am staying out of it. She's unstable." I pushed the letter aside.

"Careful!" Mom took the spoon from the sugar dish and wiggled the letter inside the gallon-sized Ziploc bag.

My phone rang; it was Will. My mother motioned for me to answer.

"Good morning Will; how are you?" I said, looking at my mom, annoyed.

"Not good. Trey's missing and so is Simon's truck. Have you seen him?" I turned the phone's speaker on.

"No. I haven't heard from him in weeks. How long has he been missing?" Same old. Trey he comes, he goes, he steals, he reappears, he steals again—repeat. Trey's cycle of self-harm would not cease until all his resources had dried up. I felt numb to this Trey-episode, and figured he sold the truck and is getting high in a drug motel somewhere, not ready to face the consequences.

"Two days. His phone was ringing, but now when we call, it's dead. And that's not all. Trey has continued to see Helga. My neighbor told me that she's coming over to my house while I am at work." I looked at my mom baffled.

I was stunned. Not because of Trey's continued affair, but because of Will's loyalty toward Phyllis. Phyllis would freak if she knew Will, her trusted ally, was going rogue telling me all this dirt. She was paying for his driver, helping with his rent, and paying him to take care of Trey's needs. She was not paying him to tell me the truth about Trey. Phyllis only kept people around her whom she could use as puppets; people who were beholden to her in some way. Surprisingly, Will was proving himself to be no puppet.

I pondered, perhaps Will did have a soul that could not be bought? Perhaps all those stories I heard about him stealing her ski suit and Simon's watch, and about him dancing around in her panties were a lie. She wanted to hurt him. Another story fabricated and used as an assault weapon to damage someone's reputation, life, social acceptability.

"I know Trey is playing everyone," he said now. "I try to reason with Phyllis about his manipulations, and she gets mad at me." Will's voice was full of frustration.

"That's why Trey will likely never recover. She needs to go to Al-Anon." I stirred in another teaspoon of sugar into my coffee.

"There's more. I wasn't going to tell you, but Trey's drug dealer called me at three a.m. He said that he has Simon's truck and will not give Trey or the truck back until we pay him five hundred dollars."

"I figured. So now he's been kidnapped?" I asked sarcastically. I looked at mom. She mouthed, "Trey-pisode."

"It appears so..." Will said, but then he chuckled.

"I don't believe it. Only Trey would kidnap himself for money. It would be the next step in his evolutionary process."

Will continued to laugh. "I am sure, but we must get Simon's truck back."

"How's Simon doing?" I glanced at my mom, who was now wiping down the dining room table where I had spilled sugar.

"Before Trey went missing, Simon called a family meeting. I didn't think he had a throw-down left in him, but he did. He yelled at all of us, mostly Trey. He said, 'If you don't want to be married, get unmarried; you're acting like a fool. You are making us all look like fools.' Trey said he wanted to work things out with you. Then Simon said, 'Without Faith, you have a twenty percent chance of getting sober. You need her. You better hope she takes you back.'"

"That's sad, Will. His last days should be peaceful and beautiful, not like this. Please try to put him first." I took a sip of coffee.

"That's why I am trying to get the truck back. If he wrecks it, Simon is liable. Let me know if you hear from Trey."

I hung up.

Mom dismissed the phone call with an eye roll, and held up the crayoned letter. "What about this?"

"I don't know. It freaks me out. Perhaps Helga is worried she's going to get fired, and she and her husband wrote it together." I thought for a moment. "Something must be going on between Phyllis and Helga. Perhaps their sisterhood is on the rocks now that Phyllis has realized Helga cannot control Trey. Or Helga and Trey are conspiring against Phyllis."

My mother nodded. She sat back down at the table.

"You know, Trey often tried to get me to conspire with him against his mother. A lot of resentment there from his childhood. There truly is something deeply wrong with him beyond his chemical imbalance."

My phone dinged. "Who is that? Do you want some chocolate chip cookies?" Mom asked.

Brad: *I am flying in tonight; can you pick me up?*

Me: *Yes, wow, that's a quick turn-around. How long will you be here?*

Brad: *I have a meeting with a business associate. I am staying at the Embassy Suites.*

Me: *Great, see you tonight.*

I looked up. "Mom, who cares about Helga's pathetic attempt to stay relevant. I am moving forward. I have a date with Brad tonight."

"Oh Lord, Brad again? Why is he woody woodpeckering around? Don't sleep with him." Mom went into the kitchen to make cookies for the kid's afterschool snack.

"Gross," I fluffed my hair.

My mom's reaction reminded me that I hadn't heard back from the doctor's office concerning my infectious disease status. I walked into the garage for privacy. I called Dr. Smith's office and told the lovely receptionist that I wanted my test results. I felt so ashamed and embarrassed even asking. At least it was a phone call and not an in-person inquiry.

"I'll transfer you to her nurse."

The nurse picked up and asked me to confirm my birthdate. Then she said, "It looks like all of your tests came back negative."

"So I don't have gonorrhea, chlamydia, Aids, crabs, the clap?" I asked in amazement.

"Um, no, Mrs. Nathaniel you are perfectly healthy."

"Oh, praise God! Thank you! Also, can you send me a script for birth control to the pharmacy you have on file for me? Thank you!"

It was close to Valentine's Day. So I decided to wear a red dress with black knee high boots for my date with Brad. I arrived at the airport right on time to pick him up. He was waiting for me at the curb, wearing a blue North Face puffer coat and blue jeans, again. He was so cute and quirky. I wondered why he had no sense of style. I pulled up next to him. To my surprise, he walked around to my side of the car and opened the door. He pulled me out and gave me a strong, tight hug, cheek-to-cheek. It felt good. He smelled good. Then, he tried to kiss me.

I turned my head. "I can't kiss you in public. What if someone sees me?"

"Then let them watch." He put his brown nylon briefcase down. He tried again. His hands interlocked around my waist.

I pulled back. "No. What would the PTO moms think?" I laughed nervously and got back into the car.

He walked around and sat in the passenger's seat. "Red is a beautiful color on you. I missed you."

"I missed you" I replied. I mean, I guess I did. I didn't know what he was up to. I wondered if he thought he was getting some action tonight. I barely knew him. What kind of lady did he think I was? I felt offended. I began to drive to our destination.

"I brought a movie for us to watch. *Out of Africa.* You remind me of the main character played by Meryl Streep." He reached for my hand.

"I haven't seen it. She must be a hot mess," I blurted out, forgetting my role as romantic receiver of compliments. The proper way to have responded when taking a lover should have been, "Thank you. I accept all flattery true and false."

"No, she's a pillar of strength," he said, watching me with eyes big and alluring.

"And which character are you?" I glanced over at him.

"Oh, I would be Robert Redford, her lover," he said, still looking at me.

"Is she married to him or to someone else?" I side eyed him.

"Someone else. A bad guy, an alcoholic and cheater. He gives her syphilis, which makes her unable to bare children. She's deeply saddened over it, but finds love and comfort in the arms of Robert Redford," he said, peering even deeper into auric field. All this intensity made me swerve, and I nearly ran onto the sidewalk. I withdrew my hand back to the steering wheel.

"Oops!" I said as I tried to focus on driving the car safely.

Then I thought, *Thank God I don't have syphilis.*

"So, she cheats on the bad husband with you, the lover?" I looked over at him.

"Yes." Brad puffed his chest up.

"Do they end up together?"

"No, because he is not the marrying type, and he dies in a plane crash. Yes, because they loved each other till the end." He put his hand on my leg.

I laughed. "You are Robert Redford."

"What? I like marriage. I am for marriage. Let's get married now." He sounded serious.

"Right, Brad, right," I said knowingly. He was a runner and a seasoned runner, too. He had been sabotaging relationships for decades. It was clear he came in deep and hard and then left just as abruptly. He probably preferred troubled women like me—an easy kill.

I pulled into the Embassy Suites and parked the car in a discreet location. Brad checked in at the front desk while I walked in the opposite direction toward the restaurant, incognito, dodging people's eyes like an adulteress. I saw the mayor's public relations officer, Larry Schmidt, and ducked behind a huge, potted plant.

Brad was walking towards me, he pointed toward the elevators. I rerouted around the plant and snuck into an open elevator. He ran in behind me. The metal elevator doors shut. We looked at each other, eyes locked, and started making out like the plane was going down, except it was an elevator, and it was going up to the third floor. Ding! The doors opened.

I jumped away from him as a precautionary measure. No one was there. We got off the elevator. I followed him into his suite. We embraced again until I decided I really wanted to watch *Out of Africa*. Perhaps, it held some sort of spiritual enrichment that would help me more than Robert Redford's tongue down my throat. I suggested it.

"Yes, of course. Let's put in on." He walked into the bedroom. He turned on a lamp and pulled back the emerald green colored bedspread.

"I think we should watch it in the living room. Don't you think?" I walked out of the bedroom into the mini living room.

"I am tired. I had such a long day at work. I need to lie down. I may fall asleep." Brad began to fluff up the pillows.

I replied, "Okay." I walked back into the bedroom.

He put on the movie. I took my shoes off and sat on the bed, four pillows stuffed behind me. We cuddled; we kissed. It was gentle and slow. In his arms, I felt safe; it felt right and effortless, for a moment.

Then he started to move his hands all over my body, like the karate kid. Wax on, wax off. I grabbed his hands. “I am not ready. I am sorry.” I gave him a comforting look of rejection.

He conceded like a gentleman. “I understand.”

Five minutes later, his hands were roaming all over my body, again. I grabbed them again.“Seriously, we can kiss, but that’s it. This is difficult for me. I need time. I do want to move on with you,” I said, trying to throw the man a bone, just not the kind he wanted.

“I’ll wait for you,” he said, dewy-eyed.

How generous. Then Brad started kissing my neck, he moved his hand underneath my shirt. I grabbed my phone to check the time. Will had called seven times. I had accidentally turned off the ringer. “Sorry,” I said, “I have to call Will.” I sat up on the corner of the bed, with my back to Brad.

“Will?” I pulled my shirt down, and stuffed my plumpish, but floppyish breast back into its harness, otherwise known as a bra.

“Trey’s caretaker. He told me earlier that Trey is holding himself for ransom along with Simon’s truck. Give me a minute.” I felt the storm chaser’s adrenaline surge through my body.

“Ugh... yeah sure,” Brad said, bewildered and less dewy-eyed.

“He’s gay, don’t worry,” I added, belatedly, before placing the call.

“Faith, oh my God,” Will shouted dramatically.

“Will, what’s happening?” I shouted back, equally dramatically. What can I say? The drama—it was contagious.

"I came home from work, and someone has thrown a bowling ball through my window! The room where Trey has been staying! There are needles and aluminum foil crinkled all over the floor. The sheets have burn holes in them. There is a hole in the wall. The entire room is trashed. He must have had some psychotic, meth-induced episode, and broke into my house. And the stupidest thing is that he has a key!" Will breathlessly panting.

"It could have been the drug dealers? Or Helga? Apparently, she smashed the windows of her home some years ago." I trailed off and told Will the story.

"Oh, my God, I knew she was creepy! I feel unsafe in my own home."

"Do you have a security system?"

"I will have one installed. I am calling the police and making a report."

"Phyllis will freak out if you call the cops on Trey. You need to tell her first and ask for help. See what she is willing to do to help you feel safe again before you do anything else. Recently, someone tried to break into my house. I have a security system, and it was the alarm that made them bolt. So I highly recommend getting one. That being said, I haven't felt safe in months. I can sympathize." Brad began to rub my back.

"Darling, I feel like I am in danger. I have to stay with my grandmother tonight."

"I am so sorry. You'll be alright. I promise. Let me know if Trey shows up."

"Faith, you have to leave him. I am all for marriages staying together, but this is unfixable.

You are young. You can start over. You can rebuild."

"Definitely something to consider," I said, glancing over at my new BFF with a ding dong. Will hung up.

"What was that?" Brad asked, wild-eyed. I did prefer the dewy-eyed look. I turned to him.

"Another day in the life of Faith Nathaniel—lights, camera, dysfunction." I heard the song inside my head *"Bad Boys Bad Boys Whatcha Gonna Do, Whatcha Gonna Do When They Come For You"*

"No, what's going on?" Brad erected his back toward me.

I thought about what I should tell him. I mean, what a romance killer—drugs, breaking and entering, ransom demands—I told him everything that had happened in the last few weeks. Brad's eyes swelled. He must have had a renewed awareness of the instability of my life. Any normal man would run.

"Trey's doing drugs?" Brad shifted his eyes around the room.

"The whole family is hooked on something. Let's face it Brad; drug users typically are not good decision-makers," I said, trying to stay level and not get nasty.

"What kind of drugs?" Brad readjusted his body.

"Heroin, meth, cocaine; anything, I suppose. He prefers heroin, though, I think." Brad looked disturbed. We all know the risks involved with IV drug users. "I've been tested; don't worry Robert Redford. God has spared me one last time, no syphilis."

"Wow, Faith. You have to leave Fairbanks. Get your children out of here." He had morphed from Seducer Brad to Life Coach Brad in no time flat.

"My friend Maria said the same thing." I curiously watched him.

"She's smart."

My phone rang—Will again. I looked at Brad. "I don't think you should answer that."

"Trey called," Will said. "He said he will hand over the truck for five hundred dollars. You were right. That fucker kidnapped himself."

"Call Phyllis; she'll pay it. Did he mention your window?"

"He apologized, and said he had to because I locked him out... but I know I gave that asshole a key."

"Whoa, don't try to rationalize. No logical human would say, 'I don't have a key, so I'll just take this bowling ball and throw it through the fucking window.' If you do that, you will start spinning in circles. Did you ask him why he trashed the room? And where the hell did he get a bowling ball?"

"We didn't get that far, but I know Helga is bowling fanatic." Will hung up, pissed off. I mean, who really wants to deal with that circus? Not me; I was done impersonating Dr. Drew on Celebrity Rehab.

"Now what?" Brad asked, pulling me close to him.

I told him.

"Well, I think I should have bought "One Flew Over the Cuckoo's Nest, instead," he chuckled.

"What? How am I crazy? I might be surrounded by crazy, but I am not crazy!" I pulled away from him in offense. I stuffed a pillow between us. "I am thinking about my kids. They're innocent and stand to lose the most. And I don't think Will is that crazy either; he's in a bad situation. He seems a whole lot more normal than I initially thought. In fact, I think I like Will."

"Why did you tell him not to call the police? He should have. You are a co-dependent, and grooming Will to become one, too. Why are you still protecting these people?" Brad asked challenging my judgement.

"Not them, Brad. Phyllis told me I wasn't family anymore. I am protecting my children. I don't need Trey's name in the paper again. It's embarrassing for the kids, and yes, for me." I looked away from him and began to breathe deeply to re-center myself.

He moved the pillow and put his hand on my shoulder. "That's not healthy. Here, I got something for you to read," Brad said, in full life-coach mode. He got out of bed and walked over to his briefcase. He pulled a book out and handed it to me. I read the title-*Codependent No More.*

"Not sure I have time for leisurely reading these days, but the thought is... kind." I gave him a fuck-you smile. This was definitely not romantic, and not what I had in mind when considering taking a lover. Who was this guy? Did he want to seduce me and be my life coach? For real?

"That book changed my life. You don't have to read all of it; just some of it," he said with a gentle, loving look. He laid back down next to me.

My phone dinged.

Will: *Will you go with me to get Simon's truck?*

Me: *No, Will, I am not a co-dependent.*

I showed the text to Brad.

He laughed. "I think we're going to have fun together."

We laid together on the bed. He kissed my hand and held it. I gazed at him suspiciously, wondering what his real motives were. He was trucking along while crazy shit hit me left and right. I wondered if he liked to observe the drama and wanted his front-row seat, or was he genuinely trying to be my friend? Could I ever trust a man again?

I arrived home late that night. The kids were asleep. Mom was waiting up for me, sitting on the sofa reading her Agatha Christie book. I told her how wonderful Brad was and showed her the book he bought me. I wanted her to like him, even though he was an unknown entity to me. I was determined to keep him separated from the negative parts of my life. Together, we attempted to read a chapter of *Co-dependent No More*. I cried at the events, feelings, and emotional roller coasters of other people's stories. Those were my stories. That was my pain; this was my life. We got to the following passage:

> "Many of the people I've worked with in family groups have been that obsessed with people they care about.

> When I asked them what they were feeling, they told me what the other person was feeling. When I asked what they did, they told me what the other person had done. Their entire focus was on someone or something other than themselves. Some of them had spent years of their lives doing this—worrying about, reacting to, and trying to control other human beings. They were shells, sometimes almost invisible shells, of people. Their energy was depleted—directed at someone else. They couldn't tell me what they were feeling and thinking because they didn't know. Their focus was not on themselves."
>
> — Reprinted from **Melody Beattie, Codependent No More: How to Stop Controlling Others and Start Caring for Yourself,**

The passage penetrated my core so deeply it was too unbearable to finish reading. It rattled me the way only the cold, hard truth could. I understood the message LOUD and CLEAR. The last eleven years of my life had been built on keeping Trey healthy. I had spent them solely on guiding Trey's life, and I was attached to its direction and outcome like a caboose to a train spiraling out of control, veering off and on the tracks by the whims of his decisions.

I had tricked myself into thinking that I was saving another human being: a high calling in the Kingdom of the Lord. I was righteous and strong in my belief. But it was a storyline I had told myself for far too long. A storyline that allowed me not to pay attention to my own life and my own life choices. A storyline where I was a noble character, rescuing another human being and sacrificing myself in the process. But was it true love or fear?

Far too long had I walked in the shadows, too insecure to step up and take control of my own life. I allowed myself to be held captive by people who would discard me as easily as keep me. I had given away my self-worth. Why? Because of fear of the unknown? Because of the fear of not being good enough? Because of insecurity in my ability to survive alone in the world.

Trey was sick, but I was sick, too. I had used him as a shield to count myself out. My approach to Trey, his family, and his addiction had been misguided. Trey and Phyllis deceived me sure, but I deceived myself more. Why didn't I love myself? Why wasn't I enough for me?

I was not responsible for Trey's choices. Jacob had once told me that asking Trey not to be a drug addict was like asking a cancer patient not to have cancer. The difference was that when someone had cancer, they chose to seek treatment, and the same level of accountability should be expected from addicts. If you have an addiction, you should choose and follow a treatment plan. Trey was recklessly avoiding treatment. The unacceptable but undeniable truth is that some people enjoy being addicts; they have no true desire to get *well*. They are living their life's plan—free of societal obligations, in the chase, in the thick of danger, high above the expectations of others, all while controlling those who love them. Addiction is a disease, but maybe, also, for the addicts not pursuing a treatment plan, it's simply a different worldview.

Drug use is not a victimless crime; there are numerous victims, but at some point, you have to either choose to continue to be a victim or to walk away, like Dick. Phyllis refused to walk away. She had never got treatment through Al-Anon or put up boundaries with Trey, and to make it worse, she had an endless pit of money to coax him along his path of destruction. She and Trey were tied to each other, not just as mother and son, but as addicts and co-dependents. Their addiction to each other bonded them in a most unhealthy and unnatural way.

I supposed we were all sick together. Phyllis must have sensed her loss of control over me, and was threatened by my relationship with Lonnie. In her mind, she had to keep control over all of us: control over Simon and Lonnie because of the money, control over Trey and me because of his addiction, and control over Helga because of the Center. What rational, loving grandmother conspires to firebomb her son's marriage? Phyllis was suffering in such a tragic way. The path she was on would never bring her happiness—but how could the mother of an addict ever be happy?

OOPS...HE DID IT AGAIN!

CHAPTER 18

Five a.m., and Simon was on the phone. "Have you seen Trey?"

"What's going on now?" I asked with no feeling.

"Trey broke into my hangar over the weekend, stole a book of checks, my gold bars, four of my guns, and three of my samurai swords," Simon wheezed.

I felt like Simon had served me a double espresso of wake-the-fuck-up. I sat up quickly. I initiated my *TapeAcall* app.

"The keys were on my truck key ring," he continued, "and he took my truck without asking."

"Have you called the police? You are liable if a crime is committed with your guns. And how many checks has he written? That is illegal!" I got out of bed and walked into my master bath for a glass of water.

"I know it is illegal, Faith. I am a member of Mensa. He's written over twenty thousand dollars in checks on my account so far. Phyllis said if I called the police on Trey, she would call the police on Lonnie for stealing her iPhone upgrade."

I blinked. How could Phyllis compare an iPhone upgrade with check fraud and gun theft? "What can I do to help you?"

"Let him live in the basement with you," Simon demanded. "I am paying the mortgage." "No! I am not having a drug user with illegal guns around my children!"

He hung up on me. I placed the phone next to my bathroom sink.

This situation was beyond my expertise. Lonnie should have stepped up and protected her dad, and called the cops on Trey. But Phyllis, who had complete control over Simon, would not have allowed it. Simon had to keep barriers between him and Lonnie to keep the peace with Phyllis. I figured Lonnie was trying to keep the waters calm to prevent further alienation. The abuse was circular and never-ending. My focus had to remain on my children.

Over coffee, I told my mother about the phone call.

My mom looked dumbfounded, sitting across from me in the family room. "Faith, you've got to move. This is insanity. Did you tell Simon about the crayon letter Helga sent?"

"Whatever that's about, it has to do with Phyllis and Helga. Whoever sent it wants a reaction, and I am not giving it to them." I stood up to pour myself another cup.

"Someone took a lot of time to paste individual letters and mail it," Mom said, harnessing her inner Sherlock Holmes. She thoughtfully gazed at the ceiling, her fingertips pressed against her chin.

"Fine, I'll call Lonnie."

I wanted to stir the pot. After all, I only had so many ways to attack back. I sat back down next to mom. I told Lonnie everything her dad had told me.

"Jesus Christ, sister, that's a felony. I'll talk to Jacob." Lonnie sounded shocked, upset, vengeful. I was hopeful Lonnie would take action. Then, after all the ranting, she said, "I didn't mean to steal her iPhone upgrade. That was the AT&T lady's fault. I am innocent." Her tone was more passionate than ever, as though the two crimes were on equal footing and would be judged so by a court of law. I concluded her fear of Phyllis's wrath would prevent her from taking action.

Next, I called Will. To see what version of the events he had been fed, "Do you know about the hangar?"

"I was told not to tell you." He sounded shocked. "Phyllis swore me to secrecy."

"Simon called me, looking for Trey. I guess you didn't get the truck back."

"Trey didn't show up. The whole hangar incident was caught on the security cameras. Sabra is seething with anger. She doesn't know how to clean up the books."

"I guess he won't be needing five hundred dollars." I took a sip of coffee and gagged. I forgot to add the sugar!

"I can't believe he's doing this," Will spoke with an ache for justice in his voice.

"Neither can I, Will. He's on a fast decline. We'll be lucky if he stays out of jail. Is Phyllis back in town?" I walked into the kitchen, added two packets of Truvia.

"Yes, last night. She's enraged. She thinks we are all picking on Trey."

And again, Trey should be treated like a celebrity bad boy, and us mere commoners should tolerate his behavior. What about Simon?

Will said, "Trey's like Britney with the umbrella," and laughed.

"Ya, 'Oops, he did it again,' except Britney is a genius and the paparazzi deserved that umbrella attack." I took a sip of coffee.

"Ya, I would have preferred an umbrella over a bowling ball."

I had another incoming call. "Will, it's Trey. I'll call you back." Mom shook her head in disbelief. I switched over and put the phone on speaker. "Trey! where have you been?" I spoke like a mother—my default mode with him. I sat back down in the family room.

"It doesn't matter. I am giving the truck back. I left it at Will's work. I am staying with a friend. I am done with him." He spoke like a victim—his default mode with me.

"Trey, go back to Will's house. He still wants to help you. He's lucid." I placed my coffee on the table in front of the couch.

"He's in love with me. He tried sneaking into my bed; that's why I threw the bowling ball."

I gasped. "What about the hangar? Did you break in and steal checks and swords? And the ball through Will's window, because he's hot for you?" Mom's face dropped. She covered her mouth giggling.

"All you care about is the truck! You don't care about me!"

I was speechless. I immediately called Will back and told him the location of the truck. "Trey also said you tried to rape him in the middle of the night, and that's why he threw the bowling ball. He didn't offer an explanation about the hangar, sorry."

Mom continued to laugh. I found myself holding back laughter, too. Perhaps it was the laughter of a madwoman who had truly lost her mind. But the thought of Will making a pass at Trey, and Trey throwing a breaking a window like a bitch—it was hysterical. The laughter was otherworldly, as if God sent it to me to reprieve me of the present moment of chaos. This, too, shall pass.

Maggie came into the room "Happy Valentine's Day" I turned the speakerphone off. I waved at her 'good morning.' Mom took Maggie upstairs to get ready for school.

"Ugh. I would not touch his dick. He's diseased. Dis-gusting. My boyfriends are gorgeous and clean. Trey Nathaniel wishes he was up to my standard. Ugh. No offense, Faith." Will declared his innocence with loathing and fervor. I continued to laugh while he kept defending himself against Trey's accusation of sexual assault.

"No offense taken. It's just him trying to redirect attention from himself to others. He's used me as the scapegoat for years; no one understands better than I do. Do you know if he still has a job at St. Mary's?"

"I think so. But they're trying to re-hire the guy they fired to make room for Trey. I guess they want to get rid of him, finally. Phyllis is fighting it."

"That's a losing fight. Why does she keep giving him resources to hurt himself and others? I am so confused." I put my feet up on the coffee table.

Regardless, it was also not a good omen for the kids and me. Trey possibly getting fired meant no paycheck coming in, which meant I was fucked. How would the kids and I survive? I realized that if I divorced him, I would likely get nothing. All the money could easily be hidden from the IRS and the state. Sabra would do anything to make the Hamiltons happy.

I had to file for divorce ASAP.

I started a Google search for attorneys on my phone. I entered, "Family Law Attorneys, Fairbanks, Alaska." My search was interrupted by a text message.

Brad: *Good Morning, Gorgeous, wishing you a peaceful day.*

Me: *Good Morning, so many adventures already circling the atmosphere #killmenow*

Brad: *What happened?*

Me: *Typical morning—breaking and entering, a missing white truck with one suspect prank-calling, venting his frustrations toward his would-be rapist—enough said.*

Brad: *He has to call the police.*

Me: *No can do, an iPhone upgrade from the evildoer AT&T lady hangs in the balance.*

Brad: *I don't understand what you're talking about.*

Me: *Neither do any other logical humans. Glad you are up to speed.*

Brad: *Come with me to California this weekend?*

Me: *I can't leave my kids. It's not safe. If they find out about us, they will punish me and then there are the PTO moms—what will they think?*

Brad: *They will think you're stupid for not sneaking away with me.*

Me: *Maybe after I am divorced.*

Brad: *Do you have an attorney? Do you need money?*

Me: *Not your mess to clean up.*

Later that day, I was in the kitchen making the kids an after-school snack—heart shaped grilled cheese sandwiches. They were outside playing in the snow with some of the neighborhood kids. Mom sat down on the twisty barstool at the kitchen counter. She drank tea from a white coffee cup. Her energy felt trapped and loaded.

"What's your plan, Faith? Now there are guns involved. The school year is ending soon. We have to leave." She rested her folded hands firmly on the countertop.

A resistance rose from my inner being. I had worked so hard to make this house a home, not just for me, but for Maggie and Alex. The remodeled floors, kitchen, bathrooms, the new washer and dryer I cherished above all other appliances. I had picked out everything—the blinds, the cup she was drinking from, the shelves, the pictures, the trinkets, the vanities, the furniture. I had envisioned my kids growing up here. I could not leave our home. I was insulted by the idea. "Maybe for the summer. This is our home." I flipped the sandwiches in the pan.

"And how are you going to keep your home? Sounds like Trey will lose his job soon. You will leave this marriage with nothing, not even a home for the kids, because they don't care." She twisted around on the barstool as I poured the kids each a glass of water. "These people want to break you. They want to enslave you as Trey's caretaker. Wake up! You're in bondage to Phyllis and Trey!" She slammed her coffee cup down.

Her words stung like needle pricks on my skin. I saw Maggie and Alex and the effect it would have on their lives if their mother chose to stay in this environment to keep a house, to keep private school, to keep the fakery of vanity. What would that say about me? What kind of legacy was I passing on to them? What would I tell them? Hey, it's okay, you're still better than everyone else because you have the greatest house and your grandparents have a private jet? I did not want my children to remember me this way—the weak woman who never left because of fear of the unknown and the comfort of money.

I asked myself what kind of man Maggie would marry. Would Alex become a drug addict like Trey? How would they respond, seeing this psychosis pass for normal during their crucial years of development, because money could tidy up exterior messes quite effectively, but interior ones not so well? What life lessons would it teach them if I stayed for a house? For a school? For a perfect picture life, void of true substance? I placed the water glasses in front of her. I avoided eye contact.

I knew in my heart that my mother was right. Deep down, we all know the truth when we hear it, but we often reject it. We run and hide from it, but the truth is never far from the surface, reminding us of its presence—good or bad.

"My vote is to pack up the house and leave after the school year ends," my mother said. I pulled a bag of Lays potato chips from the cabinet. I opened it.

"My friends are here, mom. My community, my kid's lives. Other than Trey, we're settled here." I grabbed two paper plates. I put chips on each one.

"Faith, you are going to have to start over somewhere else or take Trey back. They won't leave you alone. They'll make up lies about your character to destroy your relationships and reputation all over town. You know they will. You've seen them do it to others." I snatched the grilled cheese from the pan with a spatula. I placed them on the plates.

"It'll be a cold day in hell before I take Trey back. Have a nice lunch!" I yelled angrily. I took my phone and left the room. I walked out into the garage. I felt as if her trapped energy had been transmitted to me, I didn't know what to do. I began to rifle through things, to see if Trey hid anything illegal. I went through some totes stacked against the wall. I checked the pockets of old snow pants and fishing gear. I looked in the ice chest and underneath bags of potting soil. Finally, I wiggled into the crawl space below the stairs. I saw a dark blue towel I did not recognize draped over something. Underneath the towel, there were three small-sized cardboard boxes. My phone rang.

I answered; it was Jacob. He told me that Sabra had closed Simon's bank account. "Trey spent like twenty k in the span of a weekend. How does somebody do that? It isn't like we live in Vegas."

Trey had probably left the checkbook with his dealer. When he was high, he was like a helpless puppy being robbed left and right. If Trey were a poorer addict, he probably would have learned to be smarter by now, but money was disposable to him. "He puts himself in those situations," I said angrily as I pushed the boxes from underneath the crawl space to the open floor. "It's his choice. I say throw the book at him."

"I want to. Trust me."

I cleared my throat. I sat on the boxes. "Jacob, I need some advice. I am ready to file for divorce. Please don't tell anyone. I need a vicious attorney."

He laughed. "Kim Waters at PNL Law Firm."

"Will you go with me? I am scared."

"Yes, of course. Anything for you."

"Thank you. Love you."

"Call you back soon. Bye," Jacob said and hung up the phone.

I stood up. The outsides of the boxes were marked "St. Mary's." Inside one box was hospital grade enemas, Viagra, a unicorn mask, and a

Ziploc gallon-size bag of pot. The other two boxes contained nothing but enemas, like hundreds of enemas. I was stupefied trying to understand the possible use of these enemas and the mask. I mean, the only thing I could come up with is that he liked to dress up and blow out, I mean really blow OUT! Maybe he was addicted to enemas, too? Then, I wondered why the Viagra, was this a poopy sex kit? What kind of dirty games were he and Helga playing? Perhaps, they took turns administering them to each other? She was clearly willing to go the extra mile to please him. I felt out-of-body disgusted, like I had been exposed to some sort of underground arctic sex dungeon, where men in unicorn mask walked around fully erect defecating on the floor. I stood up and shook myself around, trying to shake off the image of nastiness I had unpacked underneath my garage stairs.

Will called. "O.M.G., Faith, I went to get the truck, and there was a drug dealer, he was like four feet tall, pants hanging down to his knees. Like a gangster—a lot of gold jewelry. He said he wasn't giving me the keys without some cash, and then he pulled up his shirt and flashed a handgun at me!" He was shrieking. "Phyllis gave me money beforehand; she must have suspected something was going to go down. If I hadn't been ambushed, I could've taken him out; he was such a teensy-weensy fucker. I threw three hundred dollars on the ground, and he threw the keys like a hundred feet away, that turd. When I turned my back, he got into a black coupe, and I swear Trey was in the passenger's seat."

Will jolted me back to the present moment. "Will. Your life is worth more than three hundred dollars. I have not had a gun pulled on me. It's time to call it a wrap on helping Trey, okay?" I began to take the content of the boxes and stuff them deep into the trash can.

"Are you okay?" Mom asked. She snuck up behind me. I jumped, then I pointed to the phone. She walked around me and picked up one of the enemas. She gave me an accusatory look, like I was the collector. I scrunched up my face and vehemently shook my head "no." Mom walked back into the house.

"It was probably a fake gun, but I am done. Divorce him. You know he said he didn't even love you and was not happy with you except for the first two months you dated?" Belatedly, he added, "Sorry."

Mom came back with a Ziploc bag. She used a white a paper towel to scoop one of enemas inside. I left her to it.

"Well Will, I am glad he's expressing his true feelings to his alleged rapist."

I AM CALLING THE COPS

CHAPTER 19

Jacob: *Meeting, PNL Law Firm, downtown, one hour. See you there?*

Me: *I haven't heard from you in weeks! This is short notice, but I can make it. Thank you.*

"Mom," I yelled from downstairs. "I have a meeting with an attorney in an hour. Can you pick up the kids?"

She could. I got dressed in a nice navy suit. I tried to look smart and professional. I even wore my eyeglasses instead of my contacts. I gathered everything in my oversized shoulder tote—documents, recordings, financial statements, and other evidence I had collected.

On my way out the door, mom approached me with two Ziploc bags one containing Helga's note, the other the enema.

"You are going to need these," She shook the bags at me.

"Oh... thanks Mom, you are the best." I put the items in my tote. She kissed me on the forehead. "I will be praying."

The C building off Tudor Road, known as the Chi-Na Building, had thirty stories. In Fairbanks, it was considered a high-rise. I parked in the frozen parking lot and rushed to the front doors to prevent from freezing to death. In the stale smoke-colored lobby, I was met by a security guard and a metal detector. Why did I have to pass through TSA to get to the top floors? I approached a formidable-looking lady wearing a black police uniform, sitting behind a desk with a mouthful of food. She slammed the bowl of chocolate pudding down, stood up, and swallowed quickly as if I were interrupting snack time.

"I need to inspect your purse," she snarled still cleansing her palate, while hiking up her pants. She licked her lips. "Hurry up over there." She pointed to the conveyor belt across from her desk. I put my tote down on the belt. She rifled through it, practically dumping it all out. She picked up the Ziploc bag containing the enemas.

"Hmm…what is this for?" Her no bullshit vibe was high.

"Oh, well…that's evidence for a potential crime. And, you have pudding right there." I pointed to the corner of her mouth. She used the back of her free hand to wipe it off. She saw the pudding, her eyes darted back to the bag of enemas. Then her eyes landed back on me. She winced in disgust, like I was some weirdo who had not only interrupted her snack time, but also gave her an image of a bowl full of chocolate pudding.

She aggressively put my purse and the enemas on the conveyor belt. She evil-eyed me through the metal detector. The sirens did not alarm. I was relieved. I certainly did not want a pat-down from her.

A directory was displayed next to the elevator; I discovered that my destination was suite 444. I entered the elevator feeling like this was already a negative experience. Something felt wrong, or off. I talked myself into believing it was the entire situation. In what world was meeting with a divorce attorney ever going to be a positive experience, right?

The law firm office was warm and cozy, with earth tone sofas and decor. Jacob sat in its lobby; he looked ready to slay a dragon. I could tell he lived for this shit. He was wearing all black like a new-age hipster, with square red-rimmed glasses, and his hair slicked back.

He gave me a big hug. I giggled nervously. I could not believe this was my life, and I was preparing to divorce my husband. Even if Trey was despicable and partook in unusual love-making practices, this was the ending of something, and it made me sad and uneasy. Jacob grabbed my hand and held it. A door opened from the back office. A blonde, plump lady in a navy suit, like the one I was wearing, appeared. She nodded at Jacob, then turned to me.

"Nice to meet you, Mrs. Nathaniel. I'm Kim Waters. How are you doing?" She was imitating compassion. We shook hands.

There was no right answer. Saying "Great!" was detached; saying "Nervous..." was weak; saying "Scared" was pathetic. I settled for, "I could be better."

Kim suggested we move to the boardroom; Jacob rubbed his hands together excitedly; the wooden front office door opened, and Lonnie entered.

I thought, How nice! She's here to be supportive. Then I thought, Is she spying on me? Trying to use me as leverage to earn favor with Phyllis?

She approached me with her arms out for a hug. "So sorry I'm late! I love your glasses." She resynched her plum-colored dress coat.

"I'm so glad to have your support." I pushed my eye glasses against my nose.

The boardroom was spacious, with floor-to-ceiling windows overlooking the city. Kim sat at the head of the table. I sat next to Kim. Jacob and Lonnie sat together, opposite me.

It was quickly clear that Kim did not have time for small talk; she was all business and on a timeline. "Faith, I am going to start by asking questions." She opened a dark red 9X12 inch folder. She clasped a pen in her right hand ready to take notes.

"Okay." I felt like a shorn sheep.

"Faith wants Trey's stake in St. Mary's," Jacob blurted out across the table.

"Trey doesn't have a stake in St. Mary's," I corrected him. "He hasn't gone to work for months. Also, he needs to have a Master's degree to be an administrator over there, and I stopped doing his homework, so that isn't going to work out for him unless his girlfriend is able to juggle the affair, her job, Phyllis's ego, Simon's health, her six children, and Trey's assignments, plus his drug addiction." I was out of breath, just saying all that.

"He hasn't gone to work for months? How does he still have a job?" Kim stiffened up.

"My family owns Saint Mary's," Lonnie looked away toward the city below.

"Ah, yes, the Hamiltons. I have heard the rumors about drugs in the family. Also, frankly, that Saint Mary's is in the red and that another group is looking to buy it any day now," Kim said snobbishly, challenging Lonnie for a reaction.

"I don't know anything about St. Mary's," Lonnie said. "It is only big enough for one prom queen." Jacob snickered. He poked Lonnie, and she yelped, "And my dad is being neglected."

Kim said, "Simon? No offense, but I saw him sue a landscaper over work she did at his house. It was brutal. By the end of the dispute, the attorney fees cost more than the twenty-seven thousand he was suing for. It was just to prove a point. He was relentless."

Was she frightened at the prospect of dealing with Simon again? I spoke up. "Simon's sick now." I gave her a quick rundown of the latest Trey-pisode, and added, "Trey has also stolen his oxy. It's a complete mess. I have it all on recordings. Simon is not the pit bull you remember." I teared up. Kim continued to take notes.

Jacob mused, "All that money, and he has no peace. If only peace could be bought..."

He was a deep thinker.

Kim rolled her eyes. "What drugs is Trey using now?"

"Heroin, cocaine, meth... I think he sells his parents' OxyContin on the streets. Maybe he barters it for the other stuff. And he might be selling enemas too."

"Enemas?" She stopped writing, a look of perplexion fell upon her face. I reached inside of my purse and slid the Ziploc bag with the enema toward her. "Ugh" She used her pen to scoot the enema back at me. "Did anyone make a police report over the break-in at the hangar?" Kim asked as she readjusted her seat.

"Phyllis would not let Simon do it. Although he wanted to," I said, moving closer to Kim.

"Yes, she threatened to have me arrested for stealing her iPhone upgrade," Lonnie broke in. "Which was a mistake made by the AT&T lady. I did not do it intentionally!"

That again. I wondered if she had internalized that she was inferior to Phyllis and her children, that whatever crazy bullshit Phyllis concocted was legit and would be upheld in a court of law and public opinion. I wanted to shake Lonnie and scream, "You're better than this; snap out of it!" And yet this behavior was the very reason I could not trust her. She was smarter and stronger than Phyllis; she just could not see it yet. I wondered if she had self-love issues?

Kim looked around at us like we were each individually crazy, in a unique and particular sort of way. Her gaze came to rest on me. "Are you working?"

"No. I have all this paper work, do you want it?"

"Not yet. Please take that with you." Using her pen, she pointed to the enema. I put it back into my purse.

"Thanks. What are your assets?" Kim.

"I want to keep the house. I don't have grand plans for a coup at St. Mary's." I glared at Jacob.

"What's your income?"

I gave her a rough estimate. "That does not include the two thousand five hundred stipend the Hamiltons give their children each month. Except Vanna, I believe. They turned her care over to the state."

"Who's Vanna?"

Lonnie said, "My sister. She's sick, and no, I don't get the family stipend, either." Lonnie's face tightened like a fist full of rage.

Kim turned to Lonnie and asked, "Why is your sister in the care of the state?"

"I don't know. When Simon and I discussed it, he seemed to be concerned about long-term care for her. She has a conservator and is only allowed a certain amount of money in her account at a time, or she loses her state care."

I asked, "How are Vanna's children doing anyway?"

"I don't know. I haven't seen them in a while." Lonnie's energy changed to sorrow.

Oh, my. I was a blind fool. Of course, Maggie and Alex were expendable. The Hamiltons had barely acknowledged the existence of Vanna's kids. They were equally as important.

Kim said, "Faith, the one thing I can tell you for certain is that the court will not give custody to a drug user." She handed me a different red folder. "Fill out this paperwork and bring in the highlighted documents. I will need a retainer of five thousand dollars. Feel free to make an appointment with the receptionist on the way out. Nice to meet everyone. Goodbye." She rose and left the room. Abruptly.

"I don't feel like anything has been accomplished," I said, feeling forlorn.

Lonnie said, "This will take over a year to be resolved. Be patient." Jacob nodded.

"Wtf, a year?" I stood to leave, distressed and agitated.

When I arrived home, I was greeted by Maggie. "Someone sent flowers!"

"Oh, how exciting!"

Maggie took my hand and led me into the kitchen. On the kitchen counter, there was a vase with twenty-four brilliant yellow roses. It was elegant, beautiful, extra aromatic. I picked up the card and read it silently. *Dear Faith, I am thinking of you. Let's work on being Co-dependent No More. Love, Brad.*

Love? Seriously? He used that word so quickly. What game was he playing? It felt suspicious. But it was sweet.

"Mommy, mommy, what does it say? Are they from daddy?" Maggie asked jumping up and down in her green plaid uniform.

"It says, To my beautiful girl, Maggy. Love, Daddy." I tucked the card into my shirt pocket.

She beamed with joy. "Can I keep them in my room?"

"Of course." We walked past Alex playing Skylanders.

I carried them up the stairs to her room and put them on her princess pink dresser. She smiled and gazed at the flowers. "When's daddy coming home?"

"Not sure. Everyone is doing the best they can." I readjusted my glasses.

My eyes began to sting. I fled before she could notice that tears streamed down my face. I hurried to my bathroom, locked the door, and sat beside the toilet. I felt sick with emotions I could not control. I was such a loser mom. How could I cushion her from the unbearable heartbreak she was going to carry with her from this?

I cried for her, for Alex, for failing both of them. For my part in exposing them so early to the perversion of the world. For being unwilling to and incapable of fixing their dad. As I was beating myself up, I realized Trey was partying to his heart's content out there somewhere. I had covered for Trey again! I had just participated in the abusive cycle I was trying to escape. As far as creating delusions was concerned, I was as guilty as the rest of them. So much for my new-found awareness of co-dependency.

My phone beeped.

Brad: *I hope your day got easier.*

Me: *Thank you for the roses. I met with an attorney, and I feel confused. Nothing resolved. It added another layer of limbo to my already fragile state of mind.*

Brad: *The journey of a thousand miles begins with one step. Good job today. I am proud of you.*

Me: *Thanks, honey.*

Brad: *I'll see you on my way back through California. I'll get us a room. Maybe you can spend the night?*

Me: *Anything is possible, I suppose.* Spend the night? He gave me a book, sent me flowers, and we were ready for an adult sleepover? HA!

I played dolls with Maggie and helped her clean her room. Then It was time for a bath. Maggie chose to shower in the hallway bathroom; Alex wanted to take a bath in my whirlpool. I agreed. He hauled in a bucketful of bath toys—duck floaties, cars, trucks, an inflatable dinosaur.

"Splish splash, baby in the bath," I sang, sitting beside the tub.

"I am not a baby. I am a big boy." He attempted to splash me.

"Hey, don't do that." I pointed at him.

My phone beeped. I dried off my hands—a text from my beloved mother-in-law, Phyllis. My throat closed, my breath tightened—was this PTSD? I had not heard from her directly since the family meeting. Now I got a text out of the blue. It occurred to me that I had blocked her months ago. How was I receiving her messages?

Phyllis: *It's my birthday, and I want to see my grandchildren.*

Bizarre. Was it even her real birthday? Had Lonnie told her about Kim?

Me: *It's a school night. Sorry, it's late.*

Phyllis: *If you don't allow me to see my grandchildren, I will sue you. I will have your heat turned off in your house. I will put your home into foreclosure.*

I was so exhausted with their antics. I went through my phone's pictures. I found the screenshot text where she was encouraging Trey to go with Helga over me because Helga had drugs. I texted the screenshot to her.

Me: *Explain.*

Phyllis: *Please delete that, please delete it.*

Me: *I am keeping it.*

Phyllis: *Please, I am sorry. I am coming over.*

Me: *No. Happy Fake Birthday.*

Without my full attention, Alex had begun to enthusiastically splash.

"Stop that!" I yelled at him and was instantly sorry. Mom came in at the commotion. I handed her my phone. "Look at this."

She read the screenshot text. "Phyllis sent this to Trey? Oh, my goodness!" She scrolled through my conversation with Phyllis, and mouthed, "Wait, is she coming over here?"

"She wouldn't," I mouthed back.

I felt adrenaline pumping through my blood. I got Alex out of the bath, I wrapped him in his red robe. I told him to get dressed, and sent him to his room. The bathroom was covered in water from floor to ceiling. I mopped it up with extra towels and returned to my son. He was cuddled in bed holding his favorite stuffed monkey "Do you want mommy to read you a bedtime story?" He smiled innocently, as though he had not sent a level two hurricane through the bathroom moments earlier.

We picked *The Ugly Duckling*. I sat down on the edge of his blue and white aeronautical bedspread. I had hardly started the story when the doorbell rang. Startled, I looked at my phone to see what time it was. Trey had been calling. He had texted, too.

Trey: *My mom is on her way over to your house. Don't let her in. She's acting crazy. Why did you send her that text message?*

Me: *Why did you stash St. Mary's enema's in our garage? Shit Happens.*

The doorbell continued to ring, manically. A moment of silence ensued, and then the banging began. I told Alex to stay in his room and went downstairs, phone in hand. Mom was standing by the door, listening. When I glanced back, the kids were peering over the balcony.

"Who's at the door?" Maggie asked.

"Is it a werewolf?" Alex asked.

"Go to your rooms and stay there!" I yelled at them. Mom walked up the stairs to escort the children back into their rooms. The ball of stress in my stomach was turning into anger. I felt violated. Phyllis literally thought she was so powerful that she could come over here and bully me into submission? She wasn't the queen of a medieval village during the Renaissance. This was America—land of the free, home of the brave!

I yelled through the door. "Phyllis, you need to leave!"

"I want to see my grandchildren!" She seemed to be sobbing, whether from sadness, despair, or fury, I could only guess. I just felt it was designed to manipulate me.

"I think you have been taking pills. You've got to leave."

"Let me in! Open the fucking door!" Phyllis beat on the door more loudly than before.

"I am calling the police." I dialed 911. The dispatcher answered. I said loudly, "Phyllis Hamilton is trespassing and refusing to leave my residence. She's beating on the door. I think she may be on pills." I hoped my voice had penetrated to Phyllis.

"Phyllis Hamilton?" The dispatcher said with some disbelief.

"Yes, Phyllis Hamilton, and she won't leave!"

Outside, Phyllis screamed, "You better not have called the cops on me!"

The dispatcher said, "I will have someone come right away."

Mom came down the stairs.

I kept the line open and spoke to Phyllis. "You better leave! The police are on their way."

She beat on the door three times. She slipped a check made out to me for $1,000 dollars under the door. Then, I heard her walk off the porch, get in her car, and drive off.

I spoke into the phone again. "She has left. You can cancel the cops."

The dispatcher said, "Do you feel safe?"

"Yes, we're fine now. But please keep the record that I called."

"It's logged."

My mom looked at me with her mouth dropped open. "You called the police on Phyllis?" She pressed her body firmly into the wall.

"Ya, but look." I lifted the check off the ground to show her. "She is paying me off like one of Trey's drug dealers, all because I had a little dirt… Who the fuck are these people?" My tone sharpened. The money made me feel unclean. Like I had unknowingly made a deal with a she-devil, except I had no intention to hold up my end of the bargain.

"I am speechless, the arctic mob." Mom stood frozen.

I walked over to the alarm system to make sure it was on. "It's good for her to know I have boundaries. She is not innocent. She is trying to let Trey fall on the sword alone. And you know what? The old Faith would have let her in, felt bad for her plight over my own, and gotten back on the hamster wheel of insanity and ran with the best of them. The new Faith gives zero fucks." I took mom by the arm. We walked up the stairs together.

The children had their TVs on, but they had fallen asleep. How had they slept through all of that?

Slowly, it dawned on me what I had done. I had called the police on Phyllis Hamilton. Where did all this courage come from? If someone had told me last year that this would happen, I would have laughed them out of the room. It seemed I was okay with someone hurting me, demeaning me, treating me like a compost pile, but when it came to my children, I guess I just became less of a lady. I suppose Phyllis and I had at least that in common.

A BROTHER IN CHRIST

CHAPTER 20

The phone rang; it was Trey. I put it on speakerphone.

"Greetings from Enema household." I was happily putting on makeup and preparing for another close encounter of the sexy kind with Mr. Rosenbloom.

"Stop it, Faith, you called the cops on my mom. I had to go over there in the middle of the night. She was threatening to kill herself. She said she took all the Demerol. Why would you do this to us?" Trey yelled.

Was Trey delusional? To us? What was he thinking? Was he unaware of everything he had done to us? Did he think after he tired of partying and sleeping around, we were going to get back together? That the white picket fence was just sitting on the back burner, waiting for his princely return?

I began to curl my hair. "Trey, she isn't going to die. She wants you to behave. She's a survivor; she will come up with a new dialogue in her head. One she can live with. Don't worry; be there for her as she is for you." I slipped into my dark denim skinny jeans.

"You've ruined everything!"

"Did you go to work today?" I pulled a Kelly green sweater over my head.

"They're trying to fire me. Can you believe that?"

"You need to keep your job. You have to help take care of Maggie and Alex." I wiggled my feet into my warm furry brown Ugg boots.

"I hate the Center. I have hated it from day one. Everyone is mean to me."

"Well, Helga was nice to you. You're the owner's son; you have it made in the shade. Numerous people would love to be in your position." I applied red lipstick.

"You don't get it." I stopped.

Suddenly, I felt intrigued by his comments. Perhaps, I did not get it. Why was Trey a habitual self-destructor? Did he not feel confident or capable of making it on his own? Perhaps, he was hiding behind his mom and drugs, like I was hiding behind him. Both his biological dad and stepdad owned successful businesses. Perhaps he felt like a loser in a successful family, unable to fulfill his role as the eldest son. So he made himself the perpetual black sheep. Maybe he raged against his own insecurities and self-worth, and when the outside pressure became too intense, he was like a suicide bomber on a mission, and all bystanders head for cover.

"I don't get it, Trey; something is missing inside of you. You need God and you need to stick to your treatment plan. You have successfully done so in the past." I grabbed my Patagonia and got into my car. I backed out of the driveway.

"It's you. I need you. It's Friday, want to go to the movies?"

"No, I am on my way to see an old friend."

I was on my way to pick up Brad from the airport. We seemed to have such an interesting, soulful connection. I was still trying to figure out how real or just how really phony he was. I didn't know, and I guessed 50/50. I enjoyed him and thought about him often between the waves of insanity charging at me. In my thought life, he had become like a cool pool of water to dip in when things got too heated.

As I pulled into the arrival area of the airport, I saw Brad waiting for me. He was wearing the same outfit—an old blue North Face jacket and worn blue jeans with white tennis shoes. He needed a makeover. I stopped myself. It wasn't my job to give him a make-over. Our relationship would not make it that far. The best I could do was to try and help him find his fashion sense for the next lady he pretended to life-coach.

I got stopped at the red light just before I was able to pick him up. I checked my phone. I had received a text from Phyllis.

Phyllis: *Please let's talk, we need you in our lives.*

Suddenly, prompted by my screenshot, she concluded I was a valuable member of the clan. To her, I should've received this text as a trophy that I had re-won she and Trey's hearts with a blackmail text message. How far we had come and how different we were. This was another attempt at fakery, staging a scene with the plot still unknown as Phyllis calculated her next move. B-O-R-I-N-G. I chose not to respond and blocked her again.

I also had received a text from Trey. I opened it. He had sent me a shirtless selfie.

Trey: *Don't I look good?*

I laughed and cringed simultaneously. Ugh! A shirtless selfie of my cheating drug-using, enema abusing, estranged husband? I wanted to text *Hell-to-the-no you don't look good!* Then I thought, at least he wasn't on the toilet. I had grown to despise him. It was more apparent that day and at that moment.

Me: *Send it to your girlfriend.*

Trey: *You're not letting that go, are you?*

Me: *How's work?*

Trey: *They got a team of lawyers together to fire me. My mom is pissed. She's fighting hard to keep my job.*

Me: *You need to start going to work. You have two children.*

Trey: *Let's meet for coffee.*

Me: *Sure, I'll wear my unicorn mask.*

I guessed that Phyllis had given him the green light to win his wife back. But Trey and Phyllis were not bringing their A-game with that shirtless selfie. What was wrong with her? Was she only capable of responding to sheer, brute force?

Brad was holding a small, yellow tin can Easter basket for me. He repeated his little maneuver by pulling me out of the car for a kiss and a hug. He handed me the basket. "Happy Easter."

"Oh, Brad, you didn't have to do that. Thank you." We both got back into the car. I looked through the basket eagerly and started eating the mini Hershey chocolate eggs. He smiled.

"Were you working on the flight again?" I asked trying to make small talk.

He nodded. "Whole time. The trust is low on funds. We have to drop the price of the beach house. We're worried it won't sell in time."

"It'll sell. I have a good feeling about it."

"I have a good feeling about you." He gave me the I-love-you look.

I smiled. I felt special. Mission accomplished, Brad.

He said, "So how are things going, Faith?"

I told him about the episode with Phyllis at my door. "That was one of the low-points of the week, for sure."

"Well, I am here now. You can relax." He reached for my hand.

At the hotel, I parked while Brad went to check-in and get his room key. I waited in the car. My phone started to ring. It was Trey, and he sounded impatient. "Where are you? I am waiting!"

"What are you talking about?"

"The coffee shop by our house. Where are you?"

"I can't meet you right now."

"Get your ass here, right now," he screamed. My body went back into high-alert mode.

"I did not agree to meet you today, and I am certainly not meeting you now."

"I need money!"

There it was, the old 'I want you; I love you, give me money. "Don't call me again!" I hung up.

My headspace had been relatively peaceful, enjoying Brad's charm; now, it was reset to anxiety and anger. I was so tired of this roller coaster. Through the window, I saw Brad motioning for me to meet him inside the hotel. I took a few deep breathes to try and re-center my energy. I got out of the car and accidentally slammed the door, which startled me all over again. My phone rang. Trey, again. I sent it to voicemail and turned off the ringer.

"Hi honey," I said with extra positivity, in an attempt to shift my mood from Trey.

"Room 111." Brad raised his eyebrows at me.

"Great." I followed him. My phone buzzed. Trey. I thought, That motherfucker. I sent the call to voicemail again.

Inside the room, Brad grabbed me and pressed my body against the wall. We kissed—he hadn't come here to cuddle. I kissed back eagerly, ready to fully participate, anything to rid myself of the anxiety Trey was throwing at me. Yes, I said to myself. Brad, you may have your wicked way with my body.

My phone buzzed again and again. I tuned it out as he slipped his hand in unholy places. My phone continued to buzz. The more it buzzed, the more I was determined to take it to the next level with Brad.

He walked to the bed. "Should you get that? Is it one of your kids? Is it an emergency?"

Maybe it was. I checked. It was still Trey, and in addition to the multiple phone calls, he had sent nasty text messages, too.

Trey: *I will give you nothing. I'll make sure my mother does nothing to help you or the kids, you bitch.*

"Fuck you," I muttered to the phone and threw it across the room. I charged Brad like a linebacker running for the goal.

"What's wrong?" Brad asked, bracing himself.

"I am passionate about you, Rosenbloom." I ripped his shirt open.

I pushed him onto the bed. My phone continued to buzz. The more it buzzed, the more I wanted to ride Brad's wild love train all the way into next week. We kissed, and kissed, and kissed until we were naked and romping. Me like a woman in exile, he like it was what he was born to do.

Making love to Brad was my way of putting up as many barriers between Trey and me as possible. Now, Trey was not the last one; now, there was another. I felt I needed this to move on and further cut myself off from Trey: emotionally, physically, spiritually. Why not Brad? I was attracted to him and enjoyed his company. He had put in some work, at least—the flowers, the book, the Easter basket, the travel, and the hotel rooms. And Brad was like a sex god, or perhaps Trey was inexperienced at it, it seemed that way. The important thing was that I could tell Brad was grateful to be with me.

The next morning, I woke before Brad. I felt good and naughty, but mostly vulnerable. It was impossible for me to separate sex from feelings. I wondered what he would he expect from me now. I felt a twinge of panic—what was our relationship status? What was happening here? Beside me, Brad yawned and stretched, and I thought, I need to get the hell out of this hotel room. I quietly got dressed. I tiptoed around to his side of the bed searching for my other boot, he opened his eyes.

"Good morning, beautiful." He caressed my arm.

"Oh, good morning," I said, overly cheerful to deflect the obvious—I was going to do the sneak-out-and-leave. Thank God he didn't live in town.

"Where are you going? Want to have breakfast?" He softly looked up into my eyes.

"I don't eat breakfast, honey. I've got to get home. My kids need me." I looked toward the door.

"Okay. Give me a hug and kiss goodbye."

I sat beside him on the bed. I hugged him lightly.

Brad whispered in my ear, "I love you."

I gasped. What? Love? No way. That word came with strings attached. What was I supposed to say? What was I supposed to do? What would Jesus do? "I love you, as a brother in Christ." Oh God, what had I said? He was neither my brother, nor was he a Christian!

He winced. "Well, what a relief to know I am loved as your brother in Christ." He was offended. He stood up and turned his back away from me.

I put my hand on his arm. "I'm sorry, Brad, but you have to understand that that word means something serious to me. You use it so readily. Do you tell a lot of people you love them?"

"I love everybody," he said nonchalantly, he walked to the restroom.

I got up and left. What a deceiver. To try that trickery on me. Was it purely for a reaction, or did he want to manipulate me into believing things were serious between us? He was a phony who wanted me to think he was shitting rainbows everywhere he went, a sweet little Care Bear, full of love and good-givings. HA!

Whatever. I had bigger problems than the Rosenbloom's bluff. Besides, I would probably not hear from him again. My real problems were as follows—Trey was losing his job, he was out of money, and he had lost this mind.

I plugged my phone into the car jack. I had thirty-three missed calls from Trey! And a some hateful text messages, of course. How would I ever survive this?

Back home, my mom was waiting for me on the sofa in the formal living room. I entered, she stood and accused. "You did it, didn't you?" She slammed her Agatha Christie book onto the coffee table.

"Um, no?" I shut the front door behind me. "Are the kids still sleeping?"

"What did you do all night, then?" Mom stood in a defensive posture with her hands on her hips.

"We cuddled and talked," I said innocently with a pure heart.

"I don't believe you." Mom circled around to me.

"Okay," I said, putting my hand against my forehead with a sigh. I walked into the kitchen to make myself a cup of coffee. She followed me. I placed a coffee pod in the Keurig. "To tell you the truth, he's impotent." My coffee began to brew. "That's why he has never been married or had children. He's fifteen years older than me. He is only capable of cuddling. He's looking for warm companionship." I smiled gently at her. "Would you like a cup of coffee?"

Ugh. I had lied to my mother—my champion, my number-one supporter. But I just could not fight with her over Brad when we had bigger disasters lurking in our midst. Perhaps I was wrong to have slept with Brad, but I was keeping him, as phony bologna as he seemed to be at times. He tried to make me feel special, and it was romantic, even if it was in a deceiving kind of way. I was keeping him, damn it.

"Oh, poor Mr. Rosenbloom!" Mom clasped her chest. "That's so sad, and those wiener medications are hard on the heart. I'll pray for him. Want me to make you some breakfast?" She was sympathetic and relieved. "No, thank you. I am going to take a shower."

After my shower, I changed into sweatpants and a sweatshirt. I sat down on my bed. I opened my nightstand drawer. I found an old packet of birth control. I took one with my coffee. I laid my head on my pillow. I closed my eyes briefly.

My phone rang. Unknown number. I answered. Why not? It was Kim from the PNL law firm. I told her about the psychotic Trey-pisode the previous night. "He kept calling and asking for money, and he was using threatening language. I think he may also be addicted to enemas. Did you find something else out?" I took a sip of coffee, feeling hopeful.

"Listen, Faith. I talked to Father Frank. My partners and I can't take your case. I'm sorry."

"What? But I made another appointment! I am gathering all the documents you need. You talked to Father Frank?" I put my coffee down.

"Our firm represents the archdiocese, and the Hamiltons are generous benefactors. It's a conflict of interest."

"Am I hearing you correctly? You cannot represent me, because one of your partners represents the archdiocese to which the Hamiltons have donated money? Surely numerous people have donated money. Do you turn down their cases?"

"The decision was made by our firm's partners. I cannot help you. I wish you the best." Kim sounded cold and utterly detached. This was a skill she had surely mastered.

"Seriously? Where does your firm and Father Frank stand on protecting children from drug users and criminals? The least vulnerable? What's your position on that?"

I was so angry. I wanted to throw my hot coffee in Kim's face. She was corrupt and so was that sneaky-snakey Father Frank. He had used my tragic circumstance to gain leverage with Phyllis. Father Frank was probably worried that I would be awarded the money meant for his statues or what other weird pagan monuments he wanted to erect. Maybe it hadn't been Lonnie who had sent Phyllis into her tailspin. Maybe it had been Father Frank. Like Brad said, "I was the most vulnerable, and I was going to get screwed." My suffering weighted for others' gain.

My kids went to a Catholic school full of great, honorable people. Right out of a storybook. I would like to think they would be so humiliated to know what I had been going through. One of their own shoved aside for fear of losing big donor money. The Bible says, You can't have two masters; you can only serve one—God or money. Perhaps Father Frank should be reminded of that. They had chosen to safeguard possible future donations over the safety and protection of my children and me, and that was despicable. I was finally able to agree with Simon. Organized religion was inherently corrupt, at least at the highest levels.

Who would ever hold the Hamiltons accountable? They had paid off everyone in advance.

Deflated, I walked into Alex's room, he was playing Skylanders. I sat next to him. I ran my fingers through his dark blonde hair. "Mommy, stay and watch me play?"

"Do you want some pancakes?"

"Later. There are a ton of Chompies." Alex said working his remote control.

I texted Jacob about Kim and the archdiocese.

Jacob: *I am sure that's unethical. Are you sure that's what she said?*

Me: *Yes, sadly. I am losing faith in people, but not in God. I'll find another way.*

Jacob: *I'll won't recommend her to anyone again. Sorry, sis.*

I felt so defeated, but I had to keep moving forward. I remembered a Pastor saying on the radio, God has the final say in my life. Not PNL, or the wayward Father Frank. I wondered whether

Trey was dead after all those psychotic rantings. I called him. "Are you okay?"

"Why wouldn't I be?"

Typical. He had forgotten about his manic episode the night before, a new day had sprung, and once again, he had swept everything under the rug. Truly, it was his only superpower. I played along. "No reason. How is your job?" Alex shushed me for interrupting his game.

"They are firing me." Trey sounded as if he had known all along.

I wondered whether he had only been pretending to be upset, but was secretly happy to be done with the Center that he hated so much. Free, once again, from all responsibility. "What are you going to do now?" I walked into the hallway.

"Mom's going to pay me to take care of Simon."

"No! I thought he had caregivers!" I yelled in horror. I felt my temperature spike. My heart sank. Trey could not take care of a pet rock, let alone Simon. "What's wrong Mommy, What's wrong?" Maggie asked walking out of her room.

I put my arm around her. "Go take a shower. We can make breakfast together?" Maggie walked back into her room.

I whispered to Trey, "So you got the guns back?"

"My mom did. She drove into Mountain View and paid two grand for them," Trey sounded satisfied.

"Really?" My voice got louder, "You let your mom go to Mountain View, alone, to meet criminals and buy back the guns you stole? You would let her do that? I don't believe you!"

"What does it matter?" Trey yelled back.

"Where are Simon's caregivers?"

"They got into a fight over medications and quit. I guess they filed a report with their agency."

I thought, *Good luck with that. I got fired by my own attorney.* "They say doctors are the worst patients."

"Yep, Simon sure is needy."

"He has a debilitating disease. I don't know if needy is the right word."

Maggie walked back into the hallway with a change of clothes. She stared at me. "What time did you get home last night."

I put the phone on mute. "Right after you went to bed. We are going to make pancakes soon." I smiled at her.

There was a short pause before Trey said, "My mom is going to Hawaii. When she gets back, do you want to go? We can stay in the house over there and take the kids."

I unmuted the phone. "Um, no, we aren't going to Hawaii. That will not solve the issues we have." I needed to change the subject, immediately. "Maggie's first communion is coming up. It's on Easter. I hope all three of you can make it. No matter what has happened, everyone should be there for Maggie." I hugged her.

"Of course, she's my baby girl!"

I rolled my eyes and told him goodbye.

"Wait, Faith. Let's do counseling."

"Okay, if you make the appointment, I'll go."

SIMON HAS FALLEN

CHAPTER 21

It was the middle of the night; my phone was ringing. I was annoyed. I was having a beautiful dream. I was resting on a blue velvet sofa. An unfamiliar lady dressed from the 1950s, with short dark wavy hair was smiling at me. It felt as if she was sending me a present, a gift, a warm feminine hug. She said, "This is your gift." Her energy vibrated unconditional love and devotion. Between the phone ringing and this dream, I briefly wondered if this was another message about new beginnings.

I picked up the phone. It was an unfamiliar number. Drug dealer? I did not want to answer it, but my high-alert body management system had already been triggered, and I felt compelled. I unplugged my phone.

"Faith, this is Rocky. Simon fell. I called 911. He thinks he broke his leg."

Rocky? Who the hell was Rocky? "What? When? Where's Phyllis?"

"Phyllis is in Maui. Simon fell in the kitchen; he didn't have his phone. He army-crawled from the kitchen to the master bathroom and called me. There's nobody else here. He said Trey left sometime yesterday."

"Seriously? They left him alone?" Anger bubbled inside me. I threw my dark red duvet to the ground.

"I was over here earlier this evening, but I came back when he called. He told me to call you."

My heart hiccupped. I hated this; it was so cruel, unfair, and undeserved. Poor Simon, he had taken care of all of us, and this was his repayment? To army-crawl on a broken leg, three hundred feet? Alone? He could afford the best care in the state of Alaska, in the world, yet this was what he received—the great, prestigious Simon Hamilton. It was beyond tragic. "I'll call his brother and daughter. Thank you for everything you've done to help him."

How detached did Phyllis have to be to leave her husband in the care Trey? But, hey, she was on white sand beaches, luxuriating. Who was I to judge? Who knew what battles she fought daily to rationalize such depravity in her own home.

I called Aunt Denali; no answer. I left a voicemail.

I called Lonnie; no answer. I sent a text.

I called Rocky back. He sounded like he knew me, but I could not remember who he was or his relationship to Simon. It felt rude to ask at this point. "I've called Lonnie and his brother's wife, Denali. I am sure I'll hear from them soon. Which hospital are they taking him to?"

"Regents."

"I'll go by and check on him in the morning. Have you heard from Phyllis?"

"She doesn't like me. I am not highfalutin' enough"

"She doesn't like anyone!" I yelled into the phone out of frustration and hung up.

I thought about calling Phyllis, but maybe it was not my place to inform her of Simon's accident. I wasn't family anymore. I walked into Maggie's room and woke my mom up to tell her about Simon's fall. We prayed for him, and for Phyllis and Trey.

The following morning, I quickly got dressed in a long teal sweater and black leggings. I decided to wear my black and gold colored Nike's. After dropping the kid's off at school, I drove to Regents. It was the first time I noticed the snow was melting. Another season was upon us, and I had still made little to no progress in changing my life. I felt like I was stuck in an airplane on a holding pattern, circling the runway, waiting for the weather to clear, to land safely. I also felt like I was running out of jet fuel and could crash at any time.

I turned on my Christian Sirius channel trying to harness spiritual truth to center myself. The Pastor said, "When someone is rude to you, keep a smile on your face. When you stay on the high road and keep your joy, you take away their power." This message was quite fitting for the situation. I told myself I would only use my words for productive communication, and if all else failed, I would leave.

Gathered in Simon's hospital room were Uncle Peter, Aunt Denali, Jacob, and Lonnie. Simon was in the bed wearing a light blue hospital gown; his leg was elevated and wrapped. He looked lucid. "Faith," he said, smiling—genuinely happy to see me. I walked over to him.

I was amazed at how tough he was. My defenses went down. I gave him a hug and a kiss on the cheek. "I think I've seen you in better shape." I rubbed his arm.

"I am sure." He seemed delighted to be around his family and getting healthy attention and care.

I asked, "So, what are we dealing with here?"

Uncle Peter spoke up. He was leaning against the wall of the room. "Broken femur. He just woke up from surgery." Peter looked despondent.

Everyone in the room shared the same look of discontent. I recalled my own surrender to codependency—first by silence, then by comfort, then by cooperation. Who in this room would be a champion for Simon? And would Simon even allow it?

Aunt Denali grabbed my hand. She was wearing a brown linen jumpsuit, her hair in a bun. "I need some coffee, Faith. You do, too; let's go." As soon as we were out of the room, and in the hallway, she asked, "How could she leave him? Where is she?"

"Maui. She left Trey to take care of him. That's what Trey said." I looked into her eyes.

"The same Trey that broke into the office and stole checks?" Poor Aunt Denali had recently married into this family; she must be traumatized. Still, she got the best of the lot, so she shouldn't be that upset.

"Has anyone seen Trey?" I asked. "Aunt Denali shook her head no. "He probably won't show his face around here without his mama to give him a false sense of superiority." I shrugged my shoulders.

"Lonnie said Simon had caregivers. I don't understand." Aunt Denali paced the floor.

"Apparently, they quit over medication being disbursed inappropriately. I heard they filed a report about it, that's what Trey said." I tucked my hair behind my ears.

"This is so wrong." We circled the hospital hallway, past the nursing station.

"As far as I can tell, Lonnie is the only one who might be able to deal with that situation, and she is terrified of Phyllis. Simon has got to stop backing Phyllis over her. Without his support, Lonnie is powerless. She told me that herself, and I believe her. I feel bad I can't help, but I have to be my own hero right now." I took a deep breath.

"It's not your responsibility, Faith. Simon has a wife and daughter. And you know Peter will not leave his side; he'll be with him as much as he is allowed to." We stopped short of Simon's room, we looked at each other.

Aunt Denali began to cry, and seeing her cry made me cry. We hugged each other. We both felt our helplessness. It was a harsh reality to grapple within a life and death situation. We turned around and again, and began to walk toward Simon's room.

I gently used my fingertips to dab underneath my eyes to avoid smudging my mascara. "Who's Rocky, by the way? He seemed nice on the phone."

"Rocky Valentine?" Aunt Denali raised her eyebrows.

What? Was he a porn star? I tilted my head like, "I guess so."

"He's Simon's neighbor, and they're old drinking buddies. I think Peter knows him. He founded Wolverine Oil, based out of Barrow."

"I hope they weren't drinking when Simon fell. How awful."

We came upon Lonnie and Jacob talking secretively outside Simon's room. I locked eyes with Lonnie; she was furious. I could practically see smoke jetting from her ears. "Oh, my God, sister." She hugged me. "I flew back from Kenai this morning. I can't believe that bitch left him. This is abuse. She's going to pay." In spite of her rage, Lonnie was whispering. She clearly didn't want to be overheard.

Aunt Denali said, "We should come up with a plan for Simon's care." Her hands on her hips. She looked at Lonnie.

"We will," Lonnie said, she clutched her green leather purse and stomped back into the room, Jacob right behind. In our absence, a new visitor had arrived. He was an older, polished-looking gentleman from ass-kicking country: cowboy boots, spurs, and a shiny golden cowboy belt-buckle medallion. I thought, *Hee-Haw, stranger.* He rose as we entered.

Lonnie said, "Hi, Rocky," and hugged him. "Thank you."

Oh wow, that was Rocky? What a man's man. He exuded a powerful masculine energy. I imagined he could goat-tie Trey with dental floss.

He turned to me. "Hi Faith," he said, in thick Southern. He took my hand and kissed it.

Simon was glaring at him. I was uncomfortable. It felt like I should leave. I had helped initiate a

Rescue Simon plan; that was all I could do. This moment belonged to Lonnie, Jacob, Uncle Peter, and Aunt Denali. It was a rare opportunity for them to discuss the reality of the situation.

"I have errands to run," I said, disentangling my hand from Rocky's grip. "I can come back later and bring everyone lunch. Text me and let me know." I gave Simon a hug and whispered in his ear, "I love you. I want you to be okay. Everyone in this room loves you. Let me know if you need anything."

"Come back to see me," he said, sounding sad. He could feel my energy shifting away from him, but it wasn't him, it was the people tied to his caboose.

"Yes, of course I will." I softly smiled at him.

Rocky interjected, "Do you mind if I walk you to your car?"

Simon cleared his throat. He gave Rocky a dirty look.

"Great!" I said, feeling awkward. "You're such a gentleman." I glanced back at him.

"I don't get accused of that often." Rocky pulled up his belt buckle to adjust his tight blue jeans.

We talked as we walked. I said, "Thanks for looking out for Simon. He needs good friends like you around him."

"Simon told me about Trey and his tomfoolery. He asked me to help you. It must be our secret, though. Phyllis cannot find out."

"Help me how?" I looked at him, skeptically.

"He wants me to pay for your attorney. Simon doesn't like Trey, and he knows that Phyllis wants to screw you over. He loves you, but he can't help you the way things are. He has to pretend to be on Trey's side. He asked me to take care of you. They won't hurt you any longer." Rocky straightened his posture.

I was dumbfounded. Who was this knight wearing spurs? Was he another Hamilton spy? Or could I trust him?

We were at my car by this point. I said, "Let's talk. You have my number, right?"

"I do. I'll be in touch." Rocky held the car door open for me.

I sat down. He reached over the driver's seat to buckle my seatbelt. "Uh, thanks." I looked at him suspiciously. I took the belt from him. He tilted his hat at me and walked away.

It was drizzling rain, I turned on my windshield wipers. What a bizarre experience. Did God send me an angel in the form of an ass-kicking cowboy? My phone dinged.

Brad: *Thinking of you.*

Me: *I met John Wayne. He wants to take care of me.*

Brad: *If you got them by the balls their hearts and minds will follow.*

Me: *LOL! Seriously though, I met this badass cowboy named Rocky.*

Brad: *He's lucky. Can I come back and see you? I miss you.*

Me: *Of course. I always enjoy our time together.*

Brad: *Love you.*

Me: *You, too.*

Oh boy. Had I written that? Things were getting complicated.

I arrived home to find my mom in the laundry room crying while she folded towels. “Mom, what’s wrong?” I stood behind her.

“Why can’t we leave after the school year? I am so worried about you and the kids.”

Was this manipulation or a mother’s honest plea? I didn’t want to leave, and I didn’t want to have this conversation again. “Maybe for the summer,” I said, to appease her. I grabbed a box of tissues sitting on the bathroom vanity nearby.

“You will not be welcome in Fairbanks by the time Phyllis is done. You can’t trust anyone here. Alaska is an oligarchy, and you’re not part of it.” Mom sniffled as she stacked towels designated for different parts of the house.

“I know, well, I am not scared of the good old boys. Phyllis is only protected because of Simon, so it’s temporary. If he doesn’t recover, she’ll only be able to wield power through charitable donations. I can make it here.” I handed her a tissue.

“How’s Simon?” She picked the towels up, she sat them back down.

“Surrounded by his family and getting attention. He must think people don’t care about him, just his money. It makes me sad.”

Mom nodded, sobbing even more. I held her hand.

“We have some terrible things in our orbit. At least we’re all physically healthy; we have a house, and clothes, and food. I heard a Pastor on the radio say, 'You may be in a tough time right now, but the enemy always fights you the hardest when he knows God has something great in store for you.'"

Mom smiled through her tears and squeezed my hand. "What do you want to do with your life, Faith? You have some good skills working on fundraisers and with charities. I am sure there are lots of organizations in Washington that could use your help."

My phone dinged. Aunt Denali. I felt saved by the bell.

Aunt Denali: *When are you coming back? Lonnie volunteered you to take care of Simon.*

Me: *Fucking Lonnie, if it was simply me taking care of Simon, I would do it in a heartbeat. He could live here. But you know it would escalate into something else.*

Aunt Denali: *I know, I took Lonnie aside and told her she has to have your back. She can't throw you under the bus like that.*

Me: *Why doesn't she take a sabbatical and take care of her dad? You only have one dad.*

Aunt Denali: *Yep.*

Me: *So glad the Rescue Simon planning committee is pulling it together. Good ole Faith will do it, right?*

Aunt Denali: *Please come back before Phyllis arrives.*

Back at the hospital, Simon's room was dimly lit. He was sleeping. Uncle Peter was napping in a chair close by. Aunt Denali was sitting quietly, working on her computer. When she saw me, Aunt Denali indicated that we needed to talk. She put her laptop in her briefcase. We walked into the hallway.

"Lonnie said that when Phyllis flew Simon to LA in the jet a month ago, Phyllis gave Trey her credit card and told him to take care of himself and Lonnie. She then took off for the desert."

Why did that not surprise me? "At least he had Lonnie."

"Apparently, Trey did not leave his hotel room, except to try and retrieve a Ziploc bag of OxyContin from Simon's hospital bathroom. A nurse told him that they'd confiscated it and made a report. Lonnie asked him for the credit card for food, and he ignored her."

I shook my head. What could I possibly say?

"And then, according to Lonnie, Phyllis made an emergency trip in the jet from the desert to Fairbanks, saw Dr. Stella, got additional oxy, and flew back to LA." Aunt Denali looked shocked.

"Wow. That's dedication." I rubbed my hands together.

"And Trey was high the whole time. Lonnie had to call Jacob to wire her money." She placed her hands on her hips.

"Why does Phyllis keep putting him in positions of power over people? It's insanity. Doing the same thing over and over again and expecting different results." I threw my hands up in frustration.

"Or perhaps," Aunt Denali began to pace "she likes to see what he will do, and they sort of ping pong off of each other. It seems they are both addicted to the drama, the fall out, the reconstructing of reality." She looked amazed, like she had fitted the last piece of a master puzzle together. I checked my phone to see what time it was. I had to pick up Maggie and Alex from school.

"Yes, and he is like her proxy, so if he is in charge, she thinks she is still in control. Clearly, there is no controlling Trey, so there is an element of denial, delusion, and codependency." I shook my head in agreement.

"Do they both do drugs?" She squinted her eyes at me.

"Yes, but they have money, so it's tolerated. Only poor drug addicts are complete social rejects."

We stood in silence for a moment. At last, Aunt Denali said, "Phyllis is flying home tomorrow."

"Maybe this will be her wake-up call," I offered, trying to be positive.

"So, what did Rocky want?" Aunt Denali asked, changing the subject. "What did he say?" I told her what he'd said, and she nodded. "Rocky's tough; you have to let him help you." She nodded her head yes emphatically.

I looked into her eyes and at her body language, trying to get a good read. After everything I'd been through, I was skittish.

She yanked my phone out of my hands, "Damn it, call him!"

"Fine, okay!" I yanked the phone back and did what she told me to.

Rocky answered immediately. "Hey darling, I didn't think you would call me so soon!" he crowed delightfully. I rolled my eyes. Aunt Denali gave me a stern look.

"I thought about what you said. When can we meet?" I gave Aunt Denali the evil eye, she gave me the thumbs up.

"Come on over anytime."

"Where do you live?"

He laughed. "A couple of doors down from Simon on the river. We've met probably a dozen times."

"I am sorry. I have a terrible memory." I hung up and glared at Aunt Denali. "Happy now?" She grinned. We walked back into Simon's room.

I had barely sat down beside Uncle Peter when my phone rang again. I silenced it and left the room again to answer.

"Faith? This is Harry. We met at Ralph's party a while back?"

I remembered that he was the guy whose wife was cheating on him and was currently going through a divorce. I asked him how he was holding up, and he told me had good days and bad days. "You're winning if you're having good days. My days are like watching an episode of *Intervention.*" I faked a laugh. Harry said, "Let's change that. Do you want to meet for sushi at the Blue Fin?" I agreed to meet him.

I quietly walked back into Simon's room. I stood near the foot of his bed by the door, my arms folded. I thought about the quality of my day-to-day life as I watched Simon fight for his. The only semi-good days I had were with my kids, and even then,

I felt like a phony. I was hiding the truth from them. I was living a lie, and being around them was a constant reminder. I was lying to the PTO moms. I was lying to my mom about Brad. And I was not a hundred percent truthful with Brad. Deception clouded all my relationships. After this mess was cleaned up, I vowed to never live like this again. I didn't want to die like Simon.

ROCKY VALENTINE

CHAPTER 22

I pulled up to Rocky's wilderness-themed log mansion. He had a beautiful view of the river, the sun sparkled on the icebergs that remained. His home was grand, powerful, and masculine—like Rocky. I parked in front of the garage doors, and found my way around to the front door. It was ten feet high and had an old-fashioned metal door knocker with the initial "V" engraved on the outside. I used it. Bang, bang, bang...three times. I heard a dog barking and rushing toward the door.

"Chuck, get back," Rocky said as he opened. "Come on in." Chuck, the blonde lab, was happy to see me. He greeted me with his tail wagging and was clearly expecting a head rub. I obliged.

"Cute dog."

"Yes, Chuck is lonely. Loves to have company over." Rocky tugged on his collar.

"Happy to be here. The kids are at school now, but I am sure they would love to meet Chuck someday."

"Bring them over!" I nodded my head. "Would you like a tour?"

"Definitely." I walked from the foyer into a massive living room.

Two mounted taxidermied lions greeted me inside. In fact, there were animal heads and bodies everywhere. Along with huge silver glass cases filled with ivory and jewelry. Rocky guided me through his living room-slash-showcase room. Countless antiques. "These artifacts are from all over the world. Do you see anything you like?"

"That ring is unique," I said. The ring was made from some pinkish crystal, it was oblong/rectangular-shaped. He opened the case and took it out.

"I got this ring in China. It's from the Ming Dynasty." He handed it to me.

"So interesting," I said, examining it closely.

"Keep it."

Was this guy for real? "I couldn't."

"No, keep it. I have plenty."

Well, why the hell not? I deserved a ring from the Ming Dynasty, and he was clearly not hurting from a lack of treasures. I gave a small shrug. "Okay." I slipped the ring on, perfect fit.

The next room was studded with more stuffed animals. A life-sized antelope stood near the bar, a wolverine hugged the patio door, and a wolf and three small foxes peered from behind the fireplace. "How many non-living animals do you have in your house?"

"One hundred and nine."

"Did you kill all of them?" I asked, getting creeped out. I am all for having a few prize kills around the home, but this was testosterone overload. I felt like I was in the Natural History Museum.

"Yes. I've hunted all over the world—Asia, Africa, Australia. See that empty space over there on the wall?" I looked and saw a small, vacant space, perhaps enough room to squeeze in a bunny carcass. I nodded. "That's where I am going to mount Phyllis's head. No embalming needed. She's already well-preserved." Rocky let out a hysterical laugh from deep within his gut. It vibrated throughout the room.

I laughed too. I knew it was a shitty thing to laugh about, but at that moment, I was unhappy with the way she and Trey had treated Simon, so I didn't care.

"Come sit down. I will make us a drink." Rocky ushered me toward an elephant hooved glass coffee table near a cognac leather sofa. He walked behind the bar, which displayed a walrus tusk, and a whale penis.

I sat down, suspiciously speculating the number of cattle he had slaughtered to make the sofa. I looked up at the gigantic brick fireplace; halfway I saw a gorilla perched on a shelf. I felt the uneasiness of dead animal eyes watching me from every nook and cranny of the house.

"What did Phyllis do to you?"

"Other than change her hair color weekly?" He guffawed. "When I was married to my last wife, we would hang out all the time, me, Stacy, Simon, and Phyllis. We went on vacations together and everything. As soon as I retired, she was done with me." Rocky handed me a lowball glass halfway full. "She doesn't even acknowledge my presence anymore. I guess she thought I was less powerful and, therefore, of no use to her. As you get older, you become invisible to people." Rocky sat beside me.

"Cheers." Rocky and I clunked glasses. I took a drink and quickly began to gag.

"Oh my God, what is that?"

"Vodka, what? Do I need to get you a nice Reisling?" He looked disappointed.

"I can't drink that, are you trying to kill me?" I locked eyes with the gorilla.

Startled, I put the glass down on the elephant table. "Did you and Simon go hunting together?"

"Yes, some. Phyllis also says that Simon drinks because of me. Can you believe that."

I looked around curiously.

"That's what she says about Lonnie."

It came as a surprise that she used that excuse for multiple people. But the drinking was an issue. I thought briefly that maybe Phyllis had a right to dislike Rocky and Lonnie for bringing alcohol around Simon. Then I remembered how she had foisted Trey on Simon—Trey, who was a far more lethal substance abuser. Did her love for Trey honestly blind her to all the terrible things he had done and was capable of—was she completely in denial? Or was this another angle, another smokescreen and mirror she used to alienate certain people from Simon's life?

"Do you get along with Lonnie?" I asked.

"Yes, but she won't call me back." Rocky took a drink from his glass.

"I am sure she's busy."

"Yes, well, she always gets ahold of me when she needs something. Do you like Sabra?"

"Sure, I guess."

"Keep your eye on that bitch. She fucked me over many times," he said with emotion.

I wondered if they had had a love affair go bad; he seemed so angry at her. Sabra had not done anything terrible to me. Lonnie disliked her. Phyllis didn't like her, either, but then she didn't like anyone, so that did not mean much. Jeez, Rocky had beef with almost everybody, or so it seemed. His guns were blazing; we were not on an African safari hunt, were we? It was clear that Rocky's decision to help me was inspired by more than the goodness of his heart. He wanted to counterattack Phyllis using me.

"So how did Simon ask you to help me?" I asked to change the subject to something positive.

"Remember when Simon called you about the hangar? He had you on speakerphone. I was with Simon. I heard everything you both said. Afterwards, he asked me to help you and the kids. He said he loves Trey, but at the same time, he hates him and can't trust him."

"Wait, he hung up on me during that conversation. I thought he was angry at me."

"He wants you to think that for Phyllis; it makes his life easier with her if he's on Trey's side." Rocky patted my knee.

"If he's so miserable, why doesn't he divorce her?"

Rocky took another sip of his drink.

"He says he's too old and sick. He says he'll lose everything he has worked for. He thinks she's cheating on him, too." Rocky pointed his finger at me while he continued to nurse his vodka tonic.

"What? He's worried about losing his money more than his life? Does he think he's going to take it all with him? I would choose freedom and peace over impermanent objects and crazy," I ignored the part about Phyllis's infidelity, even though I had heard it before. There was no proof, only gossip.

"He's scared."

"I know. I understand. So, you offered to help me. How?" I nervously looked away and scratched my head, anticipating his possible response.

"First, I need you to be a hundred percent honest when I ask you this question. Do you want Trey back?" Rocky put down his glass and looked squarely into my eyes. It was a staredown.

"Hell NO! First, there is the affair; then there is Phyllis's meddling and covering it up; then, if that weren't bad enough, there are the drugs. I don't have the desire or energy to clean up all those messes. Especially at the expense of the children."

"I get you. My fourth wife left me for my business partner." Rocky finished his glass of vodka.

"How many times have you been married?" I was trying not to judge, but I felt my eyes jump off my face.

"Seven times. Well... one of them I married twice. Simon likes to give me a hard time about that. One, the divorce lasted longer than the marriage. That was some real bullshit." Rocky poured my vodka into his glass.

Seven times? That was venturing into Elizabeth Taylor territory. I didn't know if I would survive this one divorce. How the hell was he still standing after seven? Talk about a man addicted to falling in love. Still looking for the one, always on the hunt, I supposed. Looking at him and the dead animal trophies on his walls, I concluded that it was the hunt he liked best, not the capture...not a capture with a pulse at least.

"We all kiss several toads before we find our prince. Or princess." I was pulling deep to sound encouraging. I had just met him; it was not like we were long-term friends. It felt like a safe thing to say, or maybe I had memorized too many nursery rhymes. I smiled sympathetically. On the flip side, I thought he must have the 411 on divorce attorneys, at least seven of them. I prayed silently, *thank you God for delivering me this expert. Amen.* I squeezed his arm.

Then he delivered this bombshell. "When Helga moved in next door, I knew something was wrong."

"What? What do you mean, moved in next door?" My body's emergency response system was triggered. I dove into high alert mode. It was like red flashing lights sounding an alarm inside my body: Warning, warning, emotional trauma ahead!

"Oh shit, I am sorry. I thought you knew," Rocky said, observing my reaction. "Helga lived at the Hamiltons' with Trey in November and December." He said this as if it were common knowledge. He re-offered vodka. I stared at him.

I felt paralyzed with disbelief. When I kicked Trey out of our house in October, he moved into his parent's house, and then Helga left her family to move into the Hamiltons' home with him? With all of them? All condoned by Phyllis the Great, the sophisticated lady who gave tens of thousands of dollars to charities, but attacked her own family at the deepest and most depraved levels? How could she and Trey do this to the kids and me, and with one of their employees? All the while, Phyllis had been acting so innocent and unaware of any of Trey's misdoings. "How long did she live there?" I asked. I took the vodka.

"I went over to dinner at Simon's a handful of times, and she was always there. One time, Trey's brother was in town, and she was like a member of the family, taking your spot. Everyone pretended it was normal. I knew something was up. That's when I confronted Simon about it, and all he said was that he missed seeing you." I took a gulp. I gagged again.

"And then what?" I walked to the bar. I dumped the vodka and rinsed the glass.

"Simon denied that anything was going on between Trey and Helga, but then he said he started paying closer attention. Now, he realizes Phyllis and Trey were lying to him. Simon pitched a fit. Helga moved out and into a Saint Mary's apartment. Next thing I know, Trey moved into the apartment with her. Simon felt awful, but he should have protected you. He's trying to make things right the only way he can, now."

I started to cry. Rocky sprung from the couch to comfort me. He handed me a red handkerchief out of his shirt pocket, and I snuffled, "I can't believe the lack of conscience. There are seven real children involved! That pagan priest even kept me from retaining legal counsel. The clergy's mission is supposed to protect me in this situation." I blotted my eyes. Rocky poured me a glass of water. "I know I need to get to a place of forgiveness, but they're making it exceedingly difficult. I guess I'll just have to write about it someday." I took a drink.

"I didn't think you had put all of that together." Rocky looked surprised.

I sat back down on the sofa, gently sobbing into his handkerchief.

"Hey, chin up. It's going to be a hard couple of years, but you'll be okay!" Rocky said, with hope in his voice. He put his hand on my shoulder. I thought, *What a nice man, wanting to help a lady out of a bad situation. He was a real cowboy.* "Let's focus on moving forward. Who do you recommend for an attorney?"

"Dakota Wallace. She's a bitch. I hate her." Rocky handed me the water glass.

"I am confused." I took another drink.

"She represented my ex-wife. She fleeced me. So I know she's good."

One killer's admiration for another, I supposed. "What's the name of the firm?"

"Wallace and Miller."

I called the firm and made an appointment for the following week. "I was worried you were going to say Kim Waters."

"Is that the attorney that fired you?"

I nodded. I put the water glass down.

"That's unethical. You know we call it pay-to-play? It's the real reason rich people give lots of money to charitable foundations. All those phony galas, buying prestige and power. Where does the money really go? Fake sons of bitches." Rocky pounded his fist on the coffee table.

"Yeah, totally." I pounded my fist too. But I'd never thought of giving as buying prestige or power. That must be for the six-figure donors. In this case, charity work for the Hamiltons had paid off big time. Hopefully, the money had reached some people in need, too. The way that priest was so greedy, I wondered. I asked, "Do you give money to charities?"

"Of course. I have seven ex-wives. Well, technically, six."

We both laughed. Rocky was so out there with his feelings and emotions; he didn't hold back much. Hardly the personality I had expected from the manliest man alive. He was incredibly refreshing. He may have been crass, inappropriate, and explosive, but he was being his authentic self at the moment, and that seemed to be a rare quality in this world of lies and deceit. "Any prenups?" I asked.

"Yes, but if you break a single stipulation, the entire thing is void. Some real bullshit. Wallace, that bitch," Rocky raised his voice, he seemed to be reliving a painful memory. His face soured.

I got into character as a sidekick cowboy companion. I raised my voice, "Yeah, there is a lot of bullshit flying around; that's for sure."

I left Rocky's house. On the way home, I wondered what the hell had just happened?

SPIRIT & SUSHI

CHAPTER 23

Today was the day I was to have lunch with Harry. I told my mom I was meeting a friend. I wore a green lululemon pullover, black leggings and white Nikes. I did not need her to think I had become a serial dater. The longer she stayed at my home, the more I felt like I had to report in with her. She was a tremendous help with the kids while I cycled in and out of traumatized states, but somehow, I had transcended into a subpar adult. Becoming a single mom was a huge life-shift.

I met Harry at the Blue Fin, a delicious sushi place in midtown. He was wearing a purple turtleneck and brown corduroy pants. We sat by the window. His blue eyes glimmered in the sunlight. We exchanged pleasantries, and I asked him how he'd been.

"Hanging in there. My wife's attorney is accusing me of being a deadbeat dad." Harry shuffled around in his seat.

"Attorneys make a living playing mind games." I unfolded my napkin and put it on my lap.

Harry smiled. It felt good being able to comfort someone going through the same uphill battle as me. "And how's the Nathaniel case going?"

"Slowly. I have a new attorney. Dakota Wallace, I hear she's tough."

"That's my wife's attorney," he said, irritated, but amused at the coincidence.

I laughed. "Jeez, small town!"

"I guess." He looked skeptically at me, as if I could be a double agent. Divorce and paranoia—there should be a documentary about it. A young Asian man wearing black pants and a white shirt approached, he poured us water and took our order. I ordered the sashimi. Harry ordered the Volcano roll. I looked him, "You know we are both going to get through this, right? We need faith. Do you go to church?"

"Sometimes." Harry unfolded his napkin and put it on his lap.

He looked put-off, like I was an enthusiastic Bible-thumper that was recruiting him for a conversion. "What about you?"

"I pray constantly. Right now, my circumstance is far worse than you can imagine. I am on the brink of losing everything. Some days, I have that peace that surpasses all understanding; some days, comedy gets me through; some days—the worst days—anger is my motivation. No matter what, I know the root is God. I know all of this is happening for a reason. I am being pushed out of a life that is no longer suited for me and into a better life. It's a hard push, but every day I wake up, and I say, 'God, let your will be done in my life, help me to know how best to serve you with my life.'"

"Really?" He took a sip of water.

"Joel Osteen says, 'God will give you double for your trouble if you stay in faith.'" I was surprised by how deeply the Christian channel had taken root in my inner dialogue.

Harry scooted his chair back, "I am not about the money. I want to see my child. My wife cheated, and now she's being unnecessarily cruel to me. She wants everything." Harry scooted his chair back to the table.

"Have you ever cheated on her?" Harry sat sideways; his voice became impassioned.

"She thought I did, one time. We were at a cabin with friends; it doesn't matter. It didn't happen." Harry looked away.

Suddenly, I felt there was more to this story. But I knew it was not my place to judge him; I didn't know the truth of their relationship. All I knew was what was right in front of me. He was hurting, and there was a vulnerability about him that I found so endearing. "Harry, it's okay; we don't have to talk about it. She won't be able to keep you from being a father. She's probably using it as some sort of psychological warfare, but not even she wants that for her child. I can tell you that as a mother whose children have been abandoned by their father." I unwrapped my chopsticks.

"How's Trey?"

"Terrible." I poured soy sauce in a small dish.

I spotted the waiter coming slowly towards us with our food. I could smell it before it arrived at the table. Suddenly I was very hungry, like a ravenous lioness who had been starving for days on the African savannah. Before Rocky shot it to death, that is. The waiter set the sashimi in front of me. I told Harry about Simon's accident and Maggie's upcoming first communion. "I worry that'll be a disaster."

"Simon's in the hospital? I hadn't heard." Harry straightened his chair.

We finished lunch and exchanged goodbyes.

I decided I had time to stop by the hospital. Simon was sitting up in bed, surrounded by pillows, his leg propped for comfort. The room was full of people. Dr. Stella, Lonnie, Aunt Denali, Uncle Peter, Jacob, Rocky, and other friends crowded around him. He was beaming with joy. For a moment I wondered if we were at a birthday party? I found it delightfully amusing how he received his visitors one-by-one like the Godfather.

I said a silent prayer of gratitude, "Thank you, God, for giving Simon this moment."

"I can leave tomorrow," he said, spotting me. "I'll have to continue with physical therapy, of course." He seemed enthusiastic and positive about making a full recovery.

"That's great news." I wanted to match his positive outlook, but I felt he was safer in the hospital than at home.

Aunt Denali approached me, full of intent. She whispered, "Phyllis is on her way from the airport; she should be arriving any minute. She's only communicating with Peter. She hasn't texted anyone else back."

"Maybe it's guilt." I looked at Peter. He nodded his head.

Unaware that Rocky had sidled up next to me, I heard, "We'll know when she arrives."

I was startled, where had he come from? Was he eavesdropping? He smiled at me while clasping his golden belt buckle. My defense went down.

All of Rocky's masculine energy gave me a newfound sense of security. I decided to stay in the room.

"Have you seen Trey?" Aunt Denali asked. I shook my head.

"I wonder what he stole from Simon to fund this latest binge?" Rocky hiked up his pants. "I know people who can take care of him."

"I am sure you do. You have thousands of heads mounted on your walls," I said to make him feel proud of himself for all the killing he had done, when in reality, I found it completely disturbing. Rocky smiled, flattered.

And then, Phyllis walked in. She was dressed as if she had been plucked off Rodeo Drive. Everyone stared at her. An awkward silence drifted through the air. Simon's whole body was infused with excitement. He loved her madly; through all the insanity and drama, he loved that Phyllis.

She walked to him, leaned down to give him a hug, attempting to crack a joke. "What am I going to do with you? I can't leave you alone for a minute." She snickered.

No one laughed. Just dead air and looks of judgment.

A petite Asian lady barged in, pushing Phyllis to the side. She was crying and had bags of food in Styrofoam containers in her hands. She was wearing black pants and a white shirt—a server's uniform. I recognized her from Little Toyko, Simon's favorite Asian restaurant. She was frequently our waitress. She gave Simon a hug and a kiss on the cheek, sobbing. "I bought this for you! I bought this for you!" She put the food on his bed tray.

"Thank you, Chi," Simon said with a loving look.

"Goodbye, now. Goodbye," She gave him a hug. She left, still sobbing, as abruptly as she had come. We all continued to stare. For a moment, it felt like these two ladies were playing tug a war with Simon's heart. Denali whispered in my ear, "Why couldn't he have found a nice lady like that?"

Phyllis's face scrunched; she clenched her fist. Something about Chi's presence had turned giggly Phyllis into angry Phyllis. She was unhinged by the mirror Chi unwittingly held up to her face. She ground her teeth like an agitated chihuahua.

"Well, I'll leave so you can all continue to talk about me," Phyllis yelled at everyone in the room and stomped out. We all looked around at each other, not knowing what to do. Were Chi and Simon romantic; was this his secret lover?

Simon went from complete elation to shrieking despair in a matter of seconds. He wilted like a dehydrated flower, right before my eyes. Rocky handed him a bottle of water. "Hey buddy, I got something for you."

Simon sadly took a sip. His expression loosened into a smirk. "Thanks. You're a real Navy Seal." Rocky continued to engage Simon.

Aunt Denali and I exchanged looks. She whispered in my ear, "It's alcohol."

"What? That's crazy! He's on all these medications!" I whispered back. Then I remembered the "old drinking buddies" comment. I glared at them.

"What should we do," I asked her.

"I'll tell Peter. I am not doing anything."

"Okay, well, I am going to talk to Rocky about this." I folded my arms across my chest.

Uncle Peter approached us. He handed his phone to Aunt Denali. Aunt Denali paused and then handed the phone to me.

It was a screenshot from Phyllis to Lonnie.

"Lonnie, I am moving out of the house. You can move in and take care of YOUR father," Phyllis texted.

"No, calm down. We will all take care of him, together," Lonnie texted.

FEEDING THE SHARKS

CHAPTER 24

"You look lovely," Brad said as he sat down in the car.

I was wearing a white sundress with white sandals. Typically, I would not wear this color around the children, for fear of them destroying it with snot or peanut butter. I felt special wearing all white on this glorious spring day. Flower baskets with irises and peonies and huge planters of different floral arrangements aligned the airport arrivals station.

Brad was freshly tanned from the California sun; he was wearing a mint green polo shirt and khakis, with white Van shoes. Once again, I talked myself out of the desire to give him a fresh wardrobe makeover. It was hard.

"Thank you, where's our destination?"

"I am staying at the Dimond Center Hotel, but we should go to dinner first." Brad kissed me on the cheek.

"I don't know. I don't want people to see us together. I am not divorced yet." I directed my eyes toward the road.

"Who cares? It's only dinner."

"Fine."

I pulled into Chili's, which was located right next to Brad's hotel. A kindly hostess showed us our booth. I smelled all the food around me and felt ravenous again. I could not decide which smell I wanted to eat first—the fried cheese, the jalapeno bites, the BBQ ribs. I could not remember my last meal. It was one thing to feel hunger in your stomach, like a knot turning tighter and tighter, and it was another to feel an intense, primal need to consume enormous amounts of food by the fist-full.

Our table was equipped with an ordering tablet. I looked through the options with a finger swipe. The nachos looked crunchy and delicious. Irresistible. I definitely needed the nachos, ASAP. I ordered them.

We attempted to make small talk. It felt painful and awkward, despite the fact we had seen each other naked. This relationship was happening in reverse. Our red-hot chemistry seemed to overpower our ability to connect with each other in the simplest of ways. Silence and awkward looks ensued for several minutes. Finally, Brad picked up the tablet "These things are going to put waitstaff out of work."

"No way. Restaurants will always need people for the human interaction of being waited on and catered to. It's like how everyone said reading tablets were going to destroy paper books and bookstores. Yada yada yada. People like the experience of a bookstore—it's charming."

"You're wrong," Brad said, setting the tablet back down on the table. "It's all about money and efficiency. One day, robots will be taking your order."

I became offended. I felt like he was attacking me personally. At St. Mary's, the children and I didn't align with Phyllis's master plan to manage the Center, so we were thrown away, much like these robots who would replace restaurant servers. Brad seemed cold and callous. If these people were to be displaced, what would happen to them? "People aren't replaceable! Good manners, a smiling face, a 'How was your day?' cannot be replaced by a robot for money and efficiency. People have a value higher than any value assigned to a robot." I glared at him as if his opinion was a personal attack.

A waiter approached us with water and menus.

"Thank you," I smiled. We both opened our plastic-coated menus.

"Do you want an appetizer?" Brad asked me.

"I ordered nachos from the tablet" I looked away from him.

He laughed. "Soon, you will have a driverless car. Brick and mortar stores are closing all over the country. All shopping will be done online and delivered by drones." He blinked his eyes at me to reiterate his point. He was a know-it-all. He picked up the tablet and handed it to me. "Look at all these options, instant gratification. You ordered the nachos?" He continued to delight in his own banter.

"I disagree, Brad." I put the tablet down, ignoring him. "I like going shopping with girlfriends, trying on dresses, looking at trinkets and shoes, being able to touch them and visualize in person their use for me or others. It's fun, and that's what women do."

Brad winked at me. "Yes, well in the future, there will be fewer options to choose from, less variety of clothing, and fewer stores. The middle class is shrinking. Soon it will be the very rich, the job creators, while everyone else lives off the dole. More monopolies concentrated into the hands of the few, and less competition. Far less people too." He ran his fingers through his hair and straightened his posture.

"Darwin was a glass half empty kind of guy. The world works more in cooperation than competition. You can say some people become more authentically spiritual, or they become more authentically greedy as time passes by. Either way, death is inevitable. Storing up treasures isn't going to buy you one day longer on Earth." I glared at him. "That's the balance humanity has to find. For myself, I choose to focus on creation, freedom and cooperation. What about you?" I pushed my back into the booth, waiting for him to retaliate.

"Are you kidding? It's a jungle out there. I am simply a humble job creator. I take care of my people. I also have millions of dollars of real estate, from hard work." he said, presumably to impress me.

"I am sure you're debt-free, too," I fluttered my eyes at him.

"I didn't say that!" Brad's eyes bulged. I could see him, Ebenezer counting his pennies.

We both laughed out loud.

"How is everything else going for you?" I asked Brad.

"Everything is fine," Brad sternly implied.

"How about you, Faith?" His tone softened to lover boy, as he reached for my hand.

The life coach had jumped forward. It must be his safe space with me. He wanted to know everything about me without revealing anything real about himself; it felt deceptive.

I played along. What did I have to lose? "I am looking forward to Maggie's first communion. She's my angel. What about you? Do you still want children?"

"Yes, I want children. I've always wanted children. That's why I have to date younger women," he said, like it was a heavy burden to bear, dating all those younger women...

"Such a punishment for you. Would you not consider dating someone your own age?" I raised my eyebrows at him and took a sip of water.

"No, but I would take them to lunch." He ran his fingers through his hair again.

I suspected his refusal to date a woman his own age was an artificial barrier he created to avoid having a real, committed relationship. Or maybe he was sterile and too embarrassed to tell me.

The nachos arrived, and the human waiter placed them in front of me. I took in every smell, the cheese, the meat, the beans, the lettuce—yes, lettuce has an odor—the jalapenos... I think it was the best smell I had ever encountered. I briefly considered making a nacho perfume to wear.

I forgot Brad existed. I began to scarf them down like a wild hyena who had been hunting for days. Coming up for air at last, I saw Brad looking at me with an expression that reminded me of somebody observing President Bush's shock and awe campaign. Just then, a beloved nacho fell, and salsa slipped into my lap.

"Dammit, I got salsa on my dress," I said, watching the red stain penetrate the whiteness of the linen. My mouth fell open. I looked at him, upset.

"We can always order extra salsa, you know?" He looked disturbed. "You should take it easy. I've noticed you've put on a little weight." Brad said to me as a life coach, or as a man wanting to be murdered. I could not figure out which one.

"I noticed your hair is gray," I shot back, "and I don't like it. Pass the pepper, lose the salt, that's what I say." I stuffed more nachos in my mouth.

"I like natural."

"I like natural, but I also like Botox. I have a pretty deep frown line in-between my eyes. I don't want to walk around looking like an angry bird. So I get my frown line injected once a year to look... robotic." I smirked. "You got a problem with that?"

"No, but you don't need it. You're a natural beauty," he said, giving me the love-look.

I had cheese sauce dripping down my chin. I grabbed a napkin from the napkin bin. I wiped my face. I looked back into his eyes. Sure, a natural, fat beauty. "Gee, thanks, honey."

The next morning, I gave Brad a kiss goodbye and bid him safe travels home. It was an important day for me. I was meeting Dakota Wallace, the woman that out-killed Rocky—a mighty feat. I wore light blue jeans, and a honey colored fleece. I gathered all my documents, including the crayon letter, and recordings. This time I left the enemas. I was thankful I'd had the foresight to record everything. This story was too bizarre to be believed person to person. It seemed whenever I thought we had hit rock bottom, a new level of depravity emerged. I decided to call Rocky for moral support.

"Hello, darling," he answered the phone in southern.

"I am on my way to Dakota's office. I need a pep talk. I am super nervous."

"That bitch." I heard something drop over the phone. "Don't worry. You'll be fine; everything will be easy today. It's only talking. The worst part is the waiting. Everything happens slowly in the judicial system."

I found his words comforting but negative.

Dakota's office was a small blue historic building located downtown. The outside was decorated with newly sprouted purple lupine and a garden gnome sun tanning, wearing swimming trunks. I opened the front door to bells jingling. A golden retriever greeted me along with a strong, athletic-looking woman. She had dark hair and was wearing an indigo dress with green leggings. Her demeanor was business, but her outfit was fashionista. She smiled. "You must be Faith. Welcome. My name is Porsha, this is Bella. Can I get you anything to drink?" I patted the dog on the head.

"No, thank you," I said as I sat down on a wooden armchair that was at least four hundred years old. I sat long enough to feel inadequately dressed in jeans. I should have dressed with some flare, a cheetah print? Now, I not only felt like a loser, but I also looked like one.

After several minutes, Porsha took me into a small room. I lagged behind her, a little humble and a little fearful. There was a desk in the middle of the room and a picture of a shark on the wall. I stared at the shark, suspended in time. It was a sign from the heavens. But was it good or bad?

"You can sit down on that side of the desk if you like. Are you sure you don't want any coffee or water?"

"Yes, please. Coffee with cream and two sugars, thank you."

I sat and waited and sat and waited. I felt like I was at the DMV. Time was passing ever so slowly. I was anxious. Finally, after a whole eight minutes, Porsha returned with my coffee. I drank it all in one shot, like I was at a country bar, downing whiskey. But there was no boot, scoot, and boogie; there was only fear, anxiety, and the unknown.

Finally, a tall, magnificently powerful woman walked into the room. She was such a badass she no longer dressed for clients, she was wearing jeans and an "I Love Hawaii" t-shirt. She had short, dark hair, and her aura was, "Let's cut the shit." She grabbed a box of tissues off another table in the room and slid them toward me on auto-pilot.

My aura must have been "Weepy bitch." She sat down on the opposite side of the table. She looked like she could be firm. I liked it, but I was also scared she would be mean to me.

"I am Dakota. Here are some tissues, in case you need them." She pointed to the box, as if I had failed to miss her sliding them towards me seconds earlier. Perhaps this was the best she could do for emotional support. After all, she managed people's feelings and emotions for a living. I am sure over the years, she had become burnt-out. Dakota opened a folder, and clicked her pen, preparing to write something. "Let's get started. What's the story?"

I looked up at the picture of the shark on her wall and swallowed. "My husband of eleven years has been having an affair; we have two children—one is four, one is seven. Trey was working at his parents' drug and alcohol rehabilitation center, but he has lost his job and is now using drugs." I burst into tears. I grabbed the tissue box.

She nodded her head. "I am sorry. We can't do anything about infidelity, but the drugs are bad. Do you have proof?"

I showed her my zip drives and told her about the recordings and the phone texts. "They date back to October. Also, I have witnesses, including some of his own family members. Not his mother. She moved his married girlfriend into her house, and has also been covering up the drug abuse." I blew my nose.

"Wow!" She said flatly, I could tell she had heard worse. "Good job being prepared."

"If you have got them by the balls, their hearts and minds will follow." I quoted Brad.

She smirked and re-scooted her chair to the table. "John Wayne, huh? Which Center? I haven't heard of someone owning a private Rehabilitation Center." She looked wild-eyed around the room.

"St. Mary's. His mother works there, too, along with his married girlfriend, the one she moved into her house. She even got them a condo to live in through St. Mary's after the affair was well known. Other employees told me that and the landlord of the building they rent the apartments from."

Dakota rubbed her chin, "You could have a case for alienation of affection."

"What's that?" I looked curiously at her.

"It's when you can prove a third party is responsible for the malicious and willful interference with the relationship between and husband and wife. It could be adultery of some other act that deprives the affection of a spouse." Dakota started taking notes.

"Oh, well clearly, his mother, the Center as an entity, not sure I want to sue Helga, the other woman. She has children and health issues." I tried to see what she was writing.

"We can talk about that later. What do you want from the divorce?" She made eye contact.

"I want full custody of my children. I don't want them around any substance abusers. I want my house and my kids to stay at their school. Nothing that spectacular." I began to fidget with my foot underneath the table.

"Here is a checklist of everything I need to get going on your divorce. Including ten K," Dakota said, handing me a folder similar to the one Kim gave me.

"Yikes!" My brow furrowed.

"That's only the retainer; it could be more or less, depending on your case." Dakota looked at me like, *Are you going pay or what?*

"I'll have it to you by the end of the week, but what happens after that?" I felt like a helpless kitten, shivering in the rain, purring for a blanket.

"I'll have him served with divorce papers, he will respond, then we go to court unless she wants to settle," she said, like duh! She stood up to leave. I stood up, too.

"She?" I looked at her perplexed, like she hadn't been listening at all. I wasn't divorcing a woman, was I? Dakota took a stride toward the door.

"What about after that?" I said, trying to re-engage her.

She turned her back to me. "He will have a timeline to respond. If he doesn't respond, then the judge will make a decision."

"What if he does respond?" I gathered the folder in my arms.

"Then, the judge will set a court date."

"He is on drugs, so he may not respond at all, right?" I asked her like she could predict the future.

"One step at a time." She paced toward the door.

"Thank you for your help," I said after her, looking at the shark on the wall.

I fishtailed it out of there. I felt slightly better, like I was finally making progress. At least, I had some sort of path, direction, Jaws... My phone dinged. Brad.

Brad: *Is everything alright?*

Me: *Yes, honey bunny. I met with a new attorney, and I think she's the one.*

Brad: *Glad to hear it. Let me know if you need any money.*

Gee, Brad was so amazing. He just offered to pay for my attorney. Maybe I had been hard on him. Maybe I judged him unfairly. Maybe I needed a new barometer to judge men, and I was simply a bitter, expecting the worst, old sour pus, damaged goods.

Me: *Okay, thank you. How is your flight?*

Brad: *Taking off now. Love you.*

Me: *Love you*

I drove home. I texted Rocky.

Me: *I need $10,000 as a retainer*

Rocky: *Done. I'll have a cashier's check ready for you when you come over tonight.*

I could not believe my good fortune. Rocky was like a cowboy sent from heaven.

At home, my mom was sitting in the family room, still wearing pajamas, and watching some British show on Netflix. As time passed, she had become less sad and increasingly detached. "How did it go?" She flipped through a Martha Stewart magazine.

"Good, I guess. Rocky is going to give me ten thousand dollars for an attorney. Simon asked Rocky to help me." I blurted it out without thinking.

"Now, who is Rocky? Mom seemed irritated and unamused. She slammed the magazine down, like I was yanking her chain.

"Simon's BFF. They're neighbors." I felt like I had to sell Rocky to her.

"Do you trust him?" She asked as she turned down the volume on the TV.

"I don't trust anyone. But as time goes on, I realize I have less and less to lose. Or perhaps my belief system is changing, and I care less and less." I shrugged my shoulders. "I am starving." I opened the pantry door.

"I made some pancakes this morning for the kids. Do you want some?" Mom stood up. She took the pancake batter out of the fridge.

"I feel like I can't eat enough." I sat down at the kitchen bar, emotionally spent.

"You're stress-eating. It's a terrible habit; you got it from me." She turned on the stove.

"Great! The same year I lose my marriage, I get fat!" I put my head down.

"What are you doing about Maggie's first communion this weekend?" She sprayed a frying pan with PAM.

"I arranged for family photos beforehand. I invited Trey and his parents to join us, if Simon is able."

"It's your choice if they come or not," Mom poured the batter on the pan.

"It'll be our last family photo together, if he even comes. I'll text him." I pulled out my phone.

Me: *How's Simon?*

Trey: *He's good. My mom and I are going to pick him up today.*

Me: *Praise God! I wanted to remind you of Maggie's first communion is on Sunday. She would love to see all of you there, if possible. I understand Simon had surgery.*

Trey: I would not miss it for anything.

Me: Good, let's meet for family photos, one hour before the Church service.

Trey: I'll be there.

I put my phone down. I looked up at mother, who was flipping pancakes.

"Mom, Trey says he's coming to first communion and is even going to meet us for family photos beforehand. His parents might come. I am going to invite Aunt Denali and Uncle Peter, too." I felt hopeful that Maggie would have her dad there; she missed him.

Mom muttered under her breath, "Nothing but another shit show."

"What?" I asked her innocently.

"Oh, nothing. I like this British show." She pointed at the tv from the kitchen.

I ate until 3:00 p.m., then drove to St. Joseph's to pick up the kids. Their smiles made my heart sing. They were so innocent, unburdened, so full of joy. Children are our greatest teachers. For a moment, I forgot about all the chaos.

"I want to see Grandma," Alex said, tying the shoelace of his black Nikes.

"Today, we're going to see Rocky," I told him. "He's one of Papa Simon's best friends. He also has a big puppy dog named Chuck."

"I love dogs!" Maggie squealed from the backseat.

"Can we keep him?" Alex asked.

"That's funny," I said and laughed along.

On the way to Rocky's house, I told the kids all about Chuck and tried to prepare them for Rocky's animal trophies. They were giggling with enthusiasm to meet both of them. I knocked on the door, using the iron doorknocker. The kids stood anxiously by. Chuck barked loudly on the other side. Rocky opened, and Chuck rushed the kids. He jumped on Alex and knocked him to the ground. Alex looked annoyed.

"Chuck, damn it! Get your ass back in the house," Rocky yelled, grabbing Chuck by the collar. He helped Alex up.

Maggie looked up at Rocky. "You owe me two dollars for my swear jar."

Rocky snickered. He pulled out a money clip and handed her $10.

"I like to pay in advance."

"Wow! Thank you." Maggie smiled as she took her shoes off.

"Stupid Chuck," Alex said, brushing himself off.

Rocky said, "Hey, Maggie and Alex, you can call me Uncle Rocky. Welcome to my home. Chuck is kid friendly; he gets so tickled." Rocky smiled at the children and closed the door behind them.

"I like Chuck. Where are his toys?" Maggie asked.

"Wow, look at all the animals, Maggie. Uncle Rocky, are you a veterinarian?" Alex asked, pointing at all the carcasses.

Rocky laughed. "No, Alex, your Uncle Rocky is a killer. Maggie, the toys are in the corner by his bed, downstairs. Why don't you take Chuck down there to play?" Alex froze with a blank look on his face. "Where are the toys? Downstairs?" Maggie asked. Rocky nodded. She began to walk down the stairs. Alex followed.

I said after them, "Wait, kids, Uncle Rocky is not a killer. He is a nice man, and Papa Simon's best friend." Chuck straddled my leg for a friendly, dog-humping hello. I pushed him away. Maggie, oblivious, squeaked a toy at him. "Chuck, come here." "I don't like him," Alex said, looking at Chuck.

Uncle Rocky yelled, "Chuck, get your ass downstairs." Chuck buckled down the stairs like his life depended on it. Maggie and Alex ran after him, leaving me wondering what psychological damage Uncle Rocky had imprinted on their malleable brains.

Uncle Rocky grabbed my hand and led me into the kitchen. I sat at the bar on one of his cognac leather barstools. He offered me a drink; I declined. He poured himself a straight vodka with a splash of tonic, then came around and sat next to me.

"You know, Faith, I like kids. I have two. One's about your age."

"They're such a blessing," I hummed in agreement. I put my elbows on the bar.

"Alex, he's a good-looking boy. He's going to need a strong male role model to keep him straight. He could get into a lot of trouble without someone like me to guide him," Rocky spun on the stool and gave an alluring look. I looked away.

"They both do. Sadly, Trey is not the role-model type, unless your future plans include a stint in the pen." I giggled at my cleverness.

I admired Rocky's hands-on approach, helping the children and me out, but I began to wonder if gracious old Uncle Rocky had ulterior motives. He handed me an envelope. We made eye contact.

"Here's your money. Pay Dakota tomorrow. I am ready for you to be divorced," Rocky said, claiming his prize, me, with sweet victory.

I felt a flutter in my heart, but not from cupid's arrow. My high emergency response system skyrocketed. I had not foreseen things unfolding this way. My brain screamed *Deflect! Deflect! Deflect!* "Me too," I said casually. "I can't wait to be divorced. So, did you give Simon alcohol the other day after Phyllis left?" I made my voice harsh and full of judgment, trying to change the energy of the room.

"That son-of-a-bitch, he texts me all the time to bring him vodka. I am only being there for him, trying to help ease his pain." Rocky threw his hands in the air and took a drink.

So Rocky had been enabling Simon? "You don't know what kind of medication he has in his system. It could be a toxic mix and kill him."

"How long do you think he has left? I don't think rehab is in his future. His life is hell. If I can bring him comfort, I am going to, and that's the damn truth. No sassy little lady is going to tell me otherwise." Rocky shook his finger at me.

"I understand where you're coming from, I do, but they already have a small pharmacy in their house, and he's coming home today. If I were you, I would not want to be responsible for any other medical emergencies." I felt like I was lecturing him.

"I heard about that. People are talking."

"I am worried about all of them. I pray it'll all be okay… over time."

"You know, if you lose your house, there's plenty of room for you and the kids to move in here. They won't even have to change schools. I could take care of all of you. We could travel the world together." Rocky twisted his stool to face me.

"Oh, wow, what a great offer." I twisted my stool away from him. "I am hyper-focused on getting divorced. One step at a time. I can't even begin to imagine all the healing I need to do—probably years of therapy," I said, nodding my head in fake despair.

"You'll be fine with a strong man by your side," Rocky said and scooted his barstool even closer to mine. He went in for a kiss. I ducked. He kissed my neck. I thought, *Lord, have mercy.* He was a fast old bird; he swiveled around and tried it again.

I stood up and mustered a fake tear in one eye; it slowly jotted down my cheek like a slow-moving avalanche. I manifested a weepy-looking expression. "I can't do this; you're moving too fast. I am overwhelmed."

So much for the honorable cowboy galloping in on a white horse, looking to save a damsel in distress. Who would take advantage of someone at their lowest point like this? Only a killer who hides behind high-powered weapons to mow down unsuspecting animals.

He saw the one tear roll down my neck. "You're a smart one, aren't you?"

"I don't know what that means," I said, playing dumb. Ugh! Uncle Rocky was savvy, but what was he going to do? Press a crying girl for a kiss? I had thought Brad was a smooth operator, but he had nothing on Rocky. Was everyone trying to buy my soul? Even people who were pretending to want to help me! I don't think this was what Simon had had in mind when he asked Rocky to support the covert "Rescue Faith" mission. I was profoundly deflated by this turn of events, but what was a girl to do? I had to play the hand I was dealt, so I had to keep Rocky as a friend. But first, I had to find a way to put this rascal on a leash.

"I think I should leave. I have a great deal to think about." I walked to the stairs to call Alex and Maggie.

"Wait a minute." Rocky followed behind me. He grabbed my arm. "I am sorry; you're so beautiful, I got carried away." He gave me a lusty look and puckered up his lips.

I thought, Liar—you planned this all along. I pulled away from him, "Maggie, Alex, we have got to go." I turned to him and said, "I forgive you. You must understand I am not ready to date anyone, seriously. I am delicate." I pretended to wipe another tear from my eye. "My life is falling apart. I go to church and pray for God's healing and his direction in my life. In fact, Maggie's first communion is on Sunday. Would you like to come?" I zipped my jacket all the way up to my neck.

He took a step away from me. "Now, you know that me helping you is a secret. I can't go to Maggie's communion."

"Why not?" I pressed him for an answer, hoping to find a weakness in his armor.

"Phyllis can't find out I am helping you." Rocky walked back toward the bar.

"Who cares? You said she already hates you."

"I am on the Board at Saint Mary's." He took another sip, his back faced me.

"What? You're a board member?" What a double agent. Trying to milk both sides for all they were worth. A power play for him, wedging himself right in the middle, gathering valuable insight and knowledge, then using all the information to divulge as it fit his agenda. Like Lonnie. Fucker.

On the other hand, he did genuinely seem to despise Phyllis. I did not know what was going on. I was stumped. I went back and forth, assessing his guilt.

"The Center is in chaos. It's a mess. Financially, too. Phyllis schedules board meetings around her hair appointments. The CEO told our lobbyist that she isn't being paid to babysit Phyllis. She's on the verge of quitting. It is like a soap opera; I love it," Rocky said, laughing. He turned to me to share a smile.

"Well, I am disappointed you can't make it to Maggie's first communion," I said, stone-faced. "Maggie, Alex, let's go now!"

"Why are you leaving so soon?"

I looked at my phone. "I have to take Alex to soccer," I said, trying to look inconvenienced and sad over my abrupt departure. I called the kids, again. They walked up the stairs.

"Uncle Rocky, Chuck peed on the rug," Alex said. "Please don't stuff him."

Rocky looked mad. He stomped pass Alex and down the stairs.

On the way home, I reflected on what had happened. I surmised that Uncle Rocky was in his seventies and looking for a trophy wife to mount on his wall for his geezer friends to ooh and aah over. All while pissing off Phyllis—a double win for him.

It seemed everyone had their own agenda. Most were looking for money, some were looking for love, some wanted sex, others wanted drugs. I only wanted to keep my kids safe and get away from crazy people. Should have been simple, right?

THE CUPID SHUFFLE

CHAPTER 25

I was in my bedroom, getting dressed for Maggie's first communion. I was wearing a nude dress with low heels. My dark hair was pulled back in a French twist. I was feeling sentimental about the kids. I sat down on the tufted bench by the beveled windows. I saw something sticking out from underneath the bed. I reached down to pick it up. It was a picture of Trey and the kids in Disney Land's Toontown. Alex was a baby, barely walking. Maggie was on Trey's shoulders wearing a Princess Ariel costume. We looked so happy. I sniffled. I texted Trey with a slightness of hope that things could still turn around.

Me: *Hi, how are you? Are you going to be able to meet us at the church for family photos?*

Trey: *Yes. What should I wear?*

Me: *A nice, clean, suit.*

Suddenly, I felt an uneasiness flood the pit of my stomach.

"Mom zip my dress up," Maggie yelled from the hallway. She looked nervous.

I walked over to her. She wore a puffy sleeveless white dress, replete with a veil, satin gloves, and a diamond cross necklace her grandma Phyllis had given her. She was beautiful and the epitome of purity from head to toe. She warmed my heart. Alex was wearing a grey suit and a bright red bow tie. He was chewing a wad of turquoise gum three sizes too big for his mouth. Grandma Kate looked well put together in a green ladies coat and plaid pants. She also looked weary. We drove in silence to the church.

I turned on the Christian Sirius Channel for support and comfort. The pastor declared, "All is well in the Kingdom of the Lord." I felt better, believing sacred spaces were impenetrable by evil.

In St. Joseph's, a line had formed for family photos. I grabbed a program. I got in the line while the kids roamed around the church with Grandma Kate and their friends. Trey was nowhere in sight.

Me: *Where are you?*

Trey: *Coming.*

In Trey-time, "coming" could be five minutes, thirty minutes, or two days. We were nearly to the front of the line, and he had still not arrived. How humiliating it would be to take a single-mom family photo in front of the PTO moms. My eyes darted around the room as I concocted Trey's alibi. What would I tell them? He is busy at the Center? Taking care of Simon? Had the flu? I felt anxious.

"Faith, how have you been? Where is Trey? Is everything okay?"

I felt the judgement of a PTO mom. My back stiffened. I turned around, it was last year's President. I swallowed—"Ugh" My phone beeped.

Trey: *I am here; where are you?*

Relief! Trey was actually in the building. What a miracle. All is well in the Kingdom of the Lord. He had made it. I felt hopeful things would turn out well.

Me: *Downstairs, by the gym.*

"We are great. Trey is on his way now. I hope all is well with you. Thanks for asking." I walked to the other side of the room.

Trey walked through the doors as the photographer announced that we were next in line. His brown suit looked clean, and I could tell he had bathed. So far, so good. Then, he leaned in for a kiss. This was unusual, as Trey was not one for public displays of affection. How strange and sweet; then I recalled how he had lived at his parents' house with his married girlfriend, and I got angry. He had not been punished for that yet.

I dodged his kiss and glared at him. He put his arm around my shoulder. I elbowed him and whispered, "Don't fuck this up."

He stepped away from me, startled, with a sneer on his face. He started walking toward the exit. Mom began walking toward us with the kids.

I panicked. I had gone too far. I smiled at him, gently, trying to coax him back into participation mode. "Trey, it's our turn. You can't leave yet."

"I left something in the car. I'll be right back." He looked pissed.

Maggie rushed up to him and hugged his waist. "Daddy, can I go with you?"

"Look at my gum? Four pieces." Alex opened his mouth as wide as possible.

Trey glanced at Alex and then looked at Maggie, "No, stay with your mother." He stomped out of the room.

I didn't think he would "be right back." I had blown-up the family photo by not going along with his attempt at fake affection. I should have dealt with his advances and had the photo taken. Anger bubbled inside me for losing control of this situation. After all, it was Maggie's day. Mom stood pensive in the corner, holding Alex's hand.

The petite blond photographer dressed all in black approached us, "I am sorry, but we are on a schedule."

"Can we trade places with someone? We can go last if we have to."

"Sure." The photog nodded and walked off.

I second-guessed my sanity, signing up for family photos. I should have known that things could not possibly run smoothly. Was I self-sabotaging, or was I simply in denial? Maggie was all dolled up, but her eyes were full of sadness. Trey had not spent any time with her. To her, I was the lamest mom, and he was the coolest dad. She loved him so much. Trey had all the power to do great harm or great good in her life, in her soul, in her present moment. He just didn't get it.

"Come here Maggie; let me straighten your headpiece," I said. She smiled, and I made a pretense of righting her veil.

"Nathaniel," the photographer said again. "I can't stay here all day."

Trey barreled in.

"There you are! We were waiting on you. It's our turn," I said nicely, trying to get Trey to rally.

He looked fuddled. His face was red; his eyes were bloodshot, and he smelled like a toxic blend of ammonia and baby powder. He was high. He had gone to the parking lot to get high. He was high in our family's church. WTF?

Trey clumsily followed the photographer's directions to his place, breezing by me. I could practically hear him thinking, 'Fuck you, yes, I am high. Whatcha gonna do 'bout it?'

I smiled awkwardly, like this was normal, and nothing strange was happening. I told myself *All is well in the kingdom of the Lord.* The photographer posed us for the picture. She put Alex in front of Trey. Trey began laughing hysterically. Then Alex began laughing with him; it appeared to be an inside joke. I thought that's odd, but it was a celebratory day, it's okay to laugh obnoxiously, right?

"What's so funny?" the photographer asked. She was a serious artist and was not amused. She looked like she wanted to say, I am not here to babysit you damn fools. "One, two, three, smile," she said, over and over again."Maggie, turn slightly to the left. Mom, turn slightly to the right. Alex, step forward."

Alex stood still and Trey stepped forward, and there was a loud crash. Trey or Alex had tripped and both had fallen. Alex started coughing, he was choking on the gum. He was snort laughing. I pulled him up. Before I could initiate the Heimlich, he hawked the gum on the floor. Trey saw the gum fly through the air and began to laugh this otherworldly noise deep from his gut; it sounded like a cat being strangled. Everyone within a hundred feet stopped and stared at us. I looked around and chuckled as if to say, 'All is well in the Kingdom of the Lord.' I grabbed Trey's arm to pull him up. Alex grabbed his gum and popped it back into his mouth before I could stop him. I started laughing too, so people would think we were just a kooky clan.

"Alex, go spit the gum out, please." I patted him on the back. He shook his head "no."

"Are you okay?" the photographer asked.

My mom was glaring at me, as if to say, 'Told you so.'

Trey was down, but he seemed jolly. He pushed me aside and jumped up with renewed energy. "I am fine," he said and straightened his suit jacket. We started the shoot again.

The photographer stopped, "Can the boy get rid of his gum, please?" Mom walked over with a tissue to Alex, "spit."

Alex shook his head "no" and gave her the stare down.

I whispered in his ear. "No video games when we get home." He spit the gum out.

Trey grabbed my hand.

I elbowed him. "Don't touch me," I whispered curtly.

"Mom, Dad, move closer," the photographer said. I took a tiny step toward him.

"Closer, please," she said again, rolling her eyes. Trey pulled me to him by the waist. I grinned and endured it. I told myself, *This is Maggie's day; this is Maggie's day; this is Maggie's day.*

She snapped one last photo. "Dismissed," she called out. We dispersed.

I said a prayer. "Thank you, God, that the family photoshoot from hell is over. Amen." Trey walked toward the exit. "Trey, where are you going?"

"I have to go get my mom and Simon." He shouted for all to hear as he kept his pace towards the parking lot.

I walked briskly after him and lowered my voice, "Can you drive? The ceremony is beginning any minute."

He shrugged his shoulders and scurried up the stairs. I turned and found my friends Chelsea and Sabine taking pictures of Maggie with their daughters.

"Three child brides make three times the trouble."

Chelsea laughed.

"Oh, how are you?" Sabine asked.

I gave them hugs and caught them up on my latest life events. I felt re-centered, watching Sabine take photos of the girls—that was what this day was about. Today was a great day. A beautiful day, and no one was going to make it ugly. Thank God for Sabine and Chelsea, they helped remind me what a normal family looked like. They did not treat me like a leper, they did not judge me. They still loved the kids and me, and they treated us as if nothing had changed.

We walked into the church together. The pews were filled. I could hardly find enough room for me, the kids, and mom to sit together. We dispersed, looking for seats. I saw Uncle Peter and Aunt Denali in the back row but didn't get a chance to speak to them. We acknowledged each other with a hand wave.

The ceremony began. The Priests were dressed in their finest purple vestments. Incense was burning to the point that a layer of smoke rested near the ceiling. I looked at mom, her eyes looked teary.

"Are you okay?" I whispered.

"The incense is overpowering. I don't know if I am going to make it," She coughed.

"Sorry."

Father John asked all the kids receiving communion to walk up to the podium. He was the Resident's Priest's, Father Cantwell, understudy. Father Cantwell spoke to us about the special occasion that the communicants had been preparing for, and were about to partake in for the first time. He called for a moment of prayer. Everyone knelt. We pulled down the bench attached to the pew in front of us. Father began to pray. "Our Father, who art in heaven...."

About thirty seconds into the prayer, I heard a ruckus. It was Trey's cat-strangling laugh. My body quivered to the size of a pea. I peeked around my shoulder. Trey was at the entrance of the church, behind the glass doors, half-ass helping Papa Simon with his walker. Phyllis, now a brunette, was following behind wearing a loud yellow tiger print dress and four-inch purple Christian Louboutin's; she could barely walk. Uncle Peter stood quickly to assist his brother. Trey saw us, dropped Papa Simon, and made a beeline toward us. I instantly wished for Harry Potter's invisibility cloak.

I tried to bury my head in the space between the benches. Trey pushed his way through the pews, displacing people around him to sit next to Alex, Mom, and me. Mom began to cough from the incense, and she moved around to make room. Trey smelled more potent than before. Suddenly, there was a competition of odors brewing. The blend began to give me a headache.

"What's that smell? Is the building on fire? I can put it out." Alex offered loudly, looking at the ceiling.

"Shush," Mom pinched him. Her eyes continued to water.

Father continued to pray, ignoring the commotion from below. A skill mastered in Priesthood. After the prayer concluded, Father Cantwell asked the children to find their families and sit with them. Our pew was overcrowded already, but Trey had no inhibitions using his rumpus to scoot people out of the way to make room for Maggie. It was incredibly rude, but not the worst thing that had happened so far that day. I kept smiling. All is well in the Kingdom of the Lord.

Father Cantwell began the homily. The chemical odor was nauseating. Out of the corner of my eye, I noticed Trey's head beginning to twitch. Every two seconds, his head would jerk to the right or to the left. I wondered if he was going to have a seizure, or if some catchy song, like the "Cupid Shuffle," was on auto-play inside his head.

I had been publicly humiliated by Trey before, but this was the big kahuna. It hurt Maggie and Alex. Maybe I should move away. Very far away. He had taken the last place that was sacred and ruined it with his tweaking head and foul-smelling odor.

At last, after twenty minutes of head jerking, Father called the parishioners to receive the body and blood of Christ. Trey was not Catholic. He had not taken communion, because by church doctrine he was not allowed to. Yet on this special day, he was the first of us to jump in line to receive the body of Christ. I allowed three people to slip in between us. I was super annoyed as I watched him jerk all the way down the aisle to the priest. Mom shook her head in disbelief. Her hands firmly placed on Alex's shoulders, guiding him toward the altar. Silently, I heard her reciting a Hail Mary. I took Maggie's hand. What was I to do? I could not control another human being; this was his choice. I was a mere bystander, in every sense of the word.

Father Cantwell knew Trey was not Catholic, but Trey stood there in front of him anyway, like, 'Duh, give me the cracker already.' A bizarre stand-off ensued. Father did the sign of the cross on his head. Briefly, I envisioned Trey growling and slinking around the altar like Linda Blair in the Exorcist, while Father doused him with Holy Water. Instead, Trey kept standing there jerking. They both looked bewildered. The communion line had come to a stand-still. Father nodded to an usher, who grabbed Trey's arm and escorted him back toward his seat.

My mom, who was standing in front of me, leaned back and whispered in my ear, "Shit show." She blotted her eyes with a tissue.

I whispered back, "All is well in the Kingdom of the Lord."

At that moment, I had two choices—calm anger or a complete, ugly, crying breakdown on the floor, hyperventilating in front of all the pleasant church folk who already knew something was terribly amiss with my family. If I chose crying, I would become the sad victim of my husband's drug-induced lunacy. With silent, contained anger, I could become the overcomer, detaching from all embarrassment. After all, it wasn't mine to own.

My inner dialogue "All is well in the Kingdom of the Lord." Smile. Repeat. Deflect. I was determined to not be the emotional victim. Being the victim only empowers your enemies further. Being the angry overcomer with the goal of forgiveness was preferable. After I received communion, I hung back to watch Maggie. I took about a dozen photos of her.

"I drank the blood of Christ! It tastes like grape juice!" she said with exhilaration. I smiled and hugged her. We all returned to our seats.

Trey was still jerking and smelling like a chemical factory. Maggie sat next to him.

"Daddy, I had the blood of Christ."

"It's red wine." He laughed devilishly.

I thought, *Get behind me, Satan.* Turning to Maggie, I said, "Honey, it is the blood of Christ because it has been anointed by a holy person, Father Cantwell," trying to reinforce the teachings leading up to this event and foiling Satan's attempt to expose it all as trickery.

Phyllis approached from behind, hobbling in those high heels. She gave Maggie a big hug. "I am so proud of you. I got this for you," she said, handing her a box from the local family jeweler, Gregory. My ring had come from Gregory, too, and in a similar box. I wondered if I could sell it back to him now.

Maggie opened the box to reveal a diamond tennis bracelet. It was gorgeous.

"Yeah! Your first tennis bracelet at the age of seven," I said, trying to sound sincere and appreciative while feeling disturbed on the bedrock level.

"What about me?" Alex asked.

Maggie hugged Grandma Phyllis again. "Thank you, Grandma Phyllis!"

Phyllis said, "I love you oodles and oodles." Maggie handed me the bracelet. I put it in my purse.

Phyllis glowered at me, "Just remember that it's your bracelet, Maggie."

I smiled gently at her.

It was somewhat sweet. Phyllis loved Maggie to the best of her ability. I did not know if Phyllis could see the bigger picture, or whether her bigger picture was not rooted in the same stuff as mine. She seemed like a strange, tormented character to me—in so many ways.

"Can we all go to Southside Bistro?" Phyllis asked, looking at everyone but me. She sounded irritated; she hated having to ask my permission for anything.

"Of course. We can meet you there around dinnertime; however long Simon needs." I gave him a hug; he seemed out of it. "Thank you for coming; I can only imagine how hard it must have been to make it here."

Simon's face was pale and puffy. "I would not have missed her chomping on that biscuit for nothing. We miss the children," Papa Simon said, looking at Maggie and Alex. Alex hugged his leg.

I asked my Mom to take the children to our car while I helped Uncle Peter escort Papa Simon to his car. Phyllis was trailing behind us. Trey seemed to have disappeared.

"Can you find Trey?" Phyllis looked through me. "We need to leave." She looked agitated.

"I thought I saw him go downstairs," Uncle Peter said to her.

Okay, I walked briskly back into the church and down the stairs leading to another exit and second parking lot, where my car was located. I had no intention of looking for Trey.

I got into the car. Mom was in the passenger side seat, the kids were in the backseat. "That was fun, right kids?" Her eyes were still watery from the incense. "Ugh, Faith..." I was about to turn on the ignition when Alex leaped over the middle console, "Mommy, look, it's daddy; can we go play with him?"

"What? Where?" I looked around, paranoid.

"Oh, brother," Mom moaned and looked as if she was cringing from the inside out.

"He's swinging with Tobin and Francesca," Maggie said and pointed to the playground.

I followed Maggie's finger with my eyes. Trey was on the tire swing, swinging with such carefree ease. His brown suit jacket lay on the gravel. There were other children playing around him and with him, pushing him occasionally. Parents looked onward with concern, wondering whether to intervene or just supervise closely. I thought, *A fine shit show indeed. One of the top three. Well done, Trey. Well done.*

"No, kids, we have to go. Sorry. Maybe another time. Buckle up your seatbelts." I cranked up the car, ready to speed away as fast as possible.

I heard knocking on my window. I jumped. It was Chelsea, she was jerking her head to mimic Trey's seizure-like episode in the church. I got out of the car and closed the door behind me so no one could hear us. I laughed, watching her. "What are you doing? You're crazy!"

She put her arm around me. "Are you okay?"

"Yep, celebrating first communion Nathaniel style, and look the party continues on the playground!"

She glanced over. "No one will remember his spasms tomorrow," Chelsea said, attempting to comfort me. "At least he didn't shit himself in the pew. Now that would have been memorable." She laughed.

"A fine point, Chelsea. A fine point," I agreed.

My mom rolled down the window. "Let's go!" she said with quiet force.

"Is she okay? Has she been crying?" Chelsea asked, her eyebrows raised.

"No, allergies...I mean, I think it is."

Chelsea hugged me. "Faith, it's not your fault. He's an adult; he makes choices for his own life." Laughing with Chelsea made me feel better. It released all the tension that I had bottled up in the church.

I sat back down in the car. I felt lighter. In between Mom's glare and the kids' angst, I watched Trey swing to his heart's content. He looked happy. Despite all the nastiness that had transpired between us, deep down, I wanted him to be happy. Rarely had I seen him so unburdened, so carefree, so at ease with a laugh. It was then I realized he would never grow beyond this point; this was simply who he chooses to be, and I had to be at peace with that. Fly little bird, fly.

It was never my right to try and change Trey, to shape him into someone completely opposite of his true nature. What kind of controlling psychopath must I have been all those years, trying to turn Trey Nathaniel into a husband, father, and member of mainstream society. I had been wrong. It was Trey's life, and he should live it the way he wanted.

That did not absolve him from the responsibilities of father and provider for his children. But it had to be his decision—to be a father, or to not be a father. Looking at him now, I saw we were right back where we started all those years ago, except I no longer felt responsible, or compelled to fix him. I could freely drive away from this parking lot and leave him to his own devices. I had changed, not Trey. We lived in two different worlds, and at that moment, I released Trey from mine. Let go and let God, that was the invaluable lesson in the Kingdom of the Lord that day.

At home I crashed on the sofa, closing my eyes. I was emotionally spent. The kids decorated eggs with Grandma Kate in the kitchen. I could not gather the energy to participate in any extra family activities; even the ones I knew would be somewhat normal somehow felt tainted. I had various thoughts running through my mind. How the hell was I going to keep up with a ten thousand dollar tennis bracelet for Maggie, or a Rolex watch for Alex? Did Phyllis think she could buy my children away from me? Or did she simply feel guilty over her bad choices and thought a tennis bracelet would make things better?

How could I protect my children from the seduction of materialism, an art Grandma Phyllis had mastered? That was how she controlled people; that was how she controlled Trey and me, Lonnie, and even clergymen like Father Frank. I worried as the children grew older, they would be bedazzled by all the toys, and it would be a gateway into a deeper state of co-dependency and emotional abuse, like it was for Trey and me. I hoped maybe growing up around it was enough, and they would not drown in the cesspool of greed and vanity.

I saw their lifestyle changing dramatically. I was scared. I had anxiety. I felt nauseous. My mouth began to water. I ran to the bathroom and dry heaved.

I had puked short of the toilet. I cleaned it up with the hand towel. The rancid taste in my mouth was toxic. I had not puked in years, and every time was like the first time, and it was always the worst time. I threw the towel in the laundry and went upstairs to my bedroom. I brushed my teeth, took my shoes off and lay down.

I awakened to my mother's voice. "Faith, we've got to go. It's time to meet them for dinner. Get up." She stood in the hallway just short of my room, frowning.

"What? What's going on? Can't you take them?" I asked, sleep still pressing near. "I thought the worst part of my day was over...please."

"Nope. Sit up; we've got to leave. I thought you were up here getting ready," Mom barked and pulled the covers.

I rustled around and tried my best to summon the energy to endure another psychotic dinner. I tried to look decent and not like I had been asleep. I fluffed my hair, put on extra undereye foundation. Maggie had gotten blue egg dye on her once-white, fairytale-princess dress. "I want to wear my bracelet," she demanded.

"It won't fit you until your 25, sorry. Please change into something casual." I unzipped the back of her dress and sent her to her room.

Alex looked as if he had been chewing on a green dye stick. I looked at him and then looked at mom.

"He may have eaten a dye tablet; don't worry, it's not toxic. I called poison control." Mom walked to the garage.

"It tasted yummy," Alex declared, patting his tummy.

"Fine. Whatever," I said, defeated.

Surprisingly, the Hamiltons and Trey were already at the restaurant when we got there. Simon had parked his walker beside the table. We exchanged pleasant words. Simon was drinking wine. Trey was drinking coffee. Phyllis was not drinking.

"Oh, Maggie, you're so amazing today. I am so proud of you," Grandma Phyllis said, squeezing her shoulders.

"Yes, kid, you did great," Papa Simon agreed gritting his teeth. He looked physically uncomfortable. He kept trying to un-bow his back.

Phyllis reached into her alligator skin purse, she pulled out a golden compact, she opened it and took one white oval shaped pill out. "Open up," she said lovingly, tickling Papa Simon's chin. She popped the pill into his mouth. He swallowed it with wine.

"I want to sit next to you!" Maggie said to Phyllis.

Alex said, "No, I want to sit next to Grandma."

They fought over her. Phyllis delighted being fought over by the children. Who could blame her? It was the most normal thing about her.

"It's Maggie's special day," she finally said to Alex. "You can sit next to Trey." She offered, looking at Alex's green mouth, mystified. Trey was still twitching, but it was not as bad as at the church. Whatever drug was in his body was clearly leaving; he was becoming tired and yawning.

"Yep, nope, okey-dokey," Trey muttered, nodding off.

Papa Simon said, "We have missed seeing you and the kids, Faith." Simon looked at me as to inspire guilt.

"We miss you guys, too." I looked away. It was partly true. I did miss Simon, and I did miss the way Phyllis used to be, and the way Trey once was.

A server came up asking whether we needed additional drinks and whether we were ready to order. Everyone decided to speed order.

Phyllis, annoyed, said, "Trey will take another coffee," presumably to sober him up. At the same time, she seemed unaware that she had popped a pill into Simon's mouth while he was drinking wine. I rated her self—awareness, on a scale from one to ten, at about one. She judged Trey so harshly, but she did not lead by example.

"Maggie, where is your bracelet?" Phyllis asked, examining her wrist.

"Mommy took it." Maggie frowned at me.

"I put it in a special place, so you can wear it when you are older."

Phyllis glared at me. "Remember it came from Grandma Phyllis!" She squeezed Maggie's hand.

There were awkward moments of silence throughout the dinner. Simon seemed happy, but as the night continued, he faltered more and more. His speech slurred, and I found it harder and harder to decipher what he was saying. I kept nodding and smiling at him.

"Simon has been practicing on cadavers at his office; he's going to be doing surgeries again soon,"

Phyllis announced proudly to the table. Simon smiled and agreed. Phyllis gleamed. Trey snarled.

I swallowed hard. "Oh, Simon? How exciting. Congratulations." I took a sip of water to prevent from choking. If it made him happy, why the hell not agree?

"What's a cadaver?" Alex asked.

"I will tell you later," Mom whispered to him.

"Dead people have tougher skins," I thought I heard him say.

"I can understand that," I said, trying to be supportive.

"He'll never operate on a living person again," Trey interjected from the fog.

Simon ignored him and kept talking. Phyllis kicked Trey under the table.

"What!" Trey yelled, unaware of time and space.

Mom said brightly, "Alex and Maggie colored eggs before coming to dinner. The kids had a great time. Alex even ate a dye tablet."

"I love coloring eggs! Do you remember when you and Papa colored eggs last year?" Phyllis asked Maggie.

"I love to color eggs with the kids," Simon said.

Maggie nodded her head. "That was fun, and then the Easter Bunny came!" Maggie wiggled.

"Yes, we will hunt eggs when we get home," I smiled at Maggie and Alex.

The two grandmas continued to discuss the children. It was a safe topic. I had nothing noteworthy to contribute. I focused on Simon while Trey swerved in and out of lucidity. At that moment, I admired my mom the most. She was still trying to keep things peaceful with Phyllis after all the disgusting behaviors she had partaken in. It was the high-minded thing to do. At the end of the day, Phyllis was their grandmother, and peace should be the goal. In years to come, would it really matter who did what to whom?

WHAT'S IN THE POUCH?

CHAPTER 26

I woke up suddenly, feeling vomitus. I rushed to my bathroom and dry-heaved, but nothing came up. My mouth watered. I was worried I had the 'real' flu. Or perhaps, I was overly stressed. I had read a book about how stress and negative thought patterns could manifest as illness and disease. I was not sure I had done a sufficient job restructuring the negative thoughts that had come into my mind to positive ones.

I decided that living a life of secrets and lies had to be at the root of my nausea. Such an unclean life, even if it was not entirely of my own making. I was trapped by a lousy marriage with uncertain finances, and my escape route was not paved in gold. Maybe I was purging those old feelings of bondage. I drank from a glass of water sitting on my nightstand, lay back down, and waited for the nausea to subside. I read Psalm 23.

The Lord is my Shepherd; I shall not want.

I rested for several minutes until I felt better. I got out of bed a second time and tried to start the day again. I put on my favorite pair of Mother jeans. They felt snug.

I was frustrated. This extra pudge had to go. I could not afford a new wardrobe right now. I decided to change into my yoga pants and a t-shirt. I went downstairs to my workout room, with its wall of mirrors. I got on the treadmill and lifted my shirt to further investigate the extra fat deposits on my body. Everything looked normal, except this oval shaped potbelly. Maybe I over ate Easter Brunch?

I was displeased. I had lost it after Alex was born, and now look at it. It was a disgrace; it bulged at me. I imagined a frowny face staring back at me. Maybe I was bloated from the onset of my period. I tried to recall when my last period had been. I could not remember having had one for several months, but I had been under tremendous stress, who knew what was going on with my body's chemistry.

I remembered reading an article, once, that women, during periods of war and extreme duress, often stopped having periods; perhaps that was what was happening to me. Still, something was not right—my increased sense of smell, the nausea, the missing periods.

Oh, Mother of God, Sweet Mary, could I be pregnant?

No. There could not be a pea in the pod. Brad's little guys weren't swimmers, he was sterile. Right? And I was on birth control. I thought I took it every day. What was happening? Fuck! I needed a pregnancy test ASAP. If I was pregnant, I needed to know immediately. I had to face everything head-on; it was the only way to not get dragged down by the truckloads of Hamilton shit coming at me.

I rushed downstairs and called to my mother. "I am going to Walgreens! Do you need anything?" I asked as a courtesy but doubted I would remember to bring anything back.

"No, hurry home. The kids are going to wake up soon. It's Easter Monday."

I jumped in the car. My Joel Osteen CD was playing. He said, "Don't hate your enemies; they are there to push you into your destiny. If you keep a positive attitude and stay in faith, God knows how to take what was meant for your harm and use it to your advantage."

I thought, *Amen, brother.* But what would he think of this situation? What would the PTO moms think? What would my mother, the good Catholic, think? I quivered with feelings of shame and unworthiness.

In Walgreens, I looked around to make sure I did not recognize anyone. I grabbed three pregnancy tests off the shelf. I waited until the line at the cash register cleared before heading to the checkout. The cashier was a sweet-looking, elderly lady with blue hair; the nametag on her blue vest read Cindy. She was a dilly-dallier.

"How are you?" Cindy asked, in slow motion.

"I am great. How are you?" Inside, I screamed, Hurry up!

"Have you heard about our red-light special?" Cindy asked, picking up my pregnancy tests and waving them around.

"No, sounds like a great program, but I'm in a hurry, thank you." I nodded my head energetically to affirm that we had to keep moving along quickly. I heard the doors slide open. I looked to see if I recognized the person entering the building. I did not. I sighed with relief.

"If you sign up today, I could discount your total purchase by fifteen percent," Cindy said, holding up my pregnancy test like the Olympic torch. What the fuck, Cindy? I peered around the store again to see who might be watching.

"No, thank you," I said, loud and clear, with a big, fake grin.

"Well, if you change your mind, you can always sign up later. I don't know if you'll get the discount, though."

She finally put the tests in a bag, looking at me like I was another loser millennial who valued nothing, not even the free fifteen percent discount. I could read her mind. It said, 'Your generation is going to hell.'

"Thank you," I said. *You crazy blue-haired bitch,* I thought.

She handed me the bag.

Back in my car, I prayed aloud. "Dear God, I am so sorry I called that nice lady a bitch in my thoughts. My poor, irresponsible decisions are not her fault. Whatever the results of this test, I know it is your will. You have the final say in my life. Amen."

I turned the engine on. Joel was still playing. He said, "God has already taken into account every detail of your life, every bad break, every negative comment, how you were raised, or what somebody did. He has factored that all into his plan. If you will stay in faith, instead of holding you back, it will propel you forward. Instead of defeating you, it will make you stronger."

I felt inspired and terrified at the same time. I needed to trust Joel's words as I reconciled a possible pregnancy with an older stranger outside of my corroding marriage.

When I arrived home, I heard Maggie and Alex in the kitchen. I snuck past them and fled up the stairs with my brown paper bag, to my bathroom. I read the instructions on the test. Positive is ++ and negative is --. I put on plastic gloves. Everything had to be clean and sterile. I could not fuck this up.

I peed on the stick midstream and set the stick on the side of the tub. Immediately, one negative line began to emerge. I felt great relief. It was negative! Hahaha!

I took a luxurious shower. I had been so stupid. I was eating my feelings like every other woman would. There was a knock on the door.

"Mom, can I have pancakes?" Maggie asked.

"Of course, honey, give me a minute. I am taking a shower."

"Hurry up!" Maggie screamed, annoyed as if she had been waiting for me all morning.

"We are hungry," Alex yelled behind her.

"Okay! Go brush your teeth!" I speed-washed my hair, jumped out of the shower, and wrapped myself in a towel. I walked around the bathroom, cleaning up all the evidence. I looked at the stick one last time before tossing it into the garbage.

The – had turned into ++.

My eyes bulged, my breath shortened, and I clasped my heart because if ever there was a time I were to have a heart attack, it would be now. I stumbled backwards to a sitting position because outright falling would have been painful. I had done that move before, and it hurt. I lay down on the floor, waiting for the big one, you know, the San Andreas. Nothing happened.

A thought crossed my mind. False positive, duh! That was why I had bought three tests. Down, but not out, I rose again. I had no bodily fluids left to spare. I decided to prepare breakfast for the kids and drink liquids in the meantime. No problem.

I self-soothed with things like, "This will all be over soon." "People are misdiagnosed every day." "What doesn't kill ya, makes ya stronger." I got dressed. I hid the evidence under my bathroom sink. I drank the rest of the water sitting on my nightstand. I took the empty glass downstairs to the kitchen sink.

"Yes, pancakes!" Maggie squealed.

"I will prepare them, now," I said, like a mom servant.

I cooked pancakes in a daze, drinking coffee and water. I was stunned, intellectually immobile, going through the motions of pancake preparation in a robotic trance. What would I do if I were pregnant? My life path would be greatly diverted.

I felt suffocated by my inability to plan for the future. Even the next several minutes could bring a heap of unforeseen challenges. I fed the children. I watched them eat the smiley faces I drew on their pancakes with whipping cream. I watched them carefully, as if I might never see them this way again.

Before I became emotional, I pulled myself back and re-focused my brain on my short term goal. Finish the last two pregnancy tests. Tears did not solve problems; they just helped purge emotional overflow until equilibrium returned. "Mom, please watch the children. I have to go use the, the, the..."

"Restroom?" She finished my sentence with a big question mark, like, 'What the hell is wrong with you now?'

In ten minutes, I would know one way or another. I was anxious. I was dreading the feeling of uncertainty that I had, but I was also dreading the certainty I might soon have. On the way up the stairs, I took the time to reflect and admire each boring, rudimentary carpeted step, pulling me toward a path unknown, undetermined, and unseen—and all because I had succumbed to the throes of red-hot passion for one night... or multiple nights.

The details weren't important. I dramatically flung open the bathroom door. I pulled the remaining tests from underneath the counter. I put gloves on again and peed midstream onto the stick. I put the test down on the edge of the tub. I set my phone timer for 5 minutes.

Brad: *Good Morning Beautiful, how are you?*

His text made me feel attacked, like he was spying on me from afar, or was testing my will power in some bizarre way. What did he want me to say? Congratulations, pops? I decided to ignore him and his meager attempt to get a rise out of me with his bullshit, "You're so beautiful text." I texted Rocky instead.

Me: *Hi, Uncle Rocky, good morning! How is Simon? Last time I saw him, he was okay... mostly.*

I waited for Uncle Rocky to respond. He did not.

I searched the AOL homepage for petty gossip to occupy my time. The latest headline was, "The Duchess of Cambridge Gives Birth to a Girl." The timer went off on my phone. I shrieked and dropped my phone.

I picked up the test. It was positive.

I had one last test to take, and this test could change the last two tests. So I would be cool as a cucumber until I had proper confirmation of a baby in the pouch.

I took the final test out of the box. I put on gloves and peed on the test midstream. I set my timer. I put on makeup and flat-ironed my hair for the day. The Duchess had a SWAT team of beauticians, and if the photos were accurate, she looked like a supermodel after birthing a human being. I should at least try to look presentable for Easter Monday, right?

I waited for news of conception, new life, mitosis. I waited and waited and applied makeup until I looked more like Tammy Faye Baker than the clean, sophisticated, beauty of Duchess Kate.

The timer went off. I felt a heaviness in my chest. I picked up the test; it read ++.

I had three positive pregnancy tests in front of me.

I clasped my heart again, but instead of having the psychotic breakdown I was anticipating, a wave of unexpected euphoria rushed over and through me, enveloping me in peace. I felt the unconditional love of a mother for her baby and the cozy vessel we shared. I rested my hands on my belly. Tears glided down my cheeks. Becoming a mother was the best thing that had ever happened to me. Out of all the darkness and black clouds encircling me, a rainbow had appeared, a new life. A new life filled with limitless possibilities, a new life that would inevitably bring blessings beyond blessings to our family because babies are God's greatest blessing.

I cleaned up all the evidence again and disposed of it properly. After the initial euphoria subsided, I tried to process this new information practically. What would my next step be on this new life path that had presented itself at 11:11 a.m.?

There was a man on the other side of this baby. A man I would have to deal with for the majority of my life. Maybe I would have to raise this baby alone. That scared me. But I was a survivor. I knew I could do it. Trey had taken so much, he was not going to take this baby from me, too. I was not going to give up the baby in my pouch, and I did not care who it offended.

After considerable thought, I decided to tell Brad. He deserved to know. His reaction would help me gauge the direction I should go. After all, he was just as responsible as I was.

The whole thing was crazy. I had been with one man for the last eleven years of my life. He had left me. I had a mini-crush on Brad; he offered to be my life coach, and then came the old "You're the most beautiful woman in Alaska, lie under the stars with me and touch my pee-pee" routine. And now, I was pregnant. How was I going to get a man to process becoming a father after just a few romantic exchanges when he had avoided a committed relationship for fifty years? It had all been so insincere to begin with. He was probably dating other women, too.

Suddenly, I was consumed with fear. My fear quickly turned to anger. I knew Brad was going to blame me for fire-bombing his playboy lifestyle. He was going to act like Trey. Maybe not the drug thing, thank God, but he would run and hide because that was what men do, right? I was in disbelief. It was all his fault, with his smooth-talking and his "Your voice is like honey" comments. Hogwash! He was a seducer and used the whole life-coach gig as a ploy to take advantage of my weakened and vulnerable state. I was the victim of the Rosenbloom Bluff!

I called Brad, ready to attack.

He said, "Hey, honey, how are you doing?"

Brad answered the phone this way? For real? I rolled my eyes. "We have an issue. I noticed I was gaining weight. I realized I could not remember the last time I had a period. Anyway, I took three pregnancy tests, and they're all positive. You're the only person I've been romantic with."

"You're pregnant?" His voice shot up ten decimals. "What wonderful news! I would marry you in a minute if our situation was not so complicated." Brad still sounded as cheerful and carefree as if I had told him the daily seafood special at Simon and Seaforts.

"Well, how's this even possible? Why didn't you use protection?"

"I thought you were on birth control. I've never gotten anyone pregnant before," Brad said, accusing me as if my womb were supernaturally fertile.

"Well, I guarantee you it's either your child or I am the next Virgin Mary, and we both know that's not true," I screamed at him.

"You need to calm down. I don't like the tone of your voice."

"Calm down? I can't be pregnant while going through a divorce! How can this be happening to me?"

"You'll have to move to Juneau."

"Juneau? What the fuck? I can't move there. I don't even know you, and we are having a baby!" I said it aloud for the first time, and it felt like someone karate-chopped me in the throat.

"I've always wanted a baby. I am happy. What if we're like peanut butter and chocolate? You know, Reese's Pieces?" Brad said with a chuckle.

"What kind of lunatic are you?" I said with dignity and hung up the phone.

He was crazy—marriage, moving, baby? My life plan less than an hour ago had been a divorce, staying, and protecting my children. Now, I had to factor in protecting an unborn child. I could not stay in Fairbanks, fight to keep my house, and protect Maggie and Alex, while Brad's seed blossomed inside of me. I would be a sitting duck. Quack. Quack. Call me Duck Soufflé.

In my mind's eye, I kept seeing Brad's commercials play over and over again in my head, "Sunday Funday, Sunday Funday." That's what he said on his commercial to advertise his business while wearing a yellow t-shirt that read "Sunday Funday!"

What a complete, unforeseen deviation in my life's plan. As if going through a divorce, with children, was not traumatizing enough.

I had to move. I needed to leave town ASAP. I could not keep up this façade. The PTO moms would hog-tie me and paint a scarlet letter on my forehead. I was so ashamed. How could I be knocked up at thirty-three? Who gets knocked up at thirty-three? And how did a fifty-year-old man knock me up? How could he have lived so long and not gotten anyone pregnant? We are intimate two times and voilà, the deed is sealed, and I am with child? What? This had to be divine intervention because I could not understand how this was happening. There had to be a spiritual lesson here that I was missing.

I told myself that I needed to stay courageous, pull it together, and move forward. I needed to keep my game face on. Downstairs, the kids were playing Twister with Grandma Kate. In a daze, I sat on the sofa and watched them. I worried about how a baby could change their lives. I felt guilty. I felt like I was a bad mom. Was I worthy of a new baby?

There were several monumental, life-changing family events on the horizon—a divorce, a move, a death, and now a baby. Each of these events represented an ending and a new beginning. I could see where a faithless person, with no spiritual tools, might contemplate suicide in my situation, or recede into the black hole of the abyss.

But I knew God loved me. I had to remain in the space of accepting all God's gifts, blessings, and tribulations into my life. I believed the Pastor, that God's grand design was for my ultimate well-being, as long as I did my part by staying faithful and helpful to His people.

I walked back upstairs and lay down. I was overwhelmed. God was really putting me through the fire of transformation. I reflected on one of Joel's sermons. "God will move the wrong people out of your way and put the right ones in." God must be fine-tuning me and Brad for something, but what? I trusted it would be revealed to me in time. I decided to text him. I needed to be able to work with him even if we weren't going to be together.

Me: *I am sorry. I freaked out. I want us to have a healthy, real relationship—whatever that may look like.*

Brad: *I love you. I am freaked out*

Chelsea interrupted.

Chelsea: *The last PTO meeting is on Thursday. Don't forget.*

Me: *Okay.*

I wondered if I should show up in a maternity dress double-fisting corndogs and ice cream. I was such a phony.

I hated the person I was, all the lies, pretending, covering up. If only Trey had kept his feeble, half-steamed pecker in his pants and stayed sober. There was plenty of blame to assign to multiple people in this situation, but ultimately, I had to take responsibility for the way I had chosen to react to the things people did to me. And I had reacted poorly at times. The whole "Taking a Lover" expedition—I probably should have waited to do that.

At other times, I had rather impressed myself, but that was the nature of all humans— good and bad. In time, I would have to learn to accept and forgive myself. My phone dinged.

Rocky: *I sleep late in the mornings. Sorry I didn't text you sooner.*

Me: *No worries.*

Rocky: *Simon is good. We're having lunch at Suite 100. Do you want to meet us?*

Me: *Who is going to be there?*

Rocky: *Me and Simon*

Me: *Perfect. I am on my way.*

I decided my baby announcement cards would have to go out at a later date. Meanwhile, I was sure my expanded waistline would earn me some extra sympathy points: Oh, poor Faith. Her husband left her, and now she's getting fat. I would accept those extra sympathy points with pride. I was desperate and only a dickhead would think that anyway.

I walked into the backyard where my mother was still in her PJs, picking raspberries with Maggie and Alex. "I am resting today," she mouthed quietly. "First Communion nearly killed me."

News of a love child would surely top her off. My lips were sealed. "I know. I am sorry about that. I love you. Thank you for always being there for me."

"I am going to meet Rocky and Simon for lunch. I've decided to move back to Washington with you. We're going to spend the last two weeks of the school year packing up the house and getting it ready to list for sale."

"Oh, Faith." She hugged me. "That's the smartest thing I've heard you say. I am so happy. You can't stay here and have the kids grow up like this."

"Yes, I know."

"So, what made you change your mind?"

"Trey embarrassed me, with the head jerking and the tire swing and stuff..." I looked away from her.

She looked sideways at me. A mother's intuition was keen.

It was true; Trey had embarrassed me. Ironically, it was not as big of a motivator as Brad's love child growing inside of my womb. If I were not pregnant, I would stay and fight, but as I kept re-processing this new information, I realized that it would be a dumb fight. A house was just a house; it could easily be duplicated time and time again.

"So, can you watch the kids while I go to lunch for an hour?"

"Yes, do what you have to do," Mom said, happily. Clearly, she had been daydreaming about getting the hell out of Alaska.

I decided to get changed before heading out. I felt like I needed to wear a looser shirt. Suddenly, I was self-conscious. I had been unaware of how big my stomach had become. Now everything I put on seemed to accentuate the roundness of my belly. Everything in my life had to change, right down to my wardrobe.

At the restaurant, Simon and Rocky were sitting at the bar. They were heavily engaged in conversation. I was happy to see they were, indeed, alone. "Hi guys, how are y'all doing?" I smiled as if all was well, and I was not pregnant—just fat and sad over being dumped.

Simon said, "Faith! We were taking bets over whether you would show up. Glad to see you."

"And who won the bet?"

"I did," Rocky said as he stood to hug me and kiss my cheeks.

"Congratulations." I sat down beside Simon. "You look amazing."

He nodded. "Faith, we have a problem. Trey's out of control. It took me twenty-five years and over a million dollars to get him off drugs, and now he's back on them. I don't have another twenty-five years to spare, and he's fucked things up at St. Mary's real good." Simon said this as if Trey were my problem.

I thought, *Seriously? Again? Did I have to repeat myself a thousand more times—Trey is 40 years old; he is his own man; his bad choices are not my responsibility?* "I'm sorry about all the chaos at the Center, and the rumors. It's the worst. You know Helga's also to blame, she's broken up two other families that I know of," I said, being duplicitous.

“I am not going to fire Helga and risk being sued. She has job security.”

“I think that’s bullshit,” I said with anger. “I’m getting a divorce. I can’t raise my kids in this situation. It has become unhealthy, and it’s not worth it to me anymore.”

“I recommended an attorney,” Rocky said.

Simon fought back a smile. He must have been waiting a long time for me to get to this place. “Well, how am I going to get him clean?” He put me on the hot seat again, but it felt like a test to pass or fail than a genuine question.

“It’s Trey’s job to get himself clean. I have no desire to try and sober him up. I hope he finds God and the inner strength to do it himself, but I am not responsible. I am responsible for my four-year-old and my seven-year-old who need at least one healthy parent.”

Simon fought back a smile, “What about the house?”

Rocky said, “She wants the house.”

“No. I have thought about it. I don’t want the house. Sell it.”

Simon shuffled excitedly around. “Really? Okay, let’s sell it. I’ll make sure you get all the money. Let’s list it immediately.”

Rocky asked, “Wait, …uh… Faith, where will you go?” He sounded sincerely concerned, like he was invested.

“I don’t know for sure. I’ll probably downsize and stay around here. I love St. Joseph’s.” I looked at Simon, “Trey’s the only person listed on the title of the house; can you get him to list it?”

"He has no choice," Simon said.

"Okay, well, I'll let you take care of that. Let me know if you need any help." I wondered how the hell he was going to get Trey to do anything. Probably by bribery. Simon turned his head toward me; he had a serious tone. "No one wants to hear your sob story. We all have one. I pulled a gun on my brother for sleeping with my ex-wife. You don't see me going around telling everyone. The best revenge is success."

"No, no, no, that's not true. The best revenge is a dish served cold!" Rocky laughed hysterically. Simon and I glared at him. "I don't want revenge, Rocky. I want to feel safe and free."

We ordered lunch. Simon and Rocky talked about the good old days. How they had jointly owned a horse in the Melbourne Cup. How they had traveled around the world hunting animals. How they had spent their time carousing with women. I watched them bicker and bust each other's balls with countless shenanigans that had spanned decades. In a perfect world, these two would grow old together like in the movie *Grumpy Old Men,* but with more cursing, alcohol, and debauchery. As I was leaving Suite 100, I received a text from Brad.

Brad: *How are you feeling?*

Me: *I am okay honey, still shocked.*

Brad: *I am flying in tomorrow night to come see you.*

Me: *Okay.*

Every blank space in my mind was once filled with anxiety over my impending divorce. Now every space was filled with determination to pack the house and leave. On the way home, I stopped off at Home Depot and bought a bunch of packing tape and boxes. Was Brad the love of my life or a lunatic? Chocolate and peanut butter, who says that? I should not have too many expectations of him; it was best to let him decide his level of participation. I decided to cool it with him for a while. What was the rush? We had a lifetime to get to know each other, one way or another, for better or for worse.

Right now, I had to focus on moving my family over 2,000 miles away.

THE LOVE TRIANGLE

CHAPTER 27

"Let's get some boxes."

"Home Depot?" Mom asked. We walked into the garage.

I nodded. We got into the car. I hit the button on the garage door opener

My phone rang. It was Sabine. I had not seen her since first communion. She must be checking on me.

"Hey girl," Sabine said, "I saw Trey."

"Trey? This early? Where?" I looked over at mom.

"He came to my work and asked to see me."

"What? Why was he at the hospital?" Mom put her hand to her forehead. She mouthed, "What?"

"He said drug dealers were holding Simon's Mercedes hostage in the hospital parking lot, and the only way he could get the car back was to pay them two hundred dollars."

"Don't give him anything!" I yelled. I felt my blood pressure boil.

"I gave him twenty-five dollars to leave. I thought you were being dramatic when you were telling me all those stories. I had no idea how bad it was."

"I wish I was being dramatic. He did the same thing to Maria's family." I felt such humiliation. How could Trey go into Sabine's work and ask her for money? They barely spoke.

"How are the kids?"

"They still don't know anything. I tell them Trey is helping Papa Simon feel better. I guess I should be telling them he's helping Papa Simon meet his maker quicker."

"I am so sorry. My father was an alcoholic. My mom left him when I was young. I understand completely what you're going through. I love you, and I am here for you."

"I am sorry that happened to you. I love you. Thank you." I hung up the phone.

I looked at my mother, who had already braced herself for another Trey-pisode. "Now he's asking fellow PTO parents for drug money, and I have a PTO meeting to go to."

She said, "I am sorry for the kids." She buckled her seat belt and stared forward.

At first, I wanted to cry, but I knew staying angry was a more productive emotion. I remembered that this was another moment where my will was being tested. I could either lie naked on the cement floor of the garage, rolling around, crying, and screaming, "Where is your humanity?" or I could stand tall and use my anger to propel me forward. To Home Depot. I backed out of the driveway, and away we went.

People say anger is bad. It is so taboo. Blah blah blah. But God gave us anger, like any other emotion, and right now I was using it to survive.

If you use your anger constructively to achieve a positive goal, like moving far away from crazy people, you can lightspeed yourself ahead of unproductive grieving that just ends up slowing you down.

"I'll get a storage unit for the kid's furniture," I told my mom. "We need to find some peaceful days."

I finished packing the theater room. I packed the kids' favorite toys from their playroom. I packed up clothes from their closets that did not quite fit them yet. Some of their things I left to pack in suitcases for the plane. I collected lamps, books, old paintings, knick-knack décor in the middle of the living room floor to donate to one of my favorite charities, Love Inc.

In my room, I tried to determine the number of boxes I would need. I had removed the remnants of Trey the night and days following my discovery of his affair, so at least that was taken care of. I opened the filing cabinet in my bedroom. It would be interesting to see if any of those documents were actually important, now.

I pulled out a folder with old family photos. My heart sank. I sorted through the pictures, some old, some new; it was hard not to travel back in time and relive each scene. These photos only told the story of a happy, fun-loving family. I felt sadness for what our lives had become, but I also felt a detachment from these past events. My anger was creating some sort of protective shield. After all, no one takes photos of the shitty times.

The longer I looked at the photos, the less I was able to recognize Trey. I struggled to make an emotional connection. It was like looking at pictures of my infant self and trying to link my present self to the image. But looking at my babies was sweet and sad all at the same time-- for what it once had been, but was no longer. Beautiful moments that had been stamped into photos, but now were tainted and marked only by an abrupt end of something: a partnership, a future life together.

I felt the anger subside for a moment as tears welled in my eyes. There would be no more pictures like this. I did not know what role Trey would play in the kids' lives when this was over. Whatever the circumstance, going through a divorce with kids was making me feel like a loser, a failure, not good enough. The worst thing was we all looked so normal. Were we ever really normal? Was anyone ever really normal? Surely, most people were not this abnormal.

I felt my heart soften toward Trey. I decided to create a folder with his name written on the outside. I collected pictures and documents he might need or enjoy in the next chapter of his life and placed them inside. I left the folder in his nightstand drawer. Ding-text message.

Chelsea: *FYI, PTO meeting 6:30.*

Me: *I'll be there.*

Oh, shoot. Brad was flying in. I would have to figure this out. I texted him.

Me: *What time are you arriving, honey?*

Brad: *5:00.*

Me: *I'll pick you up, but I have to leave shortly after. I have a meeting at 6:30.*

Brad: *Are you meeting an attorney?*

Me: *PTO meeting for the kids.*

Brad: *You're such a good mom.*

Me: *Yes, they are throwing me a baby shower.*

Brad: *Really?*

I rolled my eyes. Me: *No. They're probably mad at me. I've only been to two meetings all year. This is the last one. I must go into the fire of affliction and beg for forgiveness #loserptomom*

Brad: *You can't always schedule life.*

Brad was right, you could not schedule or predict a Trey-pisode. I packed for several hours, and rented a storage unit. I arranged for movers to come. Ding! Text message.

Rocky: *We need to talk.*

Me: *I always enjoy talking with you. What's up?*

Rocky: *Come over to my house.*

I thought, Au contraire, you romancer. Me: *Let's meet for lunch in an hour?*

Rocky: *Little Italy. They know me there.*

Me: *I am sure you're known everywhere.*

My packing time had been cut short; I had to get ready for the day. I took a shower, did my makeup, and got dressed in loose-fitting clothes. Luckily, Little Italy was only five minutes from my house, and pasta fagioli sounded delicious.

My mother was in the living room, wrapping five 3 feet tall, golden candlesticks in bubble wrap. "Are you going somewhere?"

"I am meeting Rocky for a quick lunch."

"How's the packing going upstairs?"

"I think I am about done. Once I set a goal, I like to knock it out." I laughed, nervous.

"We do have a timeline," she said, as if it was the only thing keeping her going. She hiked up her black paisley pants and grabbed some trinkets off the mantel.

"We sure do. I'll be back within an hour."

Rocky's enormous, monster truck was parked outside Little Italy. Every cowboy had a horse or at least a mounted horse head, and a monster truck, right? I bypassed the hostess, trying to spot Rocky. I could not see him anywhere. I was puzzled; maybe he was in the bathroom?

I didn't have all day to wait for him while he was in the loo. I was starving. I locked eyes with a young man, walking by carrying pizza boxes. I gave him the bemused customer look. He said, "Can I help you?"

"I am looking for Rocky; he says he's known here."

"Mr. Valentine is at the bar." He pointed to an adjacent room with a small entrance. I had not noticed it before. Such a strange layout for a restaurant, I thought. Beyond the entrance, the room opened up to a large, grand, European-styled dining area with antique chandeliers and lots of grape and olive patterns imprinted on the walls.

Rocky was at the bar, pounding a glass of vodka. Great. He was either drunk or working on it. He had his fancy elephant-skin cowboy boots on, and a matching Stetson hat. He was all dolled up, man bracelets and all. I sat on the empty barstool next to him.

"What are you drinking?" I asked fiercely, not to be trifled with.

"Vodka tonic," he said, like a man with something on his mind. "Would you like anything?"

"It's early for me. No, thank you," I said, and batted my eyes with a smile.

"Let's eat." Rocky motioned for the bartender. "We'll have the stuffed mushrooms, escargot, and the seafood fettuccini to share."

"Yummy, nice spread, thanks for ordering for me. So, what do we need to talk about?"

"Simon told me Phyllis and Trey have talked about not letting you leave the state with the kids. If that happens, they won't let you keep the house, and you'll be homeless. Simon can only do so much to help you. He has to be on Trey's side—you know that." Rocky sounded matter-of-fact, like he was the judge, trial, and jury of my divorce case.

"No one is going to give kids to an active drug user. I don't care how many people the Hamiltons have bought off. Trey can't keep me here; he has no job, and only Phyllis's pocket purse as a resource. The last time I checked, she has no control over him. He's going around town asking my friends for money to pay off dealers. It's humiliating for all of us. What judge would find him to be a fit parent?"

Rocky swiveled his barstool around to face me head-on. His eyes looked straight through me. "It's more than that. You're accustomed to a certain kind of lifestyle. You have two kids. Not very many men are going to want to take that on. The way I see it, the dating pool for you is small. Men don't want to date women with kids, and you're spoiled." He took a gulp of vodka and moved three inches closer to my face. I leaned away from him. "You could never date Bill from Best Buy." I felt his vodka breath kiss my face. He put his hands on either side of my bar stool. "The only solution is for us to get married." He stared at me, in some sort of hypnotic trance. I wondered if he had a superpower where he killed people with his mind? I squinted my eyes to break the spell.

"What?" I asked, in a high-pitch squeak.

I was in disbelief over the words coming out of his mouth. This was perhaps the most unromantic and insulting marriage proposal in history. I felt queasy. I briefly wished I possessed the superpower of projectile vomit. If so, I would shower him with vomit now. A man who plays on a woman's fears is nothing short of an abuser. How dare he try this obscenely manipulative tactic on me? What was I supposed to say? Jeez, Rocky thank you for taking one for the team, the kids and I are such losers without you?

"I don't have a lot of years left," he added. "When I die, you'll be a millionaire. I'll leave everything to you."

"What about your children and grandchildren? They're my age, right? You should leave everything to them."

"They're taken care of; don't worry about it." He took another sip of his drink.

"So, your proposal is that we get married because no man wants a woman with two kids, and I've been spoiled?" I wanted him to confirm that this was indeed his thought pattern.

"Yes, but I'll take care of all of you. The kids don't have to change schools; we can all live in my riverside home. It's plenty big, don't you think?" Rocky said, raising his eyebrows, as if he had just offered me the sun, the moon, the stars, and an endless supply of dead animal heads to gaze upon, all at once.

"Rocky, I am trying to take it one day at a time." I turned away from him, I put my hands over my face. "I am divorcing Oedipus, for God's sake!" I never want to get married again! It is going to take me years to unpack all of the trauma I've endured." Rocky laughed. "I can tell you that I will not date a man who doesn't love my children. I need a lion, not a sheep. Even though you are a lion and have killed plenty of them, I am going to have to decline your generous offer of marriage at this time."

What a whacko! I would mount his head on his own wall, next to Grandma Phyllis. Some people seemed to think if you're kind, or gentle, or in a weakened state, they could take advantage. Surely after abandonment and betrayal, a woman would be desperate for love and acceptance? Well, kindness was not synonymous with weakness or stupidity. My self-worth was not dependent on external treasures or rewards, it was dependent on God. The strongest people are the kindest people. Anything you do to them speaks volumes—not about them, but about you. And at this moment, Rocky Valentine was failing the test.

I was not prey for him to kill, stuff, and display in his house, along with his other trophies. I vowed to get to a place in my life where I could give and receive love openly again, but I would reserve the right to tell someone to fuck off when appropriate. I had seen the darkness of others, and it could no longer be unseen or undetected. I would never fall for anyone's manipulations or be a co-dependent ever again.

"We could travel the world together," Rocky said, annoyed he was being rejected, but still willing to bargain. "I'll be waiting for you to reconsider." I gave him a blank look.

The waiter approached us with two plates and three trays of food. It smelled so good. Especially the seafood fettuccini. I took a bite. "This is delicious. Could we go on a food tour in Italy, please?" I asked, stuffing my face with five thousand calories of pasta and cream sauce, trying to forget about the unpleasantries he had dumped on me.

I began to simmer down. I was offended by Rocky's proposal; he had no tact. But underneath that offer was a vulnerable man, willing to give me his fortune in exchange for fake romantic love and companionship. An unnatural compromise. A cop-out on all things pure and true. There was a deep sadness and loneliness there that someone might easily exploit—if they hadn't been dealing with Rocky Valentine, professional romancer and killer of the jungle.

"I notice you've been gaining weight. Now is not the time to get fat." He scooted the escargot away from me.

I rejected him, and now he wanted to attack me by alerting me to the sad truth about myself: alone, spoiled, with two children, and now, at last, fat, as well? "Wow! Being Mrs. Valentine would be so delightful. How about we diet together? You should start by quitting alcohol. Lots of empty calories in alcohol."

He laughed. I laughed. We made peace in between the insults. I enjoyed certain aspects of Rocky's fiery personality. He was strong, courageous, and said what he thought. He was pretty funny in a rather cruel way, which, admittedly, I found entertaining. He was also untrustworthy, manipulative, and predatory. He was good and bad, like all of us in some measure.

Rocky asked, "When is Trey being served divorce papers?"

"I don't know. Any time, I suppose." I scooted the escargot back in front of me.

"We'll have to celebrate. You'll let me know, right?"

"Totally," I said, nodding, wondering why the hell anyone would celebrate their ex-partner being served divorce papers. It was one of the saddest of times.

When I picked the kids up from school, Alex asked, "Mommy, Mommy, guess what happened today?" He buckled himself into the car.

"What Alex? You got to go in Mrs. Laura's treasure chest?"

"Yes, and Ryder brought in his dog for show and tell, and it peed on the teacher's chair; it was epic!" Alex laughed mischievously.

"Alex, you don't even know what that word means." Maggie was full of scorn.

"It means awesome." Alex gave her the evil eye.

"Maggie, how was your day?" She looked annoyed.

"When's daddy coming home?" Maggie asked, her hands folded nicely in her lap.

I couldn't keep dodging this question. I had to tell them. I was running out of time. I couldn't move them away one day, and come home with a baby the next. "We're going to talk about that when we get home," I said. "But right now, I need to know what you want for dinner. I have to go back to your school for a PTO meeting later."

"Pizza," Alex said. He raised both of his hands in the air.

"Is that all right, Maggie?"

"Yeah, sure." She flipped her hair and peered out the window.

At the Alaska Pizza Company, I picked up two pizzas, breadsticks, and red sauce. Alex fell asleep on the way home. I carried him into the house and laid him on the sofa. He started laughing.

"Were you fake sleeping?" I pretended to be amazed. "Good one! Now go eat."

I refereed as the kids ate pizza. They argued over who had the bigger pizza slice, who had the most breadsticks, how to divide the sauce.

Afterward, I refreshed my makeup and changed my clothes, trying to make myself presentable. I had over indulged on fettuccine and was feeling rather sickly. I dreaded the talk that was coming with the kids.

I prayed, "Please, God, be present and help me to console my children. Give me your wisdom and keen insight as to how best to navigate this situation. Amen."

Downstairs, the kids were watching TV. In a normal situation, I would be having this discussion with Trey present, but unfortunately, he had more important things to do. Like sell Papa Simon's Mercedes. I called them into the living room. "Have a seat. We're going to have a family meeting. Wait. Alex, go get your grandmother."

Alex yelled at the top of his lungs, "Grandma, Grandma, Grandma, come here!"

"Alex, I meant for you to walk over to the other room and tell Grandma in a normal tone to join us in the living room, not yell through the walls."

"Oh!" Alex laughed again. Everything was funny to this four-year-old. What a jokester he had become. Perhaps he took on that role to balance out Maggie's sadness. Grandma walked in forlornly; she looked tired. I could not imagine the amount of stress all of this was putting on her. It troubled me.

"Please come in, Grandma Kate. We're about to discuss when daddy is coming home."

Grandma's eyes got big. "Oh," she said, and sat next to Maggie. Her black paisley pants looked worn and dusty. Was she cleaning the crawl space?

There was an awkward pause. "Maggie and Alex, there's no easy way to tell you this. Sometimes two people love each other, but no longer want to live with each other. Do you know what the word divorce means?"

"Yes. Regan's mom and dad are divorced, and her dad lives in Texas. She goes and visits him sometimes," Maggie said.

"Wait, wait, are you and daddy getting a divorce?" Alex asked, pointing his finger at me.

"Yes, although we still love each other, and most importantly, we love each of you. But your dad has not been feeling well. You may not see him for a while, but I want you to know that he loves you, and although he may not be in your life every day, he's always thinking of you." Maggie burst into tears. I held her in my arms. "I'm sorry. You'll always be taken care of, you'll always be safe, and you'll always be loved." I began to cry. Grandma Kate was also crying. Alex looked perplexed. "Alex, are you okay?"

"Wait, wait, one thing, are we moving?" Alex looked at the boxes lined up against the walls.

"Yes, we are moving for the summer to be closer to Grandma Kate. Who knows what the fall will bring," I said, trying not to rattle their mainframe, too much.

"Does this have anything to do with daddy's special friend? I don't want you to get a divorce." Maggie continued to sob.

Now my eyes got big. I looked at Grandma Kate. How quickly feelings of compassion can turn to murder.

"Who's daddy's special friend?" I asked her, with obligatory gentleness.

"This old lady with blonde hair; daddy told me to call her his special friend and not tell you about her. Please don't get a divorce." Maggie said, still crying.

I eased up my tight hug on her and scooted away. "Oh... you should not keep secrets from your parents about anyone, even another parent. That's unhealthy. I am sorry he put you in that situation." I gritted my teeth, ready to explode like a microwaved baked potato.

"Where did you meet daddy's special friend?" Grandma Kate asked, softly.

"We would go to Grandma Phyllis's, and she was always there. One time, they locked themselves in the bedroom and would not come out, and I banged and banged on the door. She yelled at me. She had beady, black eyes. I hid in the closet. But then we went to a movie; it was fun." Maggie breathlessly panting.

"Oh, Grandma Phyllis was there with daddy and his special friend?"

"Yes, sometimes she would leave to get her nails or hair done," Maggie said.

"Where was Papa?"

"He didn't leave the bed. I don't want to move."

My tone sharpened. "In the future, do not keep secrets from me, okay?"

"Okay," Maggie said.

"Can we still play Xbox?" Alex yelled, standing up and bolting out of the room. He appeared to be unphased.

"Maggie, I think your brother will be okay. Do you have any questions?"

"I don't want you and daddy to get a divorce," she said, crying heavy. Grandma Kate handed Maggie a tissue from her pants pocket.

I could no longer muster any tear to share with her. All I saw was red for the blood I wanted to spill and black for the bruises I wanted to inflict.

"I know, honey, but sometimes things don't work out between adults. It's not your fault. Adults are responsible for their own decisions and actions. Not kids. Your dad makes a lot of bad choices, and all we can do is pray for him and Grandma Phyllis to make healthier choices. Daddy's special friend was not a good person for our marriage, and I am sorry they exposed you to that. They need prayers."

"Okay," Maggie said sadly. Grandma Kate hugged her. Maggie's eyes were still big and teary.

I had to get out of there. I could not breathe in that room. I was torn between comforting my daughter as an innocent co-conspirator in Trey's and Grandma Phyllis's love triangle and reconciling a new level of betrayal from each of them. Right when I thought I had hit rock bottom with these people, a new level of depravity would emerge. "If you need anything, call me, and I'll come home." In the other room, I gave Alex a hug and kiss goodbye. He did not notice; he was consumed by his video game. Perhaps that was his coping mechanism, or perhaps he did not understand what was happening.

I realized I was late picking up Brad. By now, I felt less angry than fatigued. I was subdued over Maggie's confession. Only God knew how long they had been bringing my precious little daughter around their twisted love triangle, all while Simon lay ill in the next room. All those months while I searched fruitlessly for the identity of Eve, my seven-year-old daughter knew everything. All I would have had to do was ask her.

Then, I flashbacked to ten years ago, in a therapy session with Trey. He told me when his parents were still married, his mother had an affair with his soccer coach. She would take him over to his coach's house and leave him on the sofa for hours while she and the coach were in the back bedroom. She swore him to secrecy. I sympathized. Then, Trey said, "*Don't worry, after a while, coach bought me a Nintendo, so it wasn't so bad.*"

Phyllis did it to Trey, Trey did it to Maggie, I wondered who did it to Phyllis? They were grooming Maggie, initiating her with secrets to be like them—passing on this cocktail of narcissism, lies, and generational dysfunction like one would pass along the family crest. Their coat of arms must read "*If you are not born with a personality disorder, don't worry we will give one.*"

I prayed, "Dear God, help me teach my children to walk in the light of the Lord. To serve you before money, for you are the one true resource for all of us, and what is given can be taken away. I pray that my children will be free from manipulative relationships and generational abuse. Thank you for saving Maggie. Amen."

PTO MELTDOWN

CHAPTER 28

I parked outside Alaska Airlines departures. I pulled down the visor to look into the mirror. I was a mess. I had a raccoon face again. I tried to wipe the mascara from underneath my eyes and the black streaks off my cheeks. It smudged across my cheek bones. I was permanently looking like a sobbing hot mess, and it was not cute. I felt I was walking around with a sign saying, Someone Commit Me, but not to the same institution as the Hamiltons, please!

In the rearview mirror, I saw Brad approaching. He was wearing a baby blue t-shirt, jeans, and white tennis shoes. He was holding a bundle of red roses. He walked around to the driver's side, opened the car door, and pulled me out. He embraced me so tightly it took my breath away.

"I've missed you," he whispered in my ear. I pulled back to look at him, and he was teary-eyed too, but for a different reason. My guard was up so high these days, always ready to combat the next attack, but suddenly this space between us transformed me, and I softened to his kindness.

I felt vulnerable but safe. We shared something deep. I did not know what it was, but I felt it in the energy between us. I didn't have the need to define it at that moment. We had mountains to climb before things normalized even slightly for us. I did know one thing for certain: Brad was happy. He was happy over this baby.

It blew my mind to think his happiness could be real. The more I thought about it, the more frightened I became. If his happiness was real, then he might have an expectation—an expectation I was too broken to fulfill.

My fight or flight instinct kicked back in. I pulled myself back and talked myself into being logical. This could be an act. He was a politician. He was playing to the audience. I could not allow myself to succumb to the Rosenbloom bluff. Besides, I did not need to get this emotional again right now. I had to keep my game face on. I still had to face the PTO moms.

"We should go. I am sorry. I have that meeting, remember?" I pulled away from him. "Are we going to our usual place?" I put the roses on the back seat and drove toward the Dimond Center Hotel. I did not want him to feel rejected, but I had about a thousand marathons to run before I could meet him at an authentic emotional level. "I am glad you're happy," I said. "I am sure you're overwhelmed about becoming a father at your age," I spoke without thinking. Instantly, I regretted my statement.

"I am happy about the baby. My father is dying, and all I have is my sister. We don't talk regularly," Brad said, sounding sad now.

"A baby could change several people's lives. Maggie changed Grandma Phyllis's and Papa Simon's life. They fell in love with each other again by sharing their love for her. It was sweet to watch. Having Maggie made me a better person, having Alex even better, and this baby will make both of us better people. Unless you're a psychopath. Then having a child will have no effect on you whatsoever." I looked at him skeptically. What kind of man would happily sign up for this fiasco... perhaps, a psychopath?

"I am sure I'll change. I'll have to." Brad put his hand on my leg.

"How long do you think your dad has left on Earth?"

"He could go at any time." I put my hand on top of his hand.

"The goal should be for your father to meet the baby. How does that sound?" I asked optimistically, thinking I that had deflated him earlier.

"I don't know. I don't want to get my hopes up."

"We should make it a priority. I'll start praying."

"Are you going to move to Juneau? You should at least come for a visit." Brad looked over at me.

"I don't think I can, not yet. It would be hard on the kids. Maybe I'll visit after I move to Washington." I looked out the driver's side window.

"That makes sense. I remember when my dad left us. It was devastating. They're going to hate me." Brad took his hand off my leg.

"Not Alex; he's four, and Trey has hardly spent any time with him. I don't think there's a real attachment there. Maggie could be a challenge, but we are light years away from that happening." I grabbed his hand again.

"Nine months. But I should get to know them before that," Brad sounded serious and thoughtful.

"That's plenty of time, really, especially if we change scenery. A fresh start." I smiled at him, thinking, *More like six months, oops!*

I walked into the hotel with Brad this time. I didn't care anymore who saw us. What was the point? I was moving. I no longer cared what people thought about me, Trey taught me that lesson.

Brad checked in; we walked into room 333, lay on the bed, and cuddled. Brad held me for several minutes in silence. Between the innumerable nonverbal messages being exchanged in Brad's warm embrace, I fell asleep.

I awoke to him nudging me. I had no sense of time or place. I was just annoyed my naptime had been interrupted. "What?"

"Your meeting..."

"Oh, Oh... Oh shit! PTO, I gotta go!" It was six p.m. already, and the meeting was starting. I drove like a madwoman.

As I was parking my car at St. Joseph's, I realized it might be the last time I was in the same room with those wonderful ladies. Even though they likely detested me because of my less than satisfactorily level of participation. I loved them. I loved this school. I loved the principal; I loved the school secretary. They were wonderful, loving human beings. It was a special place, one of a kind. I would not be able to replicate this environment for the kids, and it made me feel like a failure all over again.

I began to tear up. My emotions were like waves whooshing in and out on the seashore. I wiped the tears and told myself to pull it together and suck it up. I adjusted my clothing and walked into the PTO meeting in the library. "I am sorry I am late."

Chelsea, Ella, Sabine, Amelia, and some other moms I had not seen in a while, were all there. My grand entrance was poorly received. Eyes darted away from me.

Chelsea handed me an agenda. I sat down beside her in a toddler-sized chair.

"What about yearbook?" Amelia asked.

"We don't have a chair for yearbook yet," Chelsea said.

Amelia turned to me. "Faith, would you be willing to chair yearbook? You haven't done anything this year."

I had not been seated for one minute, and already I felt the first slash of the PTO Mom's warrior's tongue. "I am sorry. I know I've been awful this year. I wish I had helped St. Joseph's and the kids. I let everyone down. I am sorry." Once again, tears were painfully swelling in my eyes. I was trying to fight them back, but the hysterical, ugly cry demanded to be set free.

Chelsea and Sabine got up and hugged me. Their sympathy only propelled the ugly cry. Now the tears were gushing like the Niagra Falls, and I could not breathe. I started to hyperventilate. "She needs a paper bag," I heard someone yell.

A grown mother, violently crying at her kids' PTO meeting. Surely, I was not the first mother to cry at a PTO meeting, but perhaps the first at this school from complete heartbreak. Day-in and day-out, my kids walked these halls putting on smiley faces to people who might have been our friends, as they watched our world crumble inside-out, and all around, while remaining as helpless as us, to do anything. Why burden them?

I had stayed away because I hated pretending. I hated lying to good people, and also I did not want the pity. I did it to protect my kids, to shelter them from others' judgments. A fake smile here, a fake smile there. How is the weather? Sorry to hear you have to reschedule your vacation to Costa Rica. We aren't going anywhere because we're taking care of Simon.

When in reality, we were not going anywhere because Trey was a lunatic on drugs, and I was scared he would break into the house and sell everything inside while we were away. Not to mention, I might have had chlamydia. It had all lead to this moment, and I let it all go.

I felt lightheaded. "I can't breathe, I can't breathe," I said.

Amelia looked stumped but seemed to realize quickly that the issue was broader than the vacant yearbook chair position. She was witnessing an emotional breakdown, a head-on collision of the inner and outer worlds I had been living in. "I'm so sorry. Please forgive me," she said, with love and tears in her eyes. She didn't know what was going on, but she was an empathetic person and saw, now, beyond the perfect picture into my true state of being.

It was not her fault. It was my fault. How was she to know Trey had abandoned us for his mother's BFF and then later for heroin? Every day I had been here, I had smiled and kept the conversation pleasant, protecting Trey and his mother for my children's sake. Our lives for the past eight months—longer—had been a lie. A lie I had kept close to the vest, to get through to this moment of unrepressed surrender.

I muttered through the tears and labored breathing, "Don't be sorry. You're a good person, Amelia. I am sorry for letting everyone down and not fulfilling my obligations."

"Come on. Let's get out of here," Sabine said, always the logical one, keeping things calm and steady.

"We'll walk you to your car," Chelsea said.

I was immobile, stuck on the toddler-sized chair. Sabine helped me up. As we walked, I became centered. "I can't believe I had a meltdown in the PTO meeting. Ugh!"

"Stop it. You're completely fine," Sabine said.

"No one will remember tomorrow," Chelsea said.

"Really?"

"One day you'll look back, and it'll all be like a bad dream," Chelsea said.

"Let's focus on moving forward," Sabine said.

I heard her on a deep level. Something was triggered inside of me. Brad was waiting on me in room 333. I had to get back to him. "Ladies, I love you. But I do need to get out of here. My job is done for the year; sadly, the quality of work is questionable..."

I pulled down my visor to look at my makeup. I looked like a party girl who had been up for three days straight, and it was not pretty. But how much pretending could a normal person do before they combusted and spewed shrapnel on everyone and everything? Brad was a politician; he must understand, better than most, the toll that pretending took on one's soul.

I arrived back at the hotel room and knocked on the door. He opened it. "That was quick...Whoa, are you okay?" he asked, examining my face.

"Well, honey, it turns out I do have a breaking point." I face-planted myself on the bed and laid there like dead meat, waiting for the vultures to pick at my corpse. I was beyond exhausted. Seriously, I did not think I could breathe or purge any more bodily fluids. My phone dinged. I thought about ignoring it and then rationalized it could be Grandma Kate, texting about the kids.

Brad asked, "Do you want your phone?"

"Hand it to me," I said, weary. I wanted five minutes, just five minutes, alone. The text was from Trey.

Trey: *You think you can divorce me? I am going to destroy you.*

After the day I'd had, this was how it should end, right? The icing on the cake.

Me: *How long do you think this spoiled, rich teen act is going to last? You're in your forties. Grow up and be a father; take care of your kids.*

Trey: *Fuck you bitch. You'll get nothing. You are nothing.*

Suddenly, a Trey-being-served-divorce-papers celebration à la Rocky sounded like a swell time. A non-alcoholic one. Perhaps we could do pedicures. Older men like pedicures...right?

GOODBYES & GRATITUDE

CHAPTER 29

We were getting on a plane in less than forty-eight hours. The movers were scheduled to come the following day. I tried to divide our household goods as equitably as possible. All I wanted was the kids' bedroom suites, their playroom furniture, and the treadmill. Trey would be left with everything else: our bedroom furniture, our dining room suite, our family room furniture, the formal living room furniture, his elliptical machine and bench press. As a bonus, I decided to leave him our wedding photos, too.

I did not want any personal items related to us as a couple. Keeping mementos or photos or anything from the past was unhealthy, especially if they made you sad or angry. Life was short. Let it go. I was moving into the future; I was not staying in the past. So why would I keep something that was only going to bring me down and remind me of a failure? Faith 2.0 was going to be proactive with her mental health. I wished to keep it simple, keep it positive, keep it moving.

I took pictures of everything to document how I was leaving the home so that, if Trey damaged the place, I would not be held liable. I needed a third-party, unbiased eye witness as well. I called the only real estate agent I knew—man-boy dimples: Luke. I asked him to list the house for sale; he said he'd be right over. I decided that I would leave a set of house keys with him. He could coordinate with Simon.

At times, I was heart-broken over leaving our house. I had to remind myself frequently to be grateful to get out of here without enduring bodily harm, and with healthy children in tow. I was sure I would lose a lot of things before this was over. Thank God Phyllis would be distracted weaving webs to hide money, while I took Maggie and Alex by the hand and across the sea.

I pulled a basket full of random junk from the kitchen cabinet. Pencils, a tape measure, paperclips, a screwdriver, a box of thank-you cards. I was going to have to throw most of this away or leave it for Trey to deal with. A pen from Simon's practice made me feel melancholy and powerless over his current state. I hated to leave Papa Simon, although we had rarely seen each other the last several months. I had to trust that Aunt Denali and Uncle Peter would work with Lonnie to make sure he was okay. I worried I would not see him again. I felt a deep sadness.

But I did not have time to wallow in self-pity with many things left to do. I picked up the thank-you cards and decided to put Papa Simon's pen to good use. I wrote thank-yous to Maria, Sabine,

Chelsea, Aunt Denali, Lonnie, Jacob, Rocky, Luke, my attorney Dakota, and some of the other PTO Moms. Writing these cards out made me feel like I was tying up loose ends and leaving things on a positive note with the special people in my life, the people with whom I wished to maintain a relationship. Expressing gratitude would help me to stay grounded in reality and not lose focus on what was truly important.

Phyllis and Trey would not be making the thank you card list this year, although I reserved the right to send one to Helga at a later date. Perhaps I would write it in yellow crayon? The thought made me laugh. I did pray for Helga's healing because normal people do not go around destroying families, other people's and even their own. After surviving a decade with Trey, I should write him a final letter, but not right now.

I had to figure out how to ship my car, and I knew a cowboy who had multiple automobiles.

"Hey, darling," Rocky answered.

"I need a favor." I paced the kitchen floor.

"Anything for my favorite Georgia peach."

"Cut the shit, Rocky."

He laughed. He had a sarcastic sense of humor, what can I say.

"I am shipping my car to Washington for the summer. May I borrow one of your cars only for a day?"

"I'll do you one better. I'll drive you to the airport," Rocky said.

"You're the best! Can you meet me at Auto Transport tomorrow at ten?"

"You're coming back here, right?"

"Of course, once everything is settled." I rifled through the kitchen draws, throwing useless junky items away.

"I thought you called to tell me that Trey was served."

"Were you there? How did he take it?"

"Everyone is upset, even Simon. He says he was blindsided."

"Why is he upset? We talked about this, you were there. Such crazy shit...blindsided?"

"I know. But now Trey's missing again, and they're upset; they're blaming you." Rocky continued to laugh.

So this particular Trey-pisode was from me serving him divorce papers, but what about all the other Trey-pisodes? The Mercedes? The guns? The checkbooks? The stolen oxy? Did I also influence Trey to do those things? I said, "He never lets a good tragedy go to waste, and Phyllis never stops finding ways to be the victim."

Rocky laughed. "That's a good one. Trey-pisode."

I saw where all of this was going. Phyllis was already assuming her natural role as spin doctor, making Trey and herself out to be the victims. When she found out about Brad's and my baby, it would be fuel to the flames. The story would be, "Trey was doing so well at the Center, and then he discovered Faith was having an affair with Brad Rosenbloom. Helga comforted Trey as a friend. Faith's betrayal was devastating. Trey trying to cope, started using drugs. And he was doing so well at the Center. She's an awful person, and she destroyed Trey's life, and she won't let us see the kids."

Maybe one day, Trey and Phyllis would meet me in an honest space and apologize. Until then, I had to accept that forgiveness was not contingent on two parties coming to terms. True forgiveness, like life, was a solo journey. I chose to work on myself in order to work on forgiving Phyllis. In fact, I felt sorry for Phyllis. All her conniving, all her machinations, did not produce one single winner, only varying degrees of losers. The greatest legacy people leave behind are not buildings, towers, or monuments built and erected in their own names. The greatest legacy people leave behind are their children, given from God. And her child was sick. Perhaps, in the upside-down world we live in, if the roles had been reversed, I would have done the same thing for my child. I don't want to think I would, but how could I ever know the depths of my own darkness without it being tested? After all, there is nothing as powerful as a mother's love.

I wrote Lonnie a thank-you card because I did love her, and there was a part of her that genuinely cared about the kids and me. Who could understand what she had gone through better than I did? I was sure she had already turned on me to court Phyllis. She would do anything for Phyllis's approval and love because of her father. I prayed that Lonnie would remove herself from the cycle of abuse one day. She would never get anything but expensive clothes and small handouts every now and then to keep her quiet and distracted.

My heart hurt for her, mostly because she did not realize her enormous potential to do good in the world. It exceeded any perception Phyllis had of her. She was stronger and smarter than Phyllis. That's why Phyllis kept her down and tried to make her feel inferior. Phyllis tried to stomp out her light, but Lonnie was meant to shine, and I hoped one day she would find her self-worth and do so again.

Luke finally arrived. He was in fine form, wearing a pair of dressy jeans and a navy suit jacket. I invited him in. "Look around. I will be in the kitchen." The basket was still sitting on the counter. I grabbed a large white envelope and put documents and house keys into it for him. I also tucked his thank you note inside. I sat on a kitchen stool at the bar and waited for Luke to finish his tour.

I decided to write a quick note for Trey.

> Dear Trey, I am not supportive of your current life path. I will not allow the kids around an active drug user. I cannot, yet, forgive you for what you have done, but God never stops forgiving. In my heart of hearts, I always wished you would be a great champion for God because who could have a better testimony than you? To walk that close to darkness and then shine the light on it, that's powerful, and you have it in you. I pray this for you more than anything. I believe that the biggest obstacle

> for you to overcome is your lack of self-love, which, I think, is the root of your drug abuse. To be clear, vanity is not a reflection of self-love; it's a reflection of narcissism. It's an illusion, a distraction from what is real and powerful on the inside. The inside is where God does his greatest work. Start there, by being mindful of the dialogue inside of your head. Our journey here on Earth is a lonely one, and the ultimate goal and highest aim is to do the inner work of learning how to properly love ourselves as God loves us so we may mirror that beauty everywhere we go. I want you to heal. Our children deserve the best version of you. I will be waiting for it to show up as an honest loving father. Regardless of your decisions and future choices, I'll always love you. You have helped me to grow as a person. You have helped me to rediscover myself in the darkest of hours, and for that, all I can say is God Bless You. Faith.

I folded it and put it neatly in a white envelope. I felt good about it. It was not sappy, or rehashing the years together, or overly scornful of his behaviors. It was truthful, and hopefully, he would read it, and it would plant a little seed of hope somewhere. In the meantime, I was going to keep making decisions in the best interests of my family.

Luke walked around the corner. "Faith, great house. Do you want to price it to sell quickly?" He flashed his man-boy dimples at me.

"Sure, the sooner, the better. I am not on the title anyway. Simon's working with Trey to put me on the title."

"Oh? I am working with Simon on a project already. Lonnie helped me get the deal."

"Hm. Interesting... I'm happy for you." I handed him the envelope with his name marked on the outside. "The keys to the house are in here. I left an envelope for Trey, too; please make sure he gets it. Thank you for all your help." I stood up to walk him to the front door.

"Faith, are you coming back to Fairbanks?"

Was he another double agent? "Of course! I love Fairbanks. I'm leaving for the summer. A lot of negative things have happened here. The kids and I need a break."

"Be careful with Lonnie." Luke put his hand on my shoulder.

"I know, I will." At the door, I said, "Hey, the house is in good condition, right?"

"It looks great." He gave me the thumbs up.

"Remember that, because if Trey moves in here, he'll turn it into a flophouse."

OLD SPICEY BALLS

CHAPTER 30

Today was my last day in Alaska, and it was pouring rain. I had my hair in a scrunchie, no makeup, and a matching black sweat suit. I had deposited the check from Phyllis. I was going to need the extra money to ship the car. I pulled into Auto Transport and parked next to Rocky, who was sitting in a white Lexus SUV. He rolled down his window as I approached. He was wearing a Blue Jays baseball cap, a matching white sweatshirt and extra cologne. I found it unusual that I could smell him through the rain. "I am going to drop off the car keys. Be right back."

"Okay, Peaches, I'll be waiting right here." He had an elfin grin on his face.

The mobile office of Auto Transport had a tiny lobby. Maximum occupancy must have been five people. There was a middle-aged woman behind the counter, with dark, curly hair that was beginning to grey; she looked grumpy. "Can I help you?" she asked, void of emotion, brushing off her orange vest with her hands.

"I am dropping off my SUV for shipment to Seattle," I said brightly.

"We don't ship to Seattle. You mean Kent?" She corrected me as if I was a dumbass.

"My apologies, Kent," I said, remaining positive.

"Huh, I need your driver's license and car title." She curled her lip.

"I'll be right back." I handed her my license. The title of my car was in Trey's name. This could go badly. I walked back to the car. I noticed that Rocky had brought his dog Chuck with him.

He rolled down the window. "Is everything alright?" Chuck stuck his head out of the window.

I told him the problem. "What should I do?" I asked him as if he had some sort of secret weapon to use on grumpy-face.

"You go in there and say what you have to say. Trey's not going to sign over the car to you."

I turned my back to walk away without responding. He banged on the outside of his car door. I turned around. Chuck jumped into the passenger seat.

"Hey, make it work." Rocky pointed his index finger at me.

I thought, What does that even mean? What stupid advice. Do I fake a family death? Do I cry hysterically? Do I get angry and throw something?

I walked back into the shack that was impersonating an office. I was damp from the rain. I tried to blot my mascara with my fingertips and shake off the excess droplets. I looked toward Mrs. Grumpy-face, whose aura was, "I don't want to help no damn body." I handed her the title.

"Is Trey meeting you here?"

"He's already in Seattle. I am going down to meet him."

"He has to be the one to sign off on shipping the car since his name is on the title, not yours." She looked at me like I was stupid and lacked good judgment from standing in the rain. Her name tag read Heather.

"Heather, please help me. I have two children. I am moving all by myself. He left me to take care of everything. Once I get to Washington, I won't have a car for my children. Please help me. Nothing illegal is happening here." I looked her in the eyes, this time with the veil lifted.

She saw the real me. The real torment. The sleepless nights, the moist mascara, the desperation. I was a pitiful sight indeed when the fake smile wore thin. She stared briefly into my eyes then looked at her computer screen.

"Eight hundred dollars, Visa or MasterCard."

I handed her my card. I had thought it was eleven hundred. Was she giving me a discount? I decided not to say anything. She could still turn on me. She swiped the card and gave it back.

"Thank you." I took the car keys off my key ring. "Here are the keys." I used a flat tone and avoided eye contact. Some animals find eye contact threatening, and maybe my chirpy tone was annoying her.

"Your car will be there in 3 weeks. Sign this." She pushed a orange document in front of me.

What the fuck? Three weeks? UGH! I had thought it would be six days! I did not know if she had screwed me over, or done me a favor, or both.

Whatever, the important thing was that the car was on its way to Washington. I signed the paper and left. I had to meet the movers.

I got in the passenger's seat of Rocky's Lexus. It smelled of Old Spice. It smelled so strongly I could not breathe. I was choking on an over-cologned Rocky Valentine. I wondered if the dog had pooped in the backseat, and he was hiding it from me. I rolled down the window in the pouring rain. Chuck jumped from backseat to front.

"Hey, it's raining." Rocky rolled my window back up using his master driver controls.

"I did it, Rocky. It was an act of God, because that lady was not handing out too many favors to too many people." I patted Chuck on the head.

"Good going. I knew you could do it. Are you hungry?"

"I have to meet the movers at the house to store the valuables. You know Trey will get in there and destroy things, steal things, pawn things. You know, whatever it is he does when no one's looking." I rolled down the window again.

"So can I drop you off at your house and take the car?" I asked Rocky politely. Rocky rolled the window back up.

My phone rang. Trey. Oh great, hateful threats, I thought. Shit, what if he had found out about the car? I answered the phone, paranoid.

"Hello," I said, on edge.

"Meet me at Alyeska Title. I need to put your name on the house."

"What? Are you really going to do that?" I asked, bewildered.

"Meet me now."

I could not believe Simon had been able to rally and pull this off. What could he have offered him that he had not already taken? Wow, I had to make this happen, because Trey's emotions were fleeting and reliant on whatever substance was currently inhabiting his body. "I am on my way." I turned to Rocky. "Change of plans. We're going by Alyeska Title." I called Luke. "Trey wants to put me on the title of the house; who do you know at Alyeska Title?" I rolled my window back down.

"Everyone. They're downstairs from my office."

"Can you help me? I need everything pulled and ready to sign. Trey is a wild card."

"No problem. I'll tell them you are coming. I have your back."

"Thanks." I hung up and said, "Did you hear that? Trey wants to put me on the title of the house." I looked around Chuck at Rocky.

"Dammit, stop touching the window! Simon doesn't want Trey to have anything. He's trying to send him out of state for drug rehab." Rocky rolled my window back up.

As soon as Rocky parked the car by the title insurance company, I opened the car door for fresh air. I took several deep breaths to purge myself of Old Spice. I texted my mother to tell her the movers were on their way, and apologized for leaving her to deal with them by herself. Before I could enter the offices of Alyeska Title Company, I heard Luke calling me from behind. I turned around and saw him at a coffee stand. He was wearing a white polo shirt and khaki pants, hiding behind a structural beam.

He said, “Come here, I talked to Tina. She’s going to help you.”

“Does she know about my situation?”

“Yes, I told her. She’s going to take care of you.”

I gave him a grateful smile. “You should not be here for this. Trey would be suspicious.”

“Yeah, okay. He hates me. I get it.” Luke retreated further behind the beam.

“Don’t take it personally.”

“Any man that won’t take care of his kids isn’t worth shit to me.”

It turned out that men do judge other men. There was a man code of honor, although I imagined it was a simple one. It must state: Don’t get caught cheating on your wife, and take care of your kids. The End.

Inside Alyeska Title, I was greeted by Tina, a tall, thin, attractive lady with shoulder length, sandy blonde hair. She wore an olive pantsuit. Her aura was welcoming and kind, not like grumpy-face at Auto Transport. I was relieved.

“I don’t want this to be awkward,” I said. “My husband and I are going through a divorce, and he says he will be here any minute. Well, I hope he shows up. His behavior has been sporadic, mostly he is…” I looked toward the ceiling as I pondered the right words.

“Using drugs,” she completed.

“And he’s been threatening me.” I pulled out my phone and showed her his text messages.

“My, my,” she said, shaking her head.

“Yes, it’s ugly. He’s tricky. So please help me make sure everything is legit. He doesn’t want me to have anything, even to care for his own children, whom he doesn't want to raise either."

"I know the type. I've been married before to one like that. Alaska is a patriarchy; us girls have got to stick together. You're safe with me, sister." Tina gave me a hug.

I felt compassion exuding from her body to mine. She had been here before, and now she wanted to help me. She was beautiful. I prayed, *Thank you, God, for sending me this angel.* Tina had not shut the world away and become cold and bitter, like some people after trauma. She seemed to embrace the opportunity to be a force of light in a time of darkness for other women. She was like Aunt Denali, and Vita. I dug this chick.

When Trey walked in, he looked terrible. He was wearing dirty jeans, and tee-shirt that read "*If it ain't broke, don't fix it.*" He smelled, too, but not like Old Spice, more like old, sweaty balls. Suddenly, I missed the smell of Rocky. "I am here. What are we doing? I have to go," Trey said, fidgeting.

"This is Tina; she's going to help us," I said delicately.

"I am in a hurry; can we make this fast?" Trey barely glanced in her direction.

Tina said, "I have everything lined out in the boardroom. This can all be done in a matter of minutes. Follow me."

We followed her and took seats next to each other. His body odor overwhelmed the entire space.

"One second, I forgot something," Tina said, and left the room. Probably to barf.

"Trey," I said, "You smell like rancid, beef and cheese. You should shower." I shook my head at him.

"Faith, I don't care." He pushed back against his chair, all huffy and puffy, like he would rather be anywhere in the world than here, giving me ownership of our house.

"Clearly, you don't care. What's the big rush today?"

"I am leaving town; I am going to New York." Trey shook his legs under the table.

"Why? What are you going to do in New York?"

"Rehab." Trey pulled out his phone to check the time.

"When?"

"In about three hours." Trey began to look around the room.

"For how long?" I looked at him.

"A month." His eyes veered away from me.

"Good. I hope it works out for you."

Tina returned, and this time she sat across and away from us. "This is simple. Faith, sign here and here. Trey, sign here and here. I will notarize this, and then we'll be done." Tina placed the papers in front of us, subtly holding her breath and shifting her head to the side. We signed the documents. She notarized them.

Trey stood up. "Are we finished?"

"You are free to go," she said like a school teacher to an eager student waiting for the bell to ring for recess. I told her bye.

Trey and I walked out of the room together, but Trey picked up momentum quickly. He scurried past me. I asked loudly, "Trey, do you want to see the kids before you leave?"

"I don't think I'll have time." He said as he continued toward the exit.

"Well, I'll tell them you said goodbye. Also, you need to bathe before getting on a plane with other humans across the country. Especially if you are a middle-seater. Proper hygiene on airplanes is non-negotiable. Use some baby powder or old spice...you know," I said, pointing to his man junk. "Whatever, Faith!" Trey raced across the parking lot.

"How did that go?" Rocky asked once I was back in the Lexus. "Did Trey show up?"

I nodded. It had stopped raining, and the sun was peeking through the clouds. "It smells good in here." I sat down in the car. I noticed a rainbow taking shape over the hillside. Suddenly, I felt overcome with gratitude and grief.

"Trey says he's going to New York for a month for rehab."

Rocky laughed. "No, he's not. Simon said they are sending him to Malibu—Passages. You know where they ride horses on the beach and talk about their f-e-e-lings." Rocky spoke in a wry tone. He looked at me for a reaction.

I looked upon the rainbow hanging in the sky.

"Passages is another escape from reality. I don't think he'll ever get sober. Why would he? What's the incentive? If children aren't enough, nothing is." I fought back the tears.

"Well, that's what Phyllis told Simon. It could be another story." Rocky said. He rounded the curve to his house.

"Hmm...Trey and Phyllis like to dispense misinformation to throw people off, why? Because as long as people don't know the truth, they can spin whatever lies and stories they want. Once someone tells the truth, they have nowhere to go. They think storytelling gives them the advantage, but mostly, people, after they wise up, don't give a shit. It's all wasted energy to protect their version of reality. And the people who go along with it don't care about their health; they just want money."

"You're a lot different than the first time we met, you know that?"

OOPSY-DAISY

CHAPTER 31

I dropped Rocky and Chuck off at their house. We made plans to meet up later. I called my mom to ask how things were going with the movers.

"Great. They're almost done. There are four of them, and they're fast." Mom spoke loudly. I guessed they were within earshot of the conversation. "How did things go at the title company?"

I told her. Mom sounded surprised that Trey had shown up. She reminded me to pick up the kids at 1 p.m.

"I'll leave directly from the storage unit to get them. When we get home, we need to pack our suitcases and get on a plane."

"Yes, it'll all be over soon." Mom hung up the phone. She sounded disgruntled, but I did not have time to ponder why she might be upset.

At Pike's Storage, I parked the car in front of my rented unit and waited for the movers to arrive. I texted Brad.

Me: *Hi honey, how are you?*

Brad: *Good, it's our busy season, so I am running around today. How are you feeling?*

Me: *Good. Today we pack our suitcases and get on a jet plane. Hooray!*

Brad: *Take it easy, okay? Don't over-do it.*

The movers arrived. They parked behind me on the gravel passage way in the storage unit lot. There were three of them. The head guy was dressed in a blue, camo-printed sweat suit and hiking boots. "Is this the unit?" I nodded, and they began moving stuff into the storage unit while I stood by and watched. A text message arrived. Trey.

Trey: *Can you give me a ride to the airport?*

Me: *I don't have time.*

Trey: *Please, I want to see the kids.*

Me: *You've had opportunities to see them; you only need a ride. Call your girlfriend.*

Trey: *She isn't my girlfriend. She's blackmailing us. She's asking mom for money.*

Me: *What? I thought she was an honorable woman. I'll be praying for you guys. Have fun in NYC.*

Two of the movers got back into the truck. I settled up with the main guy. I handed him a generous tip. "Thanks," I said.

"You're welcome, but your mom already gave us the bench press and weights as a tip." He shuffled around me.

"Oh, really?" I asked, baffled.

"She also gave us a TV and some liquor."

"That was nice of her..." I stepped away from him.

"Yes, and I think Chewy got a tool chest and some power tools." He put his hands in his pockets.

"Oh...lovely," I said, smiling, not sure how I felt. "So, are you guys related? Brothers?"

"No, this is my business, all of my hires are on work-release from the pen," he maintained eye contact. I shifted my eyes away from him.

"The penitentiary?" I tightly folded my arms across my chest.

"Yes, I get a tax break for hiring them," he looked at his employees inside of the truck with regret. I wondered what they had done?

"Well, at least your helping them stay on a good path. That's something," I smiled at him.

I got back into Uncle Rocky's white Lexus, which still had the residual smell of Old Spice. I rolled down the window and wondered what the hell mom had been thinking.

At St. Joseph's, I pulled around to the pick-up lane and parked. It made me sad to think that this was the last time I would ever be in this pick-up lane for the kids. I told myself that I might come back so that it didn't hurt so badly. Maggie and Alex were bouncing up and down. What kid doesn't enjoy the last day of school? Maggie saw me waving emphatically from the car. She grabbed her brother by the arm. They walked over together.

"Hooray, your last day of school! How was it?" I asked, making myself sound extra happy to set the tone for the brutal task ahead.

"Whose car is this?" Maggie asked.

"Uncle Rocky's. We're borrowing it for the day."

"I won a gold medal at field day," Alex said as he scooted into the backseat.

"I won three silver medals. And three silver medals beat one gold medal." Maggie elbowed Alex.

"No, no, it doesn't! I am the best, and you were only second best three times." Alex held up his medal to her face.

"Shut up, Alex!" Maggie slapped his medal.

"Oh, kids, let's relax. We have a big day today. We're going home and packing up our suitcases. Then we are off on a new adventure! Hooray!" I turned down the street toward our house.

"Wait, wait, what's that smell?" Alex said.

"Where are we going? Hawaii?" Maggie asked.

"Yes, yes, yes, Hawaii!" Alex yelled, casting his vote for a tropical paradise.

"No, not this time. Washington. Where Grandma Kate lives. It's kind of like Hawaii." I realized I had not taken the kids to visit their grandparents in so long they had no memory of Washington. I wondered what kind of daughter I had been?

"Does it have palm trees?" Maggie asked.

"Um, no."

"Can we swim with the dolphins?" Alex asked.

"Um, no."

"Can we swim in the ocean?" Maggie asked.

"Well, not really. Maybe in a wet suit."

"Ah, man, it's nothing like Hawaii," Alex folded his arms.

"But it's a new adventure, and life is about having new adventures! Hooray!" I said.

"I don't want to go; it sounds lame," Maggie said.

"Me either. I'll stay home," Alex said.

"No, we're a family, and we're all going together, and that's final," I said, my tone sharpening.

"Is daddy coming?" Maggie asked.

"I am hungry," Alex said.

"Your dad is out of state on a business trip. Alex, we can eat at the airport. When we get home, please quickly change out of your uniforms, then pack your suitcases." I pulled into the driveway.

Grandma Kate sat on a black and gold dining room chair on the front lawn. She was wearing a brown sweater, jeans, and Danskos.

"Grandma, Grandma," Alex yelled and ran toward her for a hug.

"Mom, what's going on?" I approached her.

"Oh, nothing, relaxing. What an exhausting day." She motioned towards the car. "We have too much stuff; it's not all going to fit in there," she said, annoyed. "We'll have to make two trips."

Mom took the kids inside to help them pack while I called Rocky. "We have too much luggage. It won't all fit in the SUV."

"I guess I can drive over there with the truck, and then you can follow behind me. After the bags are checked, we can go drop off the SUV at my house and then I can take you back to the airport. How does that sound?"

"Do we have time to do that? We're supposed to board in two and a half hours."

"Damn it, Faith! This is bullshit! I hate this last-minute shit. Fuck. I am on my way. Be ready." Rocky hung up, and I thought, *Yeah, being Mrs. Valentine would be a real treat.*

Inside, the kids were eating crackers and peanut butter in the kitchen. I started to freak out. Rocky's reaction was contagious, and now I was frantic with anxiety about getting out of here with all our stuff in tow. "Stop eating, go upstairs, and pack, now!" I yelled at them.

"I already packed," Mom said, like, 'I am not doing another thing.'

Upstairs, I had three large suitcases to fill with clothes, shoes, and cosmetics. I grabbed a box of Ziploc bags and started loading stuff up from the drawers and cabinets of my bathroom counter—curling irons, flat irons, hair products, makeup—lots and lots of makeup. Some of it I'd had since the seventh grade. I willingly threw things away. All this crap was replaceable. I tried to take only what I needed.

The closet was next. I had already sent all my fall and winter clothes to the storage unit in boxes. I was taking only my summer clothes to Washington. I made trip after trip, grabbing clothes and shoes and throwing them in a suitcase; it was the worst feeling. I packed up my summer purses and belts. I was about done. I went to check on the kids.

Alex was sitting on the floor, crying, still wearing his school uniform. The empty suitcase lay open, and his closet was full of clothes.

"Hey, honey, what's wrong?" I asked him, freaking out inside at what little progress he had made.

"Someone took my Xbox and my bed," he said, tears rolling down his face.

I pulled him up. "Your Xbox is going to Washington. I already packed it up. Don't cry, it'll be there, waiting for you. Right now, I need you to put all your clothes in this suitcase. Fold them nicely like I taught you, okay?" I patted him on the shoulder.

"Okay, mommy," Alex said, wiping his tears with his forearm. "I love you."

I gave him a big hug. "I love you."

Next door, Maggie was bouncing on her suitcase, trying to zip it up. "This is stupid," she said and flailed her body to the floor. I opened the suitcase. She had wadded up her clothing into a big ball and stuffed it all in.

"Honey, you have to fold your clothes nicely, so they'll fit. You can't stuff clothes in a suitcase like that. You know better. We've been through this before." My mother tone was strong.

"I wish daddy was here." She slurred.

"I am sorry you miss your dad."

"I hate you. Get out of my room!"

"Hate me while you fold your clothes. We must all compromise."

How much bullshit could one person take? Suddenly, my anger from Maggie's nasty comment was directed at Grandma Kate. I thought, Why isn't she up here helping me out? What the fuck? "Mom, come up here please and help the kids? I have to pack my own suitcases!" I yelled from atop the balcony.

Muttering, Mom stomped up the stairs and passed my room to the kid's rooms. I put my clothes on my bed and began to fold them neatly into my last two suitcases. I heard Grandma Kate say, "Alex's is ready. I'll take his suitcase downstairs."

Maggie walked into my room, "Mom, I need another suitcase. My clothes won't all fit in this one."

"We have a box we can check." I retrieved it from downstairs and gave it to her. "Finish packing now." She rolled her eyes at me and ran off with the box.

Grandma Kate came back upstairs to help Maggie. The doorbell rang. Oh, shit, it was Uncle Rocky. I rushed downstairs and opened the door. The cologne hit me first.

He barreled through the door, intoxicated on alpha male energy. "If you're catching this plane, we have got to go, now," He acted as if I had just returned from the tanning salon and was dilly-dallying.

"The suitcases are over there. You can load them up. Thanks." I pointed at the suitcases stacked against the wall, near the front door.

"Is that all?" His hands pressed firmly on his hips, but in a masculine way.

"Three and a box."

"Bring them downstairs, immediately," Rocky said, taking command of the situation.

Grandma Kate came down the stairs, pulling Maggie's suitcase. Rocky sprang into action to help her. He was from the south. In the right setting, he was a true gentleman.

"Thank you," Mom said, impressed. "I want you to know that I am grateful for everything you've done to help my daughter."

"Well, somebody's got to help. A lot of boys running around pretending to be men. Real men take care of their families." Rocky straightened his belt buckle and threw out his chest.

"You're the only real man in all of Alaska," Mom said mesmerized. I felt barf bulge in my throat.

"Thank you. I appreciate that." Rocky bent down and kissed her hand.

Even though at that moment I wanted to vomit, it was true. Rocky had earned his badge of honor. He was there for me when no one else had been. He might have been a rascal, but he was also an angel that God had put in my path to help me get to this point.

I rushed back to my room, threw my last bits of clothing into the remaining suitcase, and sat on it in an attempt to zip it up. In my panicked state, I could not get the zipper to work. As I was bouncing up and down to make the threads connect, Maggie passed my bedroom, pushing the oversized box I had given her.

She gave me the stink eye. "Figures."

"Keep it moving; take the box downstairs, now!" I yelled at her.

"Alex, please go find your grandma and ask her to get everyone in the car. I am bringing the last suitcase down."

"Okay," Alex said, still teary eyed.

"We have to leave!" Rocky yelled from downstairs.

"I am coming!" I pulled the suitcase down the stairs. Rocky met me halfway on the staircase and took it from me. "Where's my Mom?" I looked around the formal living room.

"She's already in the car. We're all waiting on you." Rocky held the front door open.

"One last thing." I enabled the house alarm and said goodbye to my beautiful house. I prayed briefly that the next family that moved in would stay together.

Then I shut the front door and jumped in the car with my mom. Rocky got in his car. We tailgated it to the airport. There was tension, silence, and exhaustion. The kids were probably traumatized. My mom was angry, and I was frazzled, wondering if I had forgotten anything. I pulled into departures under the Alaska Airlines sign.

Rocky was right behind me in his truck. I looked at the clock on my phone. Our flight boarded in fifty minutes, and we still had to check bags and make it through security. We rushed. Rocky started bringing the bags and placing them by the check-in counter.

"Mom, you go inside and wait with the kids. I'll help Rocky bring in the bags."

We took turns rolling suitcases in. I said, "Rocky, I can't go back with you to drop off the car. Do you have someone you can call? I am so sorry." I gave him an apologetic face.

"Don't worry about it. I already called my friend. He's on his way." Rocky brushed passed me with the last suitcase.

"Thank you." I walked back inside with one final load. My mom was in line to check our bags.

"Do you have our boarding passes?"

She waved them at me. I guess we weren't talking. I grabbed them from her and walked to the front of the line. I gave our info to the nicely suited man in his Alaska Airlines uniform.

"How many suitcases are we checking today?" he asked.

"Eight and one box."

"Oh, this flight is boarding in forty minutes. You aren't going to make it."

"We have to. I don't care if these suitcases don't make the flight. We have to make the flight." I expostulated.

"I'll do my best." He sympathized.

Rocky started loading the suitcases on the scales.

"This one is over-weight; do you want to take stuff out?"

"No, charge me; we have to be faster." I pounded my fist on the desk.

Surely he could sense I was extremely stressed. Rocky kept loading suitcases on the belt. The agent began to move faster, more in alignment with the urgency of the mission. I handed my mom all the boarding passes except mine. "Go get in the security line. I may have to take a later flight, but you have to make it."

Mom took the kids to the TSA pat-down line. I yelled after them, "I love you!" They ignored me.

Rocky loaded up the box.

"Your plane is boarding now," the agent said and looked at me like he was helpless.

"Can you help us? We need to get on that plane." I begged.

"Seven hundred and seventy-seven dollars."

"What?" I gasped.

"Seven hundred and seventy-seven dollars for all your bags."

My mouth hung open in suspended time.

"Let me take care of this for you," Rocky said, pushing me aside.

He handed the agent a wad of cash and gave him a certain look that I did not understand, but it must have been man-code for something.

"Follow me," the agent said, suddenly cheery-faced. "My name is Dominic."

Hmm... Rocky had a killer's instinct, and survival skills to boot. What a man.

"Wait! Let me tell my friend goodbye!" I hugged Rocky. "Thank you for everything. You're one of my angels. I love you."

"No one has ever called me an angel before." Rocky blushed.

"Angels come in all packages, and you're an angel to me. I am so happy I found the courage to reach out and ask you for help." I hugged him one last time and started to walk away.

"You come back here, okay?" He looked saddened by my departure. Perhaps, he did genuinely care for me in his own way.

I turned around and smiled at him, then I followed Dominic. He led me to the front of the TSA line, past my mom and kids. I motioned for them to join me.

An announcement came over the intercom. "This is the final boarding call for flight three seventeen to Seattle."

Oh no. I surrender, God. If I am not meant to be on this flight, then so be it. I surrender. I took off my shoes and put my purse and second bag on the belt to go through the X-ray machine. The kids were coming through the line with my mom.

"Miss, please." A lady in a uniform and with a wand ushered me into the x-ray crucifixion box. I prayed that I was not wearing any metal. She let me pass. The kids were going through the TSA checkpoint with Grandma Kate on the other side of me. I grabbed all my stuff and waited for them. I heard the final boarding call for Seattle again. Everyone was through security. I felt reinvigorated. There was still a chance.

"Let's run," I said to them. "Literally, let's run for our lives." We ran like a herd of wild horses all the way from the TSA lockdown to our gate. The stewardess was about to shut the door. "Wait, wait, we're coming!" My arms stretched out as if I was going to finish first place in the triathlon.

She looked at us and began to smile, enjoying the spectacle. But she waited.

"We climbed valleys; we swam rivers," Grandma Kate said, out of breath with a red face. Behind us, Alex was barely trotting along.

"Alex, hurry up; we've got to get on the plane now!" I handed the stewardess our boarding passes.

"Can't we take Papa's jet? This is lame. I am hungry," he said rubbing his belly.

I shrugged at the stewardess. "He has quite the imagination." I ran back to Alex, picked him up, and whisked him to the gate. Maggie and

Grandma Kate had boarded the flight. I carried Alex through the sky bridge and onto the plane before putting him down to walk the rest of the way to our seats.

A flight attendant greeted us. "You made it in the nick of time. Five seconds later, and this door would have been shut."

"I know, praise God," I said and kept walking. Our seats were in the back of the plane. Maggie and Grandma Kate sat next to each other. I told the kids I would buy them food as soon as possible. Maggie began to look through the Alaska Airlines magazine. Grandma Kate was in the aisle seat with her arms folded. Alex scooched in on my side to sit by the window. I handed him his iPad and headphones.

"Mom, we made it! Can you believe it? Literally in the nick of time!" I said to her, astonished and relieved, and hoping to be met with the same response.

"Well, if you'd been there earlier for the movers, I am sure things would have gone smoother today." She had an unpleasant tone in her voice.

I was put off. I had just accomplished a rather daunting task, and to be met with such negativity sent me to a dark place. "Oh, yes, the movers, whom you gave our treasures to," I said, accusing her.

"Yes, I did. What was I supposed to do? They were creepy as hell and kept asking for stuff," she said, angrily shrugging her shoulders and looking in my direction for a stare-down.

"Oh, I am so sorry, that's messed up," I was shocked.

"Well, you could have said no," I scoffed.

"Oopsy-Daisy...well, what's next?" Mom asked, trying to change the subject.

"I am pregnant: Oopsy-Daisy."

Made in the USA
Monee, IL
23 October 2020